INTERNATIONAL TEXTBOOKS IN MATHEMATICS

L. R. Wilcox

Professor of Mathematics
Illinois Institute of Technology

CONSULTING EDITOR

ELEMENTARY
DIFFERENTIAL
EQUATIONS

ELEMENTARY
DIFFERENTIAL
EQUATIONS

L. R. WILCOX, *1912 –*
Professor of Mathematics
Illinois Institute of Technology

HERBERT J. CURTIS
Associate Professor of Mathematics
University of Illinois, Chicago

INTERNATIONAL TEXTBOOK COMPANY
Scranton, Pennsylvania

Second Printing, July, 1962

Preface

This text is intended for use in a first course in ordinary differential equations following elementary calculus and is designed to meet a variety of needs. Where a minimal coverage of techniques is the objective in a one-semester, three-hour course, Chapters 1 through 6 with all the starred material omitted should serve. At the other extreme, a serious and longer course, with some attention to fine points, may be based on the full contents of the book, including starred material. It is hoped that the book will be well suited for use in institutions where a course in differential equations is generally required, as is the case in some engineering schools.

Since there is an increasing tendency to pay attention to individual differences among students (e.g., through ability grouping by course sections or within course sections), some instructors may wish to have enrichment materials available for their more capable students. The starred subsections and accompanying starred exercises should in many cases help to fill this need.

Where possible we have attempted, even in the main portions of the text, to inject some of the modern spirit into the presentation, while at the same time respecting fully valid classical objectives centering about techniques and skills. For example, in the solution of $x\,dy + y\,dx = 0$, we deviate from the traditional practice of dividing by xy and subsequently pretending that the division had not occurred. Again, we have tried to stress what is obvious but usually avoided, that a function is not specified until its domain is given; accordingly, the search for a function (e.g., a solution of a differential equation) entails also the search for its domain.

Despite an apparent decrease in interest in operators, we have elected to include them, even with some emphasis, for four reasons: 1) they simplify the development of the theory of linear equations both conceptually and notationally; 2) they aid in the presentation of our point of view toward applications in Chapter 6; 3) many students are stimulated, and thus better motivated, by contact with the theory of operators, probably because of the high level of precision and clarity which characterizes it; and 4) the theory of operators can be especially profitable for students who have already been exposed, perhaps even in high school, to some abstract mathematics.

The Laplace transform has been included in such a way that it can be omitted entirely, touched upon briefly, or emphasized, according to the desires of the instructor. In Chapter 7 we have included a section on Fourier series primarily because the elements of this topic are needed early by engineering students but are not normally accessible in elementary texts. In this chapter and elsewhere we have freely used the summation notation. Our experience has shown that students at this level can become thoroughly familiar with it and skilled in its use; we believe that it can help students to develop good habits of expression.

The primary reason, in our opinion, for including applications in elementary mathematics books is motivation. Yet it is senseless to try to apply mathematics before having some mathematics to apply. Consequently, we feel that to intersperse applications throughout the book would have produced greater harm than benefit. We have therefore segregated them and placed them in two chapters, 3 and 6.

In selecting exercises, we have been guided by educational objectives and not by an urge to outdo other authors in respect to quantity. We have endeavored to meet the demands posed by individual instructors' tastes, while avoiding long lists of repetitious "busy-work" problems. Supplementary groups at the ends of Chapters 2 and 5 are included in order to give students an opportunity to develop judgment in the selection of an appropriate or "best" method from among many that are available. Similar groups in Chapters 3 and 6 may meet the desires of instructors who wish to stress applications.

Answers to odd-numbered exercises appear in Appendix 4; similar answers to even-numbered exercises are available separately on special order by faculty members. Where approximate numerical answers are given, they have been computed with the help of seven-place tables to ensure accuracy; use of four- or five-place tables may thus result in some discrepancies. A reasonably complete table of Laplace transforms and some miscellaneous reference materials which may be helpful to the student appear in Appendices 1, 2, 3.

We are grateful for the superb cooperation and understanding of International Textbook Company during all stages of work on the book—from the inception of the writing project, through preparation of the manuscript, and finally publication. We owe much to many colleagues who aided us directly or indirectly; outstanding among these is R. A. Struble, who was associated with our project for a time, and who contributed substantially to the development of our approach to linear equations and especially their applications. Many thanks are due also to Mrs. Herbert J. Curtis, who aided in reading proof; to Mrs. L. R. Wilcox, who typed the manuscript, read proof, and offered much valuable advice; and to our respective institutions, which furnished the proving ground for many of our ideas.

L. R. WILCOX
HERBERT J. CURTIS

Chicago, Illinois
June, 1961

Contents

ELEMENTARY
DIFFERENTIAL
EQUATIONS

1

Introduction

1–1. PRELIMINARIES

Much of mathematics is concerned with equations of one type or another. The reader is already familiar with numerical equations, such as are studied extensively in algebra. There we have a given function f of a numerical variable and are interested in those particular numbers x for which $f(x) = 0$. The statement $f(x) = 0$ is called an *equation*, and the numbers x, which when substituted into it make the statement true, are the *solutions*. Generally, an equation specifies, though indirectly, the collection of all its solutions; mathematical questions centering around the equation are directed toward learning everything possible about this collection of all solutions.

Example 1–1. If a, b are given real numbers, $ax + b = 0$ is an equation specifying a certain collection of (real) solutions. If $a \neq 0$, it is shown in algebra that this collection consists of exactly one number, and, in fact, that this number is $-b/a$.

Example 1–1 suggests that, while the task of "solving an equation," that is, finding in some specific form all solutions, is the most important one connected with an equation, it might be useful first to settle two preliminary questions:

I   Is there any solution at all?

II   If so, exactly how many solutions are there?

When the answer to Question I is *No*, one proceeds no further, and all other questions disappear. Knowledge of this fact may save considerable effort. When the answer to Question I is *Yes*, an answer to Question II gives some direction to the search for solutions.

Example 1–2. Consider $\sqrt{x} + 1 = 0$, where x is complex. Here no solution exists, because $\sqrt{x}$ is non-negative if x is real and non-negative, and is non-real otherwise; in no case can $\sqrt{x}$ be equal to -1.

Example 1–3. Consider $x^3 - x = 0$, where x is complex. The general theorems on polynomial equations tell us that a cubic equation has just three solutions. By inspection, or by factorization, we see that $0, 1, -1$ are solutions. All solutions have thus been found.

Equations of the type to be treated in this book have, to some extent, been encountered in the calculus. If f is a given function of the real variable t defined, say, for $a \leqq t \leqq b$, a and b being given, one may consider the equation

$$(1\text{–}1) \qquad\qquad \frac{d}{dt}\, y(t) = f(t).$$

Thus (1–1) is a statement about a function y of t which may or may not be true; the *solutions* of (1–1) are those functions y of t which make (1–1) true when substituted into it. It is understood that the equality in (1–1) means that y possesses a derivative for all values of t such that $a \leqq t \leqq b$, and that this derivative function is the same as the function $f(t)$.

The problem represented by (1–1) is a central one in calculus; any solution of (1–1) is called an *antiderivative* (sometimes *indefinite integral*) of $f(t)$ and is often denoted by $\int f(t)\, dt$. Questions I and II are of significance in connection with such equations as (1–1), as we shall see.

Example 1–4. Consider $\dfrac{d}{dt}\, y(t) = 3t^2$, where t is unrestricted, but real. A little knowledge of differentiation yields that the function t^3 is a solution. Thus $t^3 + c$ is also a solution, where c is an arbitrary constant (function). It is shown in the calculus that no further solutions exist (see page 5). Note that as soon as the solution t^3 is produced, Question I is answered in the affirmative; existence of infinitely many solutions gives an answer to Question II. Finally, all solutions are given by $y(t) = t^3 + c$.

Equations of the form (1–1) always have infinitely many solutions if one exists. Hence it is important to establish conditions for the existence of a solution. Under such conditions, Question II is of little value in its original form; a modified form will be given later.

The term *differential equations* will be used throughout this text to refer to equations of the form (1–1) and to certain generalizations of these equations; no attempt will be made to specify in a precise manner exactly what class or classes of equations will be so called.

Loosely speaking, differential equations "involve" derivatives (or differentials), and the "unknowns" are functions. As certain algebraic equations are classified according to "degree," so certain differential equations are classified according to "order." Thus (1-1) has *first order* because no derivatives (or differentials) of $y(t)$ of order greater than the first appear. More generally, the term *nth order* is applied to a differential equation in which derivatives (or differentials) of an "unknown" function of various orders may appear, those of all orders greater than n being absent and that of order n being certainly present. Thus,[1]

$$\frac{dy}{dt} = ty,$$

$$(t + y)\, dy = (t - y)\, dt,$$

$$\sin\left(\frac{d^5 y}{dt^5} + y\right) = \ln\left(\sqrt{t} + y\right)$$

are examples of differential equations of order 1, 1, 5, respectively. (NOTE: We have written and shall frequently write y instead of $y(t)$ for simplicity.)

*Domains of Functions. Mean Value Theorem.[2] It has been indicated that throughout this book we are concerned with functions; sometimes they are given and sometimes they are to be determined. It is important to recognize precisely what information is required in the specification of a function.

Basically, a function is a correspondence f associating with each member of a set A of objects, called the *domain*, a unique object of a set B called the *range set*.[3] In our work, the domain is almost always a set of real numbers, and the range set also consists of numbers (sometimes real, sometimes complex). In order to specify fully a function f, it is necessary to tell what the sets A and B are and then what the rule of correspondence is.

In practice, we often tend to overlook the necessity of specifying the domain and range set, because most of the familiar functions have a "natural" or "maximal" domain. Thus, if we define a func-

---

[1] The notation ln x denotes $\log_e x$. The notation log x is reserved for $\log_{10} x$.

[2] For a less comprehensive treatment of the subject, the sections marked by * can be omitted without interrupting the continuity of the presentation.

[3] The term *range* is used to designate the set of those objects in B which actually correspond to objects in the domain. It may consist of all of B or only a part of B.

tion f by the requirement $f(t) = t^2$, it is natural to assume that the domain as well as the range set consists of all real numbers t. Again, if $f(t) = 1/t$, then the "natural" domain is the set of all non-zero real numbers; if $f(t) = \sqrt{t}$, then the domain consists of all non-negative real numbers.

This practice is generally acceptable, but it can on occasion lead to difficulties. The reader is cautioned that a critical study of differential equations is not possible without the devotion of careful attention to the domains of functions which arise.

In performing the task of presenting the solution functions of a differential equation, it is often more or less satisfactory to present each function by a formula or rule of correspondence. The tacit assumption might be that the domain is the "natural" domain, while the range set is the set of all real (or complex) numbers. Yet it must be remembered that when a function is unknown, its domain is unknown too, and part of the task of determining such a function is to find its domain. Thus, in Example 1–4, the equation $y'(t) = 3t^2$ carried with it a statement that the domain of $3t^2$ was to be taken as the set of all real numbers. The solution $y(t) = t^3 + c$ has the same set as its natural domain.

A rather curious anomaly occurs, however, in case of the differential equation $y' = 1/t$, where the domain of $1/t$ is the set of all real $t \neq 0$. Here integral calculus suggests that $y = \ln |t| + c$ gives all solutions. However, if the domain of $\ln |t| + c$ is taken again as all $t \neq 0$, it is clear that further solutions exist. For example, if we define $z(t)$ for $t \neq 0$ so that

$$z(t) = \begin{cases} \ln |t| + c_1 & \text{for } t > 0, \\ \ln |t| + c_2 & \text{for } t < 0, \end{cases}$$

where $c_1 \neq c_2$, then, for every $t \neq 0$, $z'(t) = 1/t$, so that $z(t)$ is a solution of the equation. Two principles are therefore suggested:

1. Admissible solutions of differential equations shall be functions whose domains are intervals, that is, sets of the form

   all real numbers t such that $a \leqq t \leqq b$,

   or

   all real numbers t such that $a \leqq t$,

   or

   all real numbers t such that $t \leqq b$,

   or

   all real numbers t.

2. Solutions of a differential equation should have, but need not have, maximal domains subject to the restrictions in principle 1. It is not required that their domains agree with those of functions appearing in the equation.

From these principles, it appears that $\ln |t| + c \ (t \neq 0)$ would not be admissible as a solution of $y' = 1/t \ (t \neq 0)$ because principle 1 is violated. However, by principle 2, $\ln t + c \ (t > 0)$ [or $\ln(-t) + c \ (t < 0)$] would be admissible, even though its domain is less than that of $1/t$. Despite the ambiguity, we shall follow custom and write $\ln |t| + c$ to designate succinctly the two classes of solutions.

In Example 1-4, it was suggested that *all* solutions of the differential equation $y' = f(t)$ are given by $y = Y(t) + c$, where $Y(t)$ is a particular solution satisfying the equation. Before proving this result, we state the following theorem.

Mean Value Theorem. If $\phi(t)$ is continuous for $t_1 \leq t \leq t_2$ and if $\phi'(t)$ exists for $t_1 < t < t_2$, then there exists t_0 with $t_1 < t_0 < t_2$ such that

$$\phi(t_2) - \phi(t_1) = (t_2 - t_1)\phi'(t_0).$$

A proof of this theorem is to be found in most calculus books.

Let $Y(t)$ be a particular solution of $y' = f(t)$ and let $y(t)$ be any solution; it is assumed that all three functions are defined for all t such that $a \leq t \leq b$. Define $\phi(t) = y(t) - Y(t)$, so that

$$\phi'(t) = y'(t) - Y'(t) = f(t) - f(t) = 0$$

for $a \leq t \leq b$. Let t be given, and apply the mean value theorem with $t_1 = a$, $t_2 = t$; there exists t_0 between a and t such that

$$\phi(t) - \phi(a) = (t - a)\phi'(t_0) = 0.$$

If c is defined as $\phi(a)$, we have

$$y(t) - Y(t) = \phi(t) = \phi(a) = c,$$

so that $y(t) = Y(t) + c$ for all t such that $a \leq t \leq b$.

EXERCISES

In each of exercises 1 to 10, find answers to Questions I and II for the given numerical equation. Where solutions exist, find all of them. Use the real number system.

1. $x^3 - 2x^2 - 8x = 0.$
2. $x^3 + x - 2 = 0.$
3. $\dfrac{1}{x^2} - 1 = 0.$
4. $\dfrac{1}{x - 1} = \dfrac{2}{x^2 - 1}.$
5. $x = \sqrt{5x - 6}.$
6. $x = \sqrt{x + 2}.$
7. $2\sqrt{-x} + x = 1.$
8. $\sec x = \dfrac{1}{2}.$
9. $\dfrac{\sin x}{1 + \cos x} = \dfrac{1 - \cos x}{\sin x}.$
10. $\dfrac{1 - \cos x}{2} = \sin x.$

For the equation in each of exercises 11 to 14, answer Questions I and II.

11. $\tan x = x.$
12. $\sin x = x.$
13. $e^x = b$ (b a given real number).
14. $e^x + e^{-x} = 1.$

Each of exercises 15 to 21 contains an equation for an unknown real function $y(t)$ of the real variable t. For each equation find one solution; then write all solutions.

15. $\dfrac{dy}{dt} = \dfrac{1}{t^2}.$
16. $y' = \cos^2 t.$
17. $y' = \dfrac{1}{t^3 - 1}.$
18. $y' = te^t.$
19. $y' = \dfrac{1}{\sqrt{t^2 + 2t}}.$
20. $y' = t \ln t.$
21. $y' = \dfrac{t^2 + 1}{t(t - 2)}.$

In each of exercises 22 to 25, determine the order of the differential equation.

22. $\dfrac{d^3y}{dt^3} - \dfrac{dy}{dt} = 0.$

23. $(y^2 + 1)\, dy - (t^2 + y^2)\, dt = 0.$

24. $\dfrac{d^4y}{dt^4} + 3y\,\dfrac{dy}{dt} = t^2\left(1 + \dfrac{1}{t^2}\dfrac{d^4y}{dt^4}\right).$

25. $y + \sin^2\dfrac{d^2y}{dt^2} + \cos^2\dfrac{d^2y}{dt^2} = \dfrac{dy}{dt}.$

In each of exercises 26 to 29, y is an unknown function and the equation is assumed to be true for all real numbers u and v. Show that in each case infinitely many solutions exist.[4]

★26. $y(u + v) = y(u) + y(v).$

★27. $y(u + v) = y(u) \cdot y(v).$

★28. $y(u + 2\pi) = y(u).$

★29. $y^2\left(u + \dfrac{\pi}{2}\right) + y^2(u) = 1.$

★30. In exercise 19, determine the "natural" domain of each solution.

★31. In each of exercises 18, 20, and 21, specify appropriate domains for the function in the right side and the solutions found.

1-2. FAMILIES OF SOLUTIONS

Let us examine some possibilities relative to the collection of all solutions of a differential equation. It will be recalled that the equation[5]

$$(1\text{-}2) \qquad\qquad y'(t) = 3t^2$$

of Example 1-4 has an infinitude of solutions

$$(1\text{-}3) \qquad\qquad y(t) = t^3 + c.$$

Now consider the second-order equation

$$(1\text{-}4) \qquad\qquad y''(t) = 6t;$$

---

[4]Exercises marked by ★ are more difficult than the rest; they are intended primarily for students who are studying the entire text, including the sections similarly identified.

[5]As usual in the calculus, y', y'', $\cdots$ are alternative notations for $\dfrac{dy}{dt}$, $\dfrac{d^2y}{dt^2}$, $\cdots$.

one integration yields

$$y'(t) = 3t^2 + c_1,$$

and a subsequent integration gives

(1–5) $$y(t) = t^3 + c_1 t + c_2.$$

Now each of (1–3) and (1–5) represents an infinitude of functions; an essential difference exists between them, however, in that only one arbitrary constant or *parameter* occurs in (1–3), while two parameters appear in (1–5). One is thus led to speak of one- or *two*- or generally *n*-parameter families of functions.

It has been seen that (1–3) represents *all* solutions of (1–2); similarly, (1–5) represents *all* solutions of (1–4). One might expect that generally the totality of solutions of a differential equation coincides with some *n*-parameter family of functions. One might expect also that the number *n* is equal to the order of the differential equation. Actually, this is usually the case provided the proper qualifications and interpretations are made, though no proof will be attempted here.

It is natural now to raise a converse question. Suppose an *n*-parameter family of functions is given; is there a differential equation of order *n* naturally associated with the family, where we require at least that all the functions of the family should be solutions of the equation? While we do not here answer this question precisely and completely, we shall give a method of obtaining what we shall call "a differential equation of the family." Our method is quite general, although it is described for the case $n = 3$.

Given a family $y = f(t, c_1, c_2, c_3)$, differentiate three times with respect to t, assuming such differentiation to be possible, and obtain

$$\begin{cases} \dfrac{dy}{dt} = f'(t, c_1, c_2, c_3), \\[2mm] \dfrac{d^2y}{dt^2} = f''(t, c_1, c_2, c_3), \\[2mm] \dfrac{d^3y}{dt^3} = f'''(t, c_1, c_2, c_3). \end{cases}$$

If c_1, c_2, c_3 are eliminated among these three equations and the given equation, there results a relationship connecting t, y, y', y'', y''', which is the desired differential equation. When the elimination can be carried out, the resulting differential equation is *a differential equation* of the family, and the family is *the general solution of the differential equation*. When the general solution includes all solutions of the differential equation, it is called the *complete solution*. Thus the complete solution of a differential equation is a family of functions with two properties: 1) every member of the family is a solution, and 2) every solution is a member of the family.

Example 1-5. Find a differential equation of the family

$$(1\text{-}6) \qquad\qquad y = c_1 t + c_2.$$

Solution: Two differentiations yield

$$y' = c_1,$$

$$(1\text{-}7) \qquad\qquad y'' = 0.$$

Since (1–7) is free of c_1, c_2, this equation represents the result of elimination of c_1, c_2 and is the desired differential equation.

Example 1-6. Find a differential equation of the family

$$(1\text{-}8) \qquad\qquad y = c\left(t - \frac{1}{c}\right)^3.$$

Solution: Differentiation gives

$$(1\text{-}9) \qquad\qquad y' = 3c\left(t - \frac{1}{c}\right)^2.$$

By squaring the first equation and multiplying by $27c$, cubing the second, and then subtracting the results, we obtain

$$27cy^2 = y'^3.$$

Elimination of c gives

$$(1\text{-}10) \qquad\qquad 3yy'^2 = y'^3 t - 27y^2.$$

In Example 1–5 it is easily shown that the general solution (1–6) includes all solutions of (1–7). However, in the case of Example 1–6 there exists a solution of the differential equation (1–10) not included in the general solution (1–8), namely, $y = -27t^2/4$. The reader should check this by direct substitution. A detailed analysis of this situation for first-order equations is contained in the discussion which follows. It is important to understand that "general solution" and "totality of all solutions" do not necessarily mean the same thing in all cases.

*More on Elimination. The procedure of this section involves elimination of one or more parameters from a system of equations. This procedure is widely used in algebra, and generally the techniques available there are applicable here. There are certain complications, however.

Let us consider first a simple problem from analytic geometry. Parametric equations of a curve are $x = c$, $y = c^2$; it is desired to obtain the cartesian equation. Squaring the first equation and subtracting the result from the second give $y = x^2$. This last equation is a *consequence* of the given two, but it must now be shown to imply them. Thus one assumes $y = x^2$, defines $c = x$, and obtains $y = c^2$. This proves that if (x, y) satisfies $y = x^2$, then there exists c such that $x = c$, $y = c^2$. The two arguments together show that $y = x^2$ if and only if there exists c such that $x = c$, $y = c^2$.

An *eliminant* of equations $x = f(c)$, $y = g(c)$ is an equation $F(x, y) = 0$ such that for every (x, y), $F(x, y) = 0$ if and only if there exists c such that $x = f(c)$, $y = g(c)$.

It is well to recognize that an eliminant need not exist; and when it does exist, it does not necessarily arise from the simplest or most obvious technique of combining the given equations so as to eliminate c.

When x and y are functions of a variable t, there is an added point to notice. In elimination of c from $x = t + c$, $y = 1 + c^2$, for example, we may write $c = x - t$ and then $y = 1 + (x - t)^2$. In reversing steps we define $c = x - t$ and of course obtain $y = 1 + c^2$. Note that c is a function not only of x but also of t.

Let us now consider the problem of Example 1–6. It was found that c could be eliminated from

$$(1\text{–}8) \qquad\qquad y = c\left(t - \frac{1}{c}\right)^3,$$

$$(1\text{–}9) \qquad\qquad y' = 3c\left(t - \frac{1}{c}\right)^2,$$

so as to yield

$$(1\text{–}10) \qquad\qquad 3yy'^2 = y'^3 t - 27y^2.$$

There remains the task of showing, if possible, that for every pair (y, y') of functions of t satisfying the last equation, and such that the second is the derivative of the first, there exists a constant c

such that the given equations are true. Let us see how far we can proceed toward that end.

Assuming (1–10), we may clearly attempt to define c by any equation which appeared as a consequence of (1–8) and (1–9). One such equation was[6] $c = \dfrac{y'^3}{27y^2}$. Substitution of this value of c indeed shows that both (1–8) and (1–9) hold. It remains to show, if possible, that, if $c = \dfrac{y'^3}{27y^2}$ and (1–10) hold, then c must be a constant.

Nowhere in this converse argument have we used the fact that in (1–10) y' is the derivative of y. This condition becomes, when applied to (1–8) and (1–9),

$$0 = 3c\left(t - \frac{1}{c}\right)^2 - \frac{d}{dt}\left[c\left(t - \frac{1}{c}\right)^3\right]$$

$$= 3c\left(t - \frac{1}{c}\right)^2 - \frac{\partial}{\partial t}\left[c\left(t - \frac{1}{c}\right)^3\right] - \frac{\partial}{\partial c}\left[c\left(t - \frac{1}{c}\right)^3\right]c',$$

that is,

$$c' = 0 \quad \text{or} \quad \frac{\partial}{\partial c}\left[c\left(t - \frac{1}{c}\right)^3\right] = 0.$$

The first possibility leads to the desired conclusion. However, the second leads to

$$\frac{3}{c}\left(t - \frac{1}{c}\right)^2 + \left(t - \frac{1}{c}\right)^3 = 0.$$

It follows that either $c = 1/t$ or $c = -2/t$. Hence there appear to emerge from (1–10), in addition to the solutions given by (1–8) with $c = $ constant, two additional solutions, namely, $y = 0$ and $y = -27t^2/4$.

In this case, then, the elimination process which led from (1–8) and (1–9) to (1–10) introduced two solutions not present originally; (1–10) does not represent a true eliminant of (1–8) and (1–9). It follows also that the complete solution of (1–10) consists of the family (1–8) together with the two additional functions. The two "superfluous" solutions are called *singular solutions* of (1–10). They are evidently obtained from $\dfrac{\partial y}{\partial c} = 0.$

---

[6]Note that division by y suggests that the solution $y = 0$ is lost; this is actually not the case, as appears later.

When the type of analysis just given produces an entire family of "superfluous" solutions, it is no longer proper to refer to the given family as the general solution of the differential equation; in such a case, the general solution would contain both families.

Extension of these considerations to equations of higher order than the first is complicated and will not be attempted here. Similar phenomena may be expected to occur, however.

EXERCISES

In each of exercises 1 to 18, find a differential equation of the family of functions.

1. $y = ct.$

2. $y = \dfrac{c}{t}.$

3. $y = \dfrac{c}{t^2}.$

4. $y = ce^{t/c}.$

5. $y = c \ln \dfrac{t}{c}.$

6. $y = c_1 t^2 + c_2.$

7. $y = ct^2 e^t.$

8. $y = c \sin t.$

9. $\dfrac{x}{c} + \dfrac{y}{1-c} = 1.$

10. $(x - c)^2 + (y - c)^2 = c^2.$

11. $y = c_1 e^{-t} + c_2 t e^{-t}.$

12. $y = c_1 e^{5t} + c_2 t e^t.$

13. $y = c_1 (t - c_2)^2.$

14. $y = \sin(ct + c^2).$

15. $y = c\left(t - \dfrac{1}{c}\right)^2.$

16. $y = c\left(t - \dfrac{1}{c}\right)^n.$

17. $y = c(t - c)^n.$

18. $t \cos c + y \sin c = 1.$

★**19.** In exercise 15, determine whether the differential equation has any solutions beyond the general solution.

★**20.** In exercise 16, find any singular solutions which may exist.

1–3. ELEMENTARY GEOMETRIC INTERPRETATIONS; FIELD OF TANGENTS

Equations of the first order

(1–11)
$$\frac{dy}{dx} = f(x, y)$$

may be interpreted geometrically in the following manner. If $y = g(x)$ is a solution, consider the graph of this function, an arbitrary point $P(x, y)$ of the graph, and the tangent line to the curve at P. See Figure 1–1. The tangent has slope $m = g'(x)$. Since $y = g(x)$ is a solution of (1–11), we have a relationship connecting x, y, and the slope y', which holds at every point P of the curve. We say that (1–11) holds *along the curve*.

For example, the equation $y' = 2x$ holds along the curve $y = x^2$; that is, at every point of this parabola the slope of the tangent is equal to twice the abscissa at the point. Actually, the same is true at every point of each curve $y = x^2 + c$ of the family constituting the general solution of the differential equation.

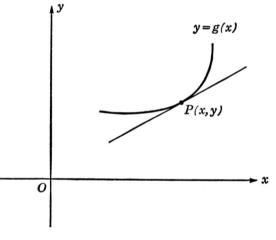

Figure 1–1

Example 1–7. At each point of a curve the slope of the tangent is equal to the reciprocal of the abscissa. Find all such curves.

Solution: The slope at (x, y) is $1/x$. Thus the differential equation which holds in consequence of this condition is

$$\frac{dy}{dx} = \frac{1}{x}.$$

The general solution is

$$y = \ln |x| + c.$$

If the general solution of (1-11) is

(1-12) $$y = g(x, c),$$

then the one-parameter family (1-12) of functions is represented graphically by a *one-parameter family of curves.* At each point $P(x, y)$ of any one of these curves the slope of the tangent to that curve is expressed by (1-11) in terms of x and y. This means that at each point P there is a tangential direction determined by (1-11) and hence a unique tangent line through P. Conceivably there may be more than one curve of the solution family passing through P, but all such curves have at P the same tangent. (See Section 1-7.) The directions so determined [one at each point of the domain of the function $f(x, y)$] constitute the *direction field* of (1-11), and the corresponding tangent lines constitute the *field of tangents.*

Example 1-8. Plot a graph showing the field of tangents for the equation $y' = x + y$.

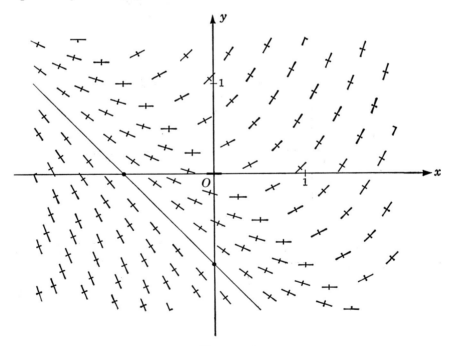

Figure 1-2

Solution: Without attempting to find the general solution, we draw through each point (x, y) a line having slope $x + y$. Thus at $(0, 0)$ the line is the x-axis; at $(1, 0)$ the line has slope 1, and so on. For convenience draw only a short segment of each line. The result is shown in Figure 1–2. Note the strong suggestion from Figure 1–2 that the lines can be grouped together so that those in each group are tangent to one curve of the solution family. It may also be expected that only one curve of the family passes through every point of the plane.

Since a differential equation is expected to have infinitely many solutions, the differential equation alone cannot specify a single solution. If we append to the equation one or more *initial* or *boundary conditions*, depending on the order of the equation, there may be singled out a specific solution. Thus, in the first-order case (1–11) we add the requirement that for a particular value of x, say $x = x_0$, y should have a specific value, say $y = y_0$. A solution $y = g(x)$ meeting this requirement satisfies $y_0 = y(x_0)$. Geometrically, a solution curve satisfying the initial condition passes through the point (x_0, y_0). This situation has already been observed in Example 1–8.

Example 1–9. The slope of a curve at (x, y) is equal to $1/x^2$, and the curve passes through $(1, 1)$. Find the curve.

Solution: The differential equation and initial condition are

(1–13)
$$\frac{dy}{dx} = \frac{1}{x^2},$$

(1–14)
$$y(1) = 1.$$

The solutions of (1–13) are given by $y = -(1/x) + c$. By (1–14), $x = 1$ implies $y = 1$, so that $1 = -1 + c$; hence $c = 2$. The solution curve passing through $(1, 1)$ thus has the equation $y = -(1/x) + 2$.

Example 1–10. A function $y = g(x)$ has the property $\frac{d^2y}{dx^2} = 1$; when $x = 0$, $y = 1$ and when $x = 1$, $y = 2$. Find the function.

Solution: Two successive integrations yield

$$y = \frac{x^2}{2} + c_1 x + c_2.$$

Since $x = 0$ implies $y = 1$, we have $c_2 = 1$; by imposing the final condition, we have

$$2 = \frac{1}{2} + c_1 + 1,$$

so that $c_1 = 1/2$. The desired function is given by

$$y = \frac{x^2}{2} + \frac{x}{2} + 1.$$

Note that two conditions are needed in addition to the second-order differential equation in order to determine a unique solution.

EXERCISES

In each of exercises 1 to 4, construct a field of tangents for the equation.

1. $y' = x^2 + y^2$.

2. $y' = x - y$.

3. $y' = \dfrac{y}{x} - \dfrac{x}{y}$.

4. $y' = 1 - \dfrac{y^2}{x}$.

5. In exercise 1, find the locus of points at which the tangents to the solution curves have a fixed slope s.

6. In exercise 4, find the locus of points at which the tangents to the solution curves pass through the origin.

7. In exercise 2, determine the set of all points P at which every solution curve through P is concave upward. (HINT: Impose the condition that $y'' > 0$.)

8. In exercise 4, find the set of all points P at which each solution curve is concave downward.

9. In exercise 1, find the curvature of every solution curve through $(1, 1)$.

$\star$**10.** In exercise 2, find all points at which a solution function assumes a maximum. Find all points at which a solution function assumes a minimum.

$\star$**11.** In exercise 3, find all points at which a solution assumes a minimum; a maximum.

1–4. EXISTENCE QUESTIONS

It has been seen that the first fundamental questions concerning a differential equation are (I) whether a solution exists and, if so, (II) how many solutions exist. It is also evident that II must be replaced by other questions, since knowledge that infinitely many solutions exist is not likely to be very helpful.

The equation of Example 1–4 has infinitely many solutions any two of which differ by a constant. We may therefore ask: if two or more functions are solutions of a given differential equation, is there a relationship among them? Or, if several solutions are known, can they be used to determine all (or almost all) others?

In Example 1–4 an equation of first order was found to have as complete solution a one-parameter family of functions; in Example 1–5 an equation of second order was found to have a two-parameter family of solutions. Generally, then, does a differential equation of order n have an n-parameter family of solutions including all, or nearly all, of them?

Again, when an n-parameter family of functions does not (as in Example 1–6) include all solutions of an equation of order n, how are all additional solutions obtained?

In Example 1–9, when an *initial* or *boundary condition* was appended to the differential equation, it was possible to find among all solutions of the equation a unique one which satisfied the condition. In general, then, one may ask how many initial or boundary conditions are required in order to single out a unique solution of a given differential equation of order n.

A detailed analysis of such existence and uniqueness questions for differential equations with or without initial or boundary conditions is deep and beyond our aims. However, we state here without proof a typical fundamental theorem bearing on this subject, which will be freely used throughout this book.

Theorem. Suppose $F(x, v)$ is continuous in x and that there exists a constant A such that

$$| F(x, w) - F(x, u) | \leq A | w - u |$$

for all values of x, w, u such that

$$| x - a | \leq b, \quad | w - c | \leq b', \quad | u - c | \leq b'.$$

Then there exists a unique function $y(x)$ defined on an interval $|x - a| \leqq b''$, such that

(1–15) $$y'(x) = F(x, y(x))$$

for $|x - a| \leqq b''$, and such that $y(a) = c$.

This theorem actually implies the existence of a one-parameter family of solutions of the equation (1–15) without initial condition. Thus for each c meeting the requirements of the hypothesis of the theorem, a solution exists depending on c. Such a solution may be written in the form $y = g(x, c)$, and a family with c as parameter results.

The existence of a suitable constant A as specified in the hypothesis of the theorem may be awkward to verify in special cases. It may be shown that, if F is defined in and on the boundary of the rectangular region in the xy-plane bounded by vertical lines $x = a + b$ and $x = a - b$ and the horizontal lines $y = c + b'$ and $y = c - b'$, and if $\dfrac{\partial F}{\partial y}$ is defined and continuous in, and on the boundary of, this rectangle, then the desired constant A exists.

It should be mentioned that the existence theorem extends to systems of differential equations, and so applies to equations of order higher than the first. For example,

$$y'' = G(x, y, y')$$

is equivalent to the system

$$\begin{cases} y' = z \\ z' = G(x, y, z). \end{cases}$$

To obtain a unique solution here, one appends boundary conditions of the form $y(a) = c$, $y'(a) = d$ (c, d being given numbers). A general theorem relating to this situation is found on page 120.

*More on Domains and the Existence Theorem. The reader should note how the statement of the existence theorem relates to the principles stated on pages 4 and 5 concerning the domains of solutions. In particular, the function $F(x, v)$ may be defined for x, v in any region of the xv-plane containing a rectangle with (a, c) as mid-point in which the conditions in the hypothesis are fulfilled. The conclusion of the theorem states the existence of a suitable interval $a - b'' \leqq x \leqq a + b''$ and a solution $y(x)$ having the interval as domain. It may well happen that the number b'' given in the theorem will be less than b; moreover, the domain of the solution given by the theorem need not be maximal.

To prove the sufficiency condition for the existence of A as in the hypothesis,[7] one uses the mean value theorem to obtain, for every x, w, u such that

$$| x - a | \leqq b, \quad | w - c | \leqq b', \quad | u - c | \leqq b',$$

a number y_1 between u and w such that

$$F(x, w) - F(x, u) = F_y(x, y_1)(w - u).$$

From function theory, we know that a continuous function defined over a rectangle and its boundary is bounded, that is, there exists A such that

$$| F_y(x, y_1) | \leqq A$$

regardless of where the point (x, y_1) may be in the rectangle. Hence

$$| F(x, w) - F(x, u) | \leqq A | w - u |.$$

Any upper bound of $| F_y(x, y) |$ will thus suffice as A.

EXERCISES

★1. For $F(x, v) = f(x) + kv$ determine directly a Lipschitz constant A as in the theorem which is effective for any rectangular domain of $F(x, v)$.

★2. For $F(x, v) = x^2 + v^2$ determine a Lipschitz constant for a rectangle of unit side with the origin at the center.

★3. For $F(x, v) = xv$ determine a Lipschitz constant for the rectangle described by $0 \leqq x \leqq 1, 0 \leqq v \leqq 1$.

★4. If the existence theorem is applied to $y' = 1/x$, $a = 1$, may the number b'' given by the theorem be any positive number? If not, what restriction must it obey? Why?

1–5. CHANGES IN FORM OF A DIFFERENTIAL EQUATION

The reader is familiar with techniques in solving algebraic equations involving replacement of a given equation by another

---

[7] Such a constant A is called a *Lipschitz constant*, and (1–15) is called a *Lipschitz condition* for $F(x, u)$.

whose solutions bear a known relation to those of the given equation. Thus an equation may be solved by solving one *equivalent* to it, that is, one having the same solutions. Or, the given equation may be replaced by one which it implies, provided solutions of the second are checked in the original so that any *extraneous* solutions may be detected and discarded. For example, $\sqrt{x} = 1$ implies $x = 1$ (obtained by squaring); here the solution of the second satisfies the first, so that no solutions are extraneous. Finally, if the given equation is implied by the second, its solutions are those of the second together with those (if any) which were lost in the transition. For example, $x^2 - x = 0$ may be solved by solving $x - 1 = 0$ and then appending the solution $x = 0$ lost through division by x.

Similar techniques are applicable to differential equations. Thus

$$y' = 1 + y^2$$

is equivalent to

$$\frac{1}{1 + y^2} \, y' = 1,$$

whence the solutions of either are those of the other. Again, in the case of

(1–16)
$$y' = \frac{\sin xy}{y},$$

it might be found expedient to change to the form

(1–17)
$$yy' = \sin xy.$$

However, one solution of (1–17) is $y = 0$, which is not a solution of (1–16), since (1–16) is meaningless when $y = 0$. The equation

(1–18)
$$y' = y$$

may be replaced by

(1–19)
$$\frac{y'}{y} = 1,$$

provided it is noted that any solution of (1–18) for which $y = 0$ for one or more values of x has been ruled out in the transition. Such solutions must be found independently and appended to the solutions of (1–19). Finally, derivative and differential forms of an equation, such as, for example,

$$\frac{dy}{dt} = y + t$$

and
$$dy = (y + t)\,dt,$$
are evidently equivalent.

Other changes in form result from transformations of variables. Thus

(1–20)
$$\frac{dy}{dt} = y$$

becomes, after substituting $y = e^u$,

$$e^u \frac{du}{dt} = e^u,$$

which is equivalent to

$$\frac{du}{dt} = 1.$$

(Note, however, the tacit assumption that y is always positive when y is replaced by e^u.) Elaboration of these procedures are best delayed until they are specifically used.

When a differential equation is written in differential form, the notation fails to convey the information as to which variable is independent. In

(1–21)
$$y\,dy + x\,dx = 0,$$

for example, such ambiguity exists. If (1–21) is replaced by

(1–22)
$$y \frac{dy}{dx} = -x,$$

the general solution is found to be $y = \pm\sqrt{c^2 - x^2}$, as the reader may show. However, if (1–21) is written

(1–23)
$$x \frac{dx}{dy} = -y,$$

the general solution is found to be $x = \pm\sqrt{c^2 - y^2}$. The two solutions thus obtained are closely related, both being obtainable from $x^2 + y^2 = c^2$, one by solving for y and the other by solving for x. In a certain extended sense to be discussed more fully in the next section, $x^2 + y^2 = c^2$ may be regarded as a solution of (1–21), since it determines the actual solution ($y = \pm\sqrt{c^2 - x^2}$ or $x = \pm\sqrt{c^2 - y^2}$) implicitly.

EXERCISES

In each of exercises 1 to 10, effect the indicated transformation of variable(s). State any restrictions introduced through the transformation.

1. $\dfrac{dy}{dx} = \dfrac{1}{\sqrt{1 - x^2}}$; $x = \sin u$.

2. $\dfrac{dy}{dt} = y + t$; $y = e^t v$.

3. $y^2 \dfrac{dy}{dx} - xy = 0$; $y = vx$.

4. $\dfrac{dy}{dx} - \dfrac{y}{x} = y^2$; $y = \dfrac{1}{u}$.

5. $(x + y)\dfrac{dy}{dx} = x - y$; $x = vy$.

6. $(x + y + 1)\dfrac{dy}{dx} = x + y + 2$; $y = -x + u$.

7. $3x\dfrac{dy}{dx} + 4y = e^x$; $x = e^t$.

8. $xy'' - 2(x + 1)y' + (x + 2)y = 1$; $y = e^x u$.

9. $x^2 y'' + xy' + y = 0$; $x = e^t$.

10. $y'' + y = 2x - 1$; $u = 2x - 1, y = v \cos x$.

1–6. IMPLICITLY DEFINED FAMILIES OF SOLUTIONS

In Sections 1–2 and 1–3 differential equations were seen to be connected with families of functions or curves involving a certain number of parameters. We shall consider here a natural extension of the ideas developed, in the special case of equations of first order.

A one-parameter family of curves has been described by an *explicit* equation $y = g(x, c)$. Somewhat greater generality can be achieved by employing instead an *implicit* equation

$$(1\text{–}24) \qquad\qquad g(x, y, c) = 0.$$

As in Section 1–2, we may attempt to obtain a corresponding differential equation. Since no assumption is to be made to the effect that (1–24) may be solved for y in terms of x and c, differentiation of (1–24) takes on the following form. We find the (total) differential of $g(x, y, c)$ and equate to zero:

$$(1\text{–}25) \qquad dg = \frac{\partial g}{\partial x}\, dx + \frac{\partial g}{\partial y}\, dy = 0.$$

Geometrically, (1–25) connects direction numbers dx, dy of the tangent lines of each curve of the family (1–24) with the coordinates x, y of the points of tangency and the parametric value c. When possible, elimination of c between (1–24) and (1–25) yields a relationship connecting x, y, dx, and dy. This last result is called a *differential equation* of the family (1–24), and (1–24) is called the *general solution* of the differential equation. It should be noted that the present extended ideas contain those of Section 1–2 as a special case.

Example 1-11. Find a differential equation of the family $x^2 + y^2 = c^2$.

Solution: Forming the differential, we obtain $2x\, dx + 2y\, dy = 0$, whence $x\, dx + y\, dy = 0$ is the desired equation, being free of c. (See the discussion of (1–21) in Section 1–5.)

Example 1-12. Find a differential equation of the family $(y - c)^2 = cx$.

Solution: Taking the differential, we have

$$2(y - c)\, dy = c\, dx.$$

Solving for c, we obtain

$$c = \frac{2y\, dy}{2dy + dx};$$

substitution in the original equation yields, after simplification,

$$y\, dx^2 - 2x\, dy\, dx - 4x\, dy^2 = 0,$$

which is the desired differential equation.

An important special case of the considerations just made occurs when c appears linearly in (1–24), so that (1–24) may be written

$$(1\text{–}26) \qquad h(x, y) = c.$$

In this case specification of (x, y) (in the domain of h) in (1–26) leads to one and only one value of c. This means that there is exactly one curve of the family (1–26) passing through every point (x, y). Here, as in Example 1–11, forming the differential

(1–27)
$$\frac{\partial h}{\partial x} dx + \frac{\partial h}{\partial y} dy = 0$$

of (1–26) gives directly the desired differential equation of the family (1–26).

The converse procedure, that of working from the differential equation to the solution family, is discussed at length for various classes of equations in Chapter 2. It is clear that when the left member of an equation can be recognized as a total differential, so that the equation is of the form (1–27), the general solution (1–26) can be written immediately. For example, the reader should note how easily the process in Example 1–11 may be reversed. It is easy to see, moreover, that under suitable conditions in this case the general solution includes all solutions, as we now show.

It suffices to prove that through any point (x_0, y_0) there is only one solution of (1–27). We shall suppose that $\frac{\partial h}{\partial x}$ and $\frac{\partial h}{\partial y}$ are continuous and that they are not both zero at (x_0, y_0). (Discussion of points, called *singular points*, at which $\frac{\partial h}{\partial x} = \frac{\partial h}{\partial y} = 0$ is beyond the aims of this book.) Suppose[8] $h_y(x_0, y_0) \neq 0$. Then by continuity $h_y(x, y) \neq 0$ for (x, y) in a suitable rectangle bounded by $x = x_0 \pm b$, $y = y_0 \pm b'$. It follows that (1–27) is equivalent to

$$\frac{dy}{dx} = - \frac{\dfrac{\partial h}{\partial x}}{\dfrac{\partial h}{\partial y}},$$

at least in the rectangle. Applying to this equation the existence theorem of Section 1–4, we see that there exists a unique solution $y = \phi(x)$ ($|x - x_0| \leq b''$) such that $y_0 = \phi(x_0)$. But $h(x, y) = c$, where $c = h(x_0, y_0)$, is also such a solution, and so must be equivalent to $y = \phi(x)$ at least for $|x - x_0| \leq b''$.

It is customary to refer to the curves of the family (1–26) as *level* curves for the function $h(x, y)$; for along each of these curves the function takes on the same value or "level."

[8] h_y means $\frac{\partial h}{\partial y}$.

Example 1-13. Find a differential equation of all circles with radius 1 and with centers on the x-axis.

Solution: We first find the equation (1-24) of the given family of curves. Let the abscissa c of the center of any member of the family be the parameter. The equation of a circle with center $(c, 0)$ and radius 1 is

$$(x - c)^2 + y^2 = 1;$$

this equation then represents the family. Differentiation as in (1-25) yields

$$2(x - c)\, dx + 2y\, dy = 0.$$

Combining the given equation with

$$(x - c)^2\, (dx)^2 - y^2\, (dy)^2 = 0$$

gives

$$(1 - y^2)\, (dx)^2 = y^2\, (dy)^2,$$

or

$$y\, dy \pm \sqrt{1 - y^2}\, dx = 0.$$

Either of the last two equations may be regarded as the desired differential equation.

Note. An equivalent derivative form of the desired differential equation may be obtained by selecting one of the variables, say x, as independent and eliminating c by substituting $x - c = -y\dfrac{dy}{dx}$ into the given equation.

EXERCISES

In each of exercises 1 to 12, find a differential equation of the given family of curves.

1. All lines in the xy-plane having slope 1.
2. The family $x^n + y^n = c$.
3. $3x^2 + 2y^2 = c$.
4. $cxy = x - y$.
5. $c(x^2 + 1) = y^3$.
6. $\dfrac{x^2}{4} + \dfrac{y^2}{c} = 1$.
7. $(x + y + 1)^2 = c(x - y)$.
8. $ce^{x+y} = y$.

9. The family of confocal conics

$$\frac{x^2}{a^2 + c} + \frac{y^2}{b^2 + c} = 1.$$

10. All tangent lines of the hyperbola $xy = 1$. Show also that this hyperbola is a solution curve of the differential equation.

11. $(y - c)^3 = (x - c)^2$.

12. $c_1 x^2 + c_2 y^2 = 1$.

13. Show that a differential equation of the family of lines $y = cx + f(c)$ is $y = y'x + f(y')$. This is *Clairaut's equation*.

*14. Find a differential equation of all circles in the xy-plane.

*15. Find a differential equation of all central conics in the xy-plane having center at the origin.

1–7. ENVELOPES; SINGULAR SOLUTIONS

It was seen in Example 1–6 that a differential equation of a family of functions (or curves) may have solutions (or solution curves) which are not members of the given family. On page 11 it was suggested that such extra or *singular* solutions arise from the equation obtained by partial differentiation of the given equation with respect to the parameter.[9] One class of singular solutions (though not the only one) has an important geometric significance and will now be studied.

The family $(x - c)^2 + y^2 = 1$ of circles satisfies the differential equation

$$(1\text{–}28) \qquad\qquad y^2(y'^2 + 1) = 1,$$

as Example 1–13 shows. As noted in Section 1–2, there may be additional solutions; in this case $y = 1$ and $y = -1$ satisfy (1–28). The relationship between these lines and the circles is clear: Each point P on each line is on exactly one of the circles, and at P the line and the circle have the same tangent.

In general, let

$$(1\text{–}29) \qquad\qquad g(x, y, c) = 0$$

[9] In the case of one-parameter families. We shall not attempt to treat more general cases in this book.

represent a one-parameter family of curves, and let

(1–30)
$$\begin{cases} x = h(c) \\ y = k(c) \end{cases}$$

represent a curve such that

(1–31) $$g(h(c), k(c), c) = 0$$

for every c in the domains of h and k. Suppose further that at $(h(c), k(c))$ the curve (1–30) has the same tangent as the curve of the family (1–29) corresponding to the parametric value c. The curve (1–30) (or the composite of all such curves if several exist) is called the *envelope* of the family (1–29).

Every curve (1–30) as described must be a solution of the differential equation of the family (1–29), since, at each point of (1–30), the coordinates x, y and the direction numbers dx, dy of the tangent are the same as those at the same point on the appropriate curve of (1–29). Now direction numbers of the tangent to (1–30) are $h'(c)$, $k'(c)$ if these are not both zero; similarly, direction numbers of the tangent to the curve of (1–29) are

$$-g_y(h(c), k(c), c), \quad g_x(h(c), k(c), c),$$

provided these are not both zero. Hence we have, for every c,

(1–32) $$h'(c)g_x(h(c), k(c), c) + k'(c)g_y(h(c), k(c), c) = 0.$$

From (1–31) and the theory of partial differentiation, we have

$$0 = \frac{d}{dc} g(h(c), k(c), c)$$

$$= g_x(h(c), k(c), c)h'(c) + g_y(h(c), k(c), c)k'(c) + g_c(h(c), k(c), c).$$

Using (1–32), we find

(1–33) $$g_c(h(c), k(c), c) = 0.$$

Since every point (x, y) of the envelope must satisfy

(1–34)
$$\begin{cases} g(x, y, c) = 0 \\ g_c(x, y, c) = 0 \end{cases}$$

for some c, it follows that (1–34) may be regarded as implicit parametric equations of a locus including the envelope. However, it must be noted that (1–34) may define loci other than the envelope. For example, (1–32) may hold when the coefficients g_x and g_y are both zero, without implying coincidence of tangents to (1–29) and (1–30). Thus (1–34) may include the locus of cusp points, if any (see Example 1–15), or the locus of points of self-intersection, if any, of the curves of (1–29).

Example 1–14. Find the envelope of the family $cy = (x - c)^2$.

Solution: Equations (1–34) become

$$\begin{cases} cy - (x - c)^2 = 0, \\ y + 2(x - c) = 0. \end{cases}$$

Elimination of x yields

$$cy - \frac{y^2}{4} = 0,$$

so that $y = 0$ or $y = 4c$. Thus we obtain two lines,

$$\begin{cases} y = 0, \\ x = c, \end{cases} \quad \text{and} \quad \begin{cases} y = 4c, \\ x = -c, \end{cases}$$

which are also represented, after elimination of the parameter, by

$$y = 0 \quad \text{and} \quad y = -4x.$$

The differential equation of the given family is

$$2y(y' + 2) - xy'^2 = 0,$$

and it is satisfied by both $y = 0$ and $y = -4x$. That these two lines, clearly not members of the family of parabolas, are actually the envelope is easily verified.

Example 1–15. Find the envelope of the family $(x + c)^2 = cy^3$.

Solution: Equations (1–34) for this case are

$$\begin{cases} (x + c)^2 = cy^3, \\ 2(x + c) = y^3. \end{cases}$$

Elimination of y yields

$$(x + c)^2 = 2c(x + c),$$

so that

$$x + c = 0 \quad \text{or} \quad x + c = 2c.$$

We thus obtain two curves

$$\begin{cases} x = -c, \\ y = 0, \end{cases} \quad \text{and} \quad \begin{cases} x = c, \\ y = \sqrt[3]{4c}. \end{cases}$$

Elimination of c gives

$$y = 0 \quad \text{and} \quad y^3 = 4x.$$

The differential equation of the family is

$$9xyy'^2 = 6y^2y' - 4.$$

Obviously $y = 0$ is not a solution of this equation and therefore is not part of the envelope. However, $y^3 = 4x$ is a solution and is the entire envelope. A sketch of the family shows that $y = 0$ is the locus of cusps of the curves of the family.

EXERCISES

In each of exercises 1 to 6, find an equation of the envelope of the given family.

1. All lines tangent to $y = x^2$.

2. $x \cos c + y \sin c = 1$.

3. $y = -x^2 \sec^2 c + x \tan c$.

4. All lines tangent to $y = x^3$.

5. $(x - c)^2 + y^2 = c^2$.

6. $y = c\left(x - \dfrac{1}{c}\right)^3.$

7. Find a differential equation of the family in exercise 3 and show that the envelope as found is a solution curve.

8. Find an equation of the family of normal lines to the parabola $y^2 = 4x$; then find parametric equations of the envelope of the family. (HINT: Use the ordinate of a variable point on $y^2 = 4x$ as parameter.)

★9. Using the results of exercise 8, show that the center of the circle of curvature of $y^2 = 4x$ at each point $(c^2/4, c)$ lies on the envelope of the family of normals.

★10. Find the envelope of the normals to the ellipse $\dfrac{x^2}{a^2} + \dfrac{y^2}{b^2} = 1$.

★11. Using the results of exercise 10, show as in exercise 9 that for each point of the ellipse the center of curvature lies on the envelope of normals.

★12. Generalize the results of exercises 8 to 11 to a curve $y = f(x)$. (The envelope of normals is the locus of centers of curvature and is called the *evolute* of the given curve.)

Chapter

2

Differential Equations of First Order

2–1. PRELIMINARIES

For the most part this chapter deals with techniques for finding the solutions of certain equations of the first order, primarily those of the form $y' = f(x, y)$ or $g(x, y)y' = f(x, y)$. It will frequently be convenient to change the form of such equations as discussed in Section 1–5, and this will be done freely; however, one must always be conscious of the possibility of losing or gaining solutions by such changes.

2–2. SEPARABLE VARIABLES

When an equation can be brought into the form

$$(2\text{--}1) \qquad\qquad f(x)\, dx = g(y)\, dy,$$

the variables are said to be *separable*. Such equations can be solved by the following procedure. One integrates the left side with respect to x, obtaining $F(x)$; one integrates the right side with respect to y, obtaining $G(y)$. The general solution of (2–1) is then

$$(2\text{--}2) \qquad\qquad F(x) = G(y) + c.$$

Justification of this result lies in verification that the family (2–2) has differential equation (2–1) in the sense of Section 1–6. Indeed, the total differential of (2–2) is exactly (2–1). It is easily shown (see Section 1–6) that (2–2) represents all solutions of (2–1).

Example 2–1. Solve $y' = y$.

Solution: Ruling out any solutions for which $y = 0$ for some value of x, we write the equation in the form

$$\frac{dy}{y} = dx.$$

30

Integration gives
$$\ln |y| = x + c_1,$$
which is equivalent to
$$|y| = e^{x+c_1} = e^{c_1}e^{x}.$$
Hence
$$y = \pm\, e^{c_1}e^{x},$$
or

(2–3)
$$y = ce^{x},$$

where $c = \pm e^{c_1}$. It is clear that the constant c may be any non-zero real number. However, if we allow $c = 0$, we obtain[1] $y = 0$, which also satisfies the given differential equation. Hence (2–3), in which c is an arbitrary constant, represents all solutions except possibly any which are zero for some values of x and non-zero for others. Now the theorem of Section 1–4 applies here, yielding one and only one solution y for which $y = 0$ when $x = x_0$. But the zero function has this property, so that any solution which vanishes for a particular $x = x_0$ vanishes for all values. It follows that (2–3) represents all solutions of the given equation.

Example 2–2. Solve $y' + P(x)y = 0$.

Solution: Separating the variables, we have (again assuming y is never zero),

$$\frac{dy}{y} = -\, P(x)\, dx.$$

Integration gives
$$\ln |y| = -\!\int P(x)\, dx + c_1,$$

where $\int P(x)\, dx$ designates a particular integral of $P(x)$. Then
$$|y| = e^{c_1}e^{-\int P(x)\,dx},$$
or

(2–4)
$$y = ce^{-\int P(x)\,dx} \qquad\qquad (c = \pm e^{-c_1} \neq 0).$$

Again the zero solution is obtained by allowing c to be zero. Thus
$$y = ce^{-\int P(x)\,dx} \qquad\qquad (c \text{ arbitrary})$$

gives all solutions by an argument similar to that in Example 2–1.

---

[1] Here $y = 0$ means the *zero function*, whose value is 0 for every x.

Example 2-3. Solve $xy' - y = 0$.

Solution: Write the equation in the form

$$\frac{dy}{y} = \frac{dx}{x},$$

and integrate; the result is

$$\ln |y| = \ln |x| + c_1 = \ln |x| + \ln c_2.$$

Thus

(2-5) $$|y| = c_2 |x| \qquad\qquad (c_2 > 0),$$

and

$$y = \pm c_2 x = cx \qquad\qquad (c \neq 0).$$

But $y = 0$ also satisfies the equation, so that the solution is

$$y = cx \qquad\qquad (c \text{ arbitrary}).$$

*Restrictions in Domains. The reader should note that the treatment of Example 2-1 (and similarly of Example 2-2) seems incomplete. That is, solutions $y(x)$ may conceivably exist for which $y(x) = 0$ for x in some interval but $y(x) \neq 0$ for x outside that interval. We recall that a solution is always sought, as indicated in Section 1-1 (page 4), having an interval as domain. It follows that if $y(x_0) = 0$, then $y(x) = 0$ for all values of x in some interval containing x_0 as central point (see the existence theorem in Section 1-4). Similarly, suppose $y(x_0) \neq 0$. Then, since y is differentiable, y is continuous; hence $y(x) \neq 0$ for x in a suitable interval about $x = x_0$.

Actually, much more can be said. Suppose $y(x_0) = 0$, and consider the set of upper endpoints $x_0 + b$ of intervals containing x_0 in which $y(x) = 0$ and for which $x_0 + b$ is in the domain of $y(x)$. Then if $y(x_1) \neq 0$ for some $x_1 > x_0$, the numbers $x_0 + b$ have an upper bound (namely, x_1). By the properties of the real number system, they have a least upper bound B. Since $B \leqq x_1$, B is in the (interval) domain of $y(x)$. By continuity,

$$0 = \lim_{\substack{x \to B \\ x < B}} y(x) = y(B).$$

Now B may be the upper endpoint of the domain of $y(x)$. Otherwise, there exists an interval about B such that a unique solution $Y(x)$ exists such that $Y(B) = 0$. On this interval, $B - \epsilon \leqq x \leqq B + \epsilon$, $Y(x)$ agrees with $y(x)$. But then $B + \epsilon$ is an upper endpoint of an interval containing x_0 in which $y(x) = 0$, contrary to the definition of B.

The contradiction proves that either $y(x) = 0$ for all $x \geq x_0$, or $y(x) = 0$ for all x such that $x_0 \leq x \leq B$, where B is the upper end-point of the domain of $y(x)$. A similar argument for values $x \leq x_0$ proves that, if a solution y of $y' = y$ [or $y' + P(x)y = 0$] has the value 0 for one value of x, then $y(x) = 0$ for all values of x in the domain of $y(x)$.

In Example 2–3, the method of solution rules out $x = 0$ from the domain of any solution function. Thus the final totality of solutions must have the set of all x such that $x > 0$, or the set of all x such that $x < 0$, as domain. Here it is clear that if $y(x)$ is any solution, then $y(0) = 0$. But if $(0, 0)$ is chosen as an initial point, it will be a singular point for the given equation when the latter is written in the form $y\, dx - x\, dy = 0$. (See Section 1–6.) The existence theorem does not apply to the origin as initial point, and indeed it is clear that infinitely many solutions exist (for example, $y = cx$) such that $y(0) = 0$. (See exercises 11, 12 of the group which follows.)

EXERCISES

In each of exercises 1 to 10, find the general solution. Where an initial condition is given, find also the solution which satisfies it.

1. $2xy' + y = 0$.
2. $y(x^2 + 1)y' + 4 = 0$.
3. $x^2y\, dx + (x + 1)\, dy = 0$ (when $x = 1$, $y = 1$).
4. $xy\, dx + e^x\, dy = 0$.
5. $y^3\, dx + \sqrt{1 - x^2}\, dy = 0$.
6. $\cos x \cot y + \sin x\, (\cos y)y' = 0$.
7. $y(x^2 - 1) + (y^2 + 1)y' = 0$.
8. $xy\, dx + \ln y\, dy = 0$ (when $x = 2$, $y = 1$).
9. $(x^3 + 1)y' + xy^2 = 0$.
10. $y^2 \sec^2 x\, dy + x\, dx = 0$.

$\star$**11.** Given that $y(x)$ ($|\, x\, | \leq b$) is any solution of $xy' = y$ such that $y(0) = 0$ and such that $\lim\limits_{x \to 0} \dfrac{y(x)}{x} = c$. Prove that $y(x) = cx$.
[HINT: Define

$$z(x) = \begin{cases} \dfrac{y(x)}{x} & (x \neq 0), \\ c & (x = 0); \end{cases}$$

then show that $z'(x) = 0$ for all x.]

★12. By means of an analysis similar to that in exercise 11, show that the only solution $y(x)$ of the equation in exercise 1 such that $y(0) = 0$ is the zero function.

2–3. TRANSFORMATIONS OF VARIABLES

It has been indicated in Section 1–5 that introduction of new variables may be useful in the solution of differential equations.

Example 2–4. Solve the equation

$$(2\text{–}6) \qquad\qquad y' = x + y,$$

in which the variables are not separable.

Solution: Introduce a new dependent variable v through the transformation

$$(2\text{–}7) \qquad\qquad y = e^x v;$$

no change in independent variable is to be made. Substitution into (2–6) yields

$$e^x v' + e^x v = x + e^x v,$$

or

$$\frac{dv}{dx} = xe^{-x}.$$

Integrating, we have

$$v = \int xe^{-x}\, dx = -e^{-x}(x + 1) + c,$$

so that, from (2–7), we obtain the solution

$$y = ce^x - (x + 1).$$

Many variations of the technique just described occur. For example, sometimes the independent variable alone is transformed and sometimes both are transformed together by equations

$$(2\text{–}8) \qquad\qquad \begin{cases} x = \phi\,(u,\, v), \\ y = \psi\,(u,\, v). \end{cases}$$

In order to ensure that the transformed equation is equivalent to the original, one should ascertain that the equations (2–8) can be solved for u, v in terms of[2] x, y. The reader should check Example 2–4 for

[2]This means that the *jacobian* $\begin{vmatrix} \phi_u & \phi_v \\ \psi_u & \psi_v \end{vmatrix}$ of the transformation is different from 0.

this requirement. (In this case, $x = u$.) There are no general rules for determining what change of variable, if any, will be effective in transforming an equation into one which may be more readily solved.

Certain simple differential equations may be grouped into classes such that a particular type of transformation is effective for an entire class. This fact is illustrated in subsequent sections, but no complete classification exists. Generally, trial-and-error methods based on experience will provide the best means of finding workable transformations.

Example 2–5. Solve $y' = xy^2 - y$.

Solution: If the equation is written in the form

$$\frac{1}{y^2}\frac{dy}{dx} = -\frac{1}{y} + x,$$

we are led to recall that

$$\frac{d}{dx}\left(\frac{1}{y}\right) = -\frac{1}{y^2}\frac{dy}{dx},$$

and hence to attempt to use the transformation

$$y = \frac{1}{u}.$$

There results

$$\frac{du}{dx} = u - x.$$

Example 2–4 suggests the transformation $u = e^x v$, which leads to the solution

$$u = ce^x + (x + 1),$$

whence

$$y = \frac{1}{ce^x + (x + 1)}.$$

Here, as frequently occurs, two or more transformations may be used in succession.

EXERCISES

In each of the following exercises, transform the equation as indicated and find the general solution.

1. $xyy' + x^6 - 2y^2 = 0$; let $y = x^2 v$.
2. $(2x^3 y + 2xy^3)\,dx + (2x^2 y^2 + 2y^4 + \ln y)\,dy = 0$;
$$\text{let } x^2 = v - y^2.$$

3. $y' = 3x^2y - 3x^4 + 2x^2 - 2y + 2x$;   let $y = x^2 + e^v$.

4. $(y + xy^2) \, dx - (x + 2x^2y) \, dy = 0$;   let $v = xy$.

5. $x \left[(x^2 + y^2)^{3/2} + 2y^2 \right] dx + y \left[(x^2 + y^2)^{3/2} - 2x^2 \right] dy = 0$;
$$\text{let } x = r \cos \theta, \, y = r \sin \theta.$$

6. $x(6x^2 + 14y^2) \, dx + y(13x^2 + 30y^2) \, dy = 0$;
$$\text{let } x^2 = 5u - 2v, \, y^2 = -2u + v.$$

7. $2y (\ln x)(\ln y) \, dx + x[(\ln x)^2 + (\ln y)^2] \, dy = 0$;
$$\text{let } x = e^{u+v}, \, y = e^{u-v}.$$

8. $xy \, dx - (y^4 + x^2) \, dy = 0$;   let $x = u^2 - v^2, \, y = u - v$.

2-4. HOMOGENEOUS EQUATIONS

The equation

(2-9)
$$\frac{dy}{dx} = f(x, y)$$

is called a *homogeneous* first-order equation if $f(x, y)$ is homogeneous of degree zero [that is, if $f(tx, ty) = f(x, y)$ for every x, y, t for which (x, y) and (tx, ty) are in the domain of f]. In this case the transformation $y = vx$ carries (2-9) into

$$v + x \frac{dv}{dx} = f(x, vx) = f(1, v).$$

Separating the variables and integrating, we have

$$\int \frac{dv}{f(1, v) - v} = \int \frac{dx}{x}.$$

The solution is then obtained by placing $v = y/x$. Note that $x = 0$ must be excluded from the domain of any solution, unless $f(x, y) = 0$.

Example 2-6. Solve $y' = \dfrac{xy}{x^2 + y^2}$.

Solution: If we let $y = vx$, we have

$$v + x \frac{dv}{dx} = \frac{vx^2}{x^2 + v^2x^2} = \frac{v}{1 + v^2},$$

whence

$$x \frac{dv}{dx} = -\frac{v^3}{1 + v^2},$$

and

$$\int \frac{1 + v^2}{v^3} \, dv = -\int \frac{dx}{x}.$$

Thus

$$-\frac{1}{2v^2} + \ln|v| = -\ln|x| + c_1,$$

so that

$$\ln|vx| = c_1 + \frac{1}{2v^2}.$$

Then

$$|vx| = e^{c_1}e^{1/(2v^2)},$$

$$vx = ce^{1/(2v^2)} \qquad (c = \pm e^{c_1} \neq 0).$$

Finally, remembering that $y = vx$, we obtain

(2–10) $$y = ce^{x^2/(2y^2)}.$$

While the method of solving excludes the solution $y = 0$, this may be included in (2–10) by allowing c to be zero.

Example 2-7. Solve the equation

(2–11) $$\frac{dy}{dx} = \frac{x + y - 1}{x - y + 3}.$$

Solution: Equation (2–11), while not homogeneous, may be brought into a homogeneous form by a transformation of variables. A *translation*

$$\begin{cases} x = u + h \\ y = v + k \end{cases}$$

leads to

(2–12) $$\frac{dv}{du} = \frac{u + v + (h + k - 1)}{u - v + (h - k + 3)}.$$

Choose h, k so that

$$h + k - 1 = 0,$$
$$h - k + 3 = 0,$$

that is, choose $h = -1$, $k = 2$. Then (2–12) becomes

$$\frac{dv}{du} = \frac{u + v}{u - v},$$

which is homogeneous. The reader should show that solution may be completed by means of the transformation $v = wu$. (See exercise 13 of the following group.)

EXERCISES

In exercises 1 to 12, solve each equation which is homogeneous.

1. $y' = \dfrac{3x - y}{x + 2y}$.

2. $y' = \dfrac{xy + 3}{5x - y}$.

3. $y' = \dfrac{y}{x} + \sin \dfrac{y}{x}$.

4. $y' = \dfrac{2xy}{x^2 - y^2}$.

5. $y' = \dfrac{2xy + 3y}{x^2 + 2y^2}$.

6. $y' = \dfrac{x^3 + y^3}{xy^2}$.

7. $y' = \dfrac{x^2 e^{y/x} + y^2}{xy}$.

8. $y' = \dfrac{x^3 + x^2y - y^3}{x^3 - xy^2}$.

9. $y' = \dfrac{y + \sqrt{x^2 - y^2}}{x}$.

10. $y' = 1 + \dfrac{3y}{x}$.

11. $y' = \dfrac{2x^2 + 2y^2 - 3xy}{xy}$.

12. $y' = \dfrac{2y^3 + 2x^2y}{2xy^2 + x^3}$.

13. Complete the work of Example 2–7.

14. Solve the equation $y' = \dfrac{4x - 3y - 17}{3x + y - 3}$ by making a translation which replaces the equation by one which is homogeneous.

2–5. EXACT EQUATIONS

It was remarked at the end of Section 1–6 that, if an equation of the form

(2–13) $$M(x, y)\, dx + N(x, y)\, dy = 0$$

is such that the left member is the (total) differential of a function $h(x, y)$, the solution is given by the implicitly defined family

$$h(x, y) = c.$$

Whenever this occurs, the equation (2–13) is called an *exact* first-order differential equation.

Our first task is to determine under what conditions (2–13) is exact. If it is assumed that

$$M \, dx + N \, dy = dh(x, y),$$

then it follows that

$$(2\text{--}14) \qquad M = \frac{\partial h}{\partial x}, \quad N = \frac{\partial h}{\partial y}.$$

If it is assumed further that h has mixed second partial derivatives at least one of which is continuous, then it is known that

$$\frac{\partial^2 h}{\partial x \, \partial y} = \frac{\partial^2 h}{\partial y \, \partial x}.$$

Differentiation of (2–14) thus yields

$$(2\text{--}15) \qquad \frac{\partial M}{\partial y} = \frac{\partial N}{\partial x}.$$

It is easy to see that not all equations (2–13) are exact. For example, $y \, dx - x \, dy = 0$ does not meet the requirement (2–15), as the reader may show.

We now indicate that (2–15) is sufficient to ensure that (2–13) is exact, and at the same time we develop a method of solving (2–13) when (2–15) holds.

In passing from h to $\frac{\partial h}{\partial x}$ we differentiate with respect to x, regarding y as constant. The reverse process, leading from $M = \frac{\partial h}{\partial x}$ to the desired function h is thus integration with respect to x with y held constant. Thus we attempt to obtain h by

$$(2\text{--}16) \qquad h(x, y) = \int M \, dx + C(y),$$

where the "constant" of integration $C(y)$ is a function of y. An attempt to determine $C(y)$ is made with the help of the equation $N = \frac{\partial h}{\partial y}$. Assuming $C(y)$ to be differentiable, we have

$$N = \frac{\partial h}{\partial y} = \frac{\partial}{\partial y} \int M \, dx + C'(y).$$

Differentiation under the integral sign gives

(2–17) $$\qquad\qquad N - \int \frac{\partial M}{\partial y} \, dx = C'(y).$$

Equation (2–17) is meaningful only if the left member does not involve x. But this may be verified by differentiation with respect to x:

$$\frac{\partial N}{\partial x} - \frac{\partial}{\partial x} \int \frac{\partial M}{\partial y} \, dx = \frac{\partial N}{\partial x} - \frac{\partial M}{\partial y} = 0.$$

Now integration of (2–17) with respect to y gives

(2–18) $$\qquad\qquad C(y) = \int \left(N - \int \frac{\partial M}{\partial y} \, dx \right) dy,$$

and substitution into (2–16) gives $h(x, y)$. The proof is easily completed by the reader by showing that $h(x, y)$ actually satisfies (2–14).

It has been shown[3] that a necessary and sufficient condition for exactness of (2–13) is (2–15). Moreover, (2–16) and (2–18) give a formula for the general solution of any exact equation.

Example 2–8. Solve the equation

(2–19) $$\qquad\qquad (x + y) \, dx + (x - y) \, dy = 0.$$

Solution: Here $M = x + y$, $N = x - y$, $\dfrac{\partial M}{\partial y} = 1$, $\dfrac{\partial N}{\partial x} = 1$, whence (2–15) holds and (2–19) is exact. The function $h(x, y)$ is given by

$$\begin{aligned}
h = \int M \, dx &= \int (x + y) \, dx \\
&= \frac{x^2}{2} + xy + C(y).
\end{aligned}$$

But

$$x - y = N = \frac{\partial h}{\partial y} = x + C'(y),$$

so that

$$C'(y) = -y.$$

---

[3] The reader who is familiar with line integration will find a more satisfactory proof in treatises on advanced calculus.

It follows that a particular choice of $C(y)$ is

$$C(y) = -\frac{y^2}{2},$$

and

$$h(x, y) = \frac{x^2}{2} + xy - \frac{y^2}{2}.$$

The solution is thus

$$\frac{x^2}{2} + xy - \frac{y^2}{2} = c.$$

[Note that the constant of integration is omitted in the formulas for $C(y)$ and $h(x, y)$, since in the end $h(x, y)$ is set equal to an arbitrary constant.]

It is clear that slight modification of an exact equation may lead to one that is not exact. For example, if in (2–19) the middle sign is changed, giving

(2–20) $(x + y)\, dx - (x - y)\, dy = 0,$

(2–15) no longer holds. Of course (2–20) [and even (2–19)] may be solved by the method of Section 2–4, in view of homogeneity.

Frequently, familiarity with simple differential expressions will aid in solving exact equations by inspection. For example, (2–19) may be written

$$x\, dx - y\, dy + (y\, dx + x\, dy) = 0,$$

or

$$x\, dx - y\, dy + d(xy) = 0.$$

Integration yields

$$\frac{x^2}{2} - \frac{y^2}{2} + xy = c,$$

which agrees with the solution found in Example 2–8.

EXERCISES

In each of exercises 1 to 10, show that the equation is exact and find the general solution. Where an initial condition is given, find also the solution which satisfies it.

1. $(x^2 y - 2x)\, dx + (y^2 + \frac{1}{3} x^3)\, dy = 0.$

2. $(3x^2y^2 - 4y)\, dx + (3y^2 - 4x + 2x^3y)\, dy = 0.$

3. $(3y^2 + y \sin 2xy)\, dx + (6xy + x \sin 2xy)\, dy = 0.$

4. $(2x + 2y - 3)\, dx + (1 - 2y + 2x)\, dy = 0 \quad (x = 1,\, y = 2).$

5. $\left(\dfrac{2x}{y} + 5y^2 - 4x\right) dx + \left(3y^2 - \dfrac{x^2}{y^2} + 10xy\right) dy = 0.$

6. $[\sec^2 (x - 2y) + \cos (x + 3y) - 3 \sin 3x]\, dx$
$\qquad\qquad + [3 \cos (x + 3y) - 2 \sec^2 (x - 2y)]\, dy = 0.$

7. $(3x^2 e^{x^3} + e^{2y})\, dx + (2xe^{2y} - 3)\, dy = 0 \quad (x = 0,\, y = 0).$

8. $\dfrac{1 - 6x^2y}{x}\, dx + \dfrac{2 + 5y - 3x^2y}{y}\, dy = 0.$

9. $\dfrac{8x^4y + 12x^3y^2 + 2}{2x + 3y}\, dx + \dfrac{2x^5 + 3x^4y + 3}{2x + 3y}\, dy = 0.$

10. $\dfrac{x^2y^5 + y^2 + y}{1 + x^2y^4}\, dx + \dfrac{x^3y^4 + 2xy + x}{1 + x^2y^4}\, dy = 0.$

★11. a. Show that the equation

$$(3x - 2y + 2y^2)\, dx + (2xy - x)\, dy = 0$$

is not exact.

b. Where does the attempt to solve the equation by the method for exact equations fail?

c. Show that the equation obtained by multiplying this equation by x is exact.

d. Solve this exact equation.

★12. a. Show that the equation

$$(2x^2y - y^2 + 6x^3y^3)\, dx + (2x^4y^2 - x^3)\, dy = 0$$

is not exact.

b. Find, if possible, numbers n and m such that the equation obtained by multiplying the given equation by $x^n y^m$ is exact.

c. Solve the exact equation (if one has been found) of part **b.**

★13. Show that the equation

$$(x^4 - 3y)\, dx + 3\, dy = 0$$

is not exact and that the device of exercise 12 will not lead to an exact equation.

2–6. INTEGRATING FACTORS

When a differential equation

$$(2\text{--}13) \qquad M\ dx + N\ dy = 0$$

fails to satisfy the condition (2–15) for exactness, it may be possible to find an *integrating factor*, that is, a function $\mu(x, y)$ such that multiplication of (2–13) by μ converts it into an exact equation

$$(2\text{--}21) \qquad \mu M\ dx + \mu N\ dy = 0.$$

Example 2–9. Solve the equation

$$(2\text{--}22) \qquad y\ dx - x\ dy = 0.$$

Solution: This equation is not exact, as has been seen. Remembering the formula for the differential of y/x, namely

$$\frac{x\ dy - y\ dx}{x^2},$$

we have a clue to a possible integrating factor. For if (2–22) is multiplied by $1/x^2$, we have

$$(2\text{--}23) \qquad \frac{y\ dx - x\ dy}{x^2} = 0,$$

that is,

$$- d\left(\frac{y}{x}\right) = 0.$$

The desired solution is $y/x = c$. Of course, (2–23) may also be solved by the method of Section 2–5 with $M = y/x^2$, $N = -1/x$. Another integrating factor of (2–22) is $1/(x^2 + y^2)$, as the reader may show.

We see that (2–21) is exact when

$$\frac{\partial(\mu M)}{\partial y} = \frac{\partial(\mu N)}{\partial x},$$

that is, when

$$(2\text{--}24) \qquad N\ \frac{\partial \mu}{\partial x} - M\ \frac{\partial \mu}{\partial y} = \mu\left(\frac{\partial M}{\partial y} - \frac{\partial N}{\partial x}\right).$$

Any solution of (2–24) is clearly an integrating factor of (2–13); existence of such may be proved under assumption of continuity of M, N, $\dfrac{\partial M}{\partial y}$, $\dfrac{\partial N}{\partial x}$, but cannot be considered here. If μ is never zero, we may write (2–24) in the form

(2–25) $$N \frac{\partial \ln |\mu|}{\partial x} - M \frac{\partial \ln |\mu|}{\partial y} = \frac{\partial M}{\partial y} - \frac{\partial N}{\partial x}.$$

Special kinds of integrating factors can sometimes be determined from (2–25). For example, if μ is to be a function of x only, (2–25) becomes

(2–26) $$\frac{\partial \ln |\mu|}{\partial x} = \frac{1}{N}\left(\frac{\partial M}{\partial y} - \frac{\partial N}{\partial x}\right).$$

Such a function μ exists only if the right side of (2–26) is a function of x only:

$$\frac{1}{N}\left(\frac{\partial M}{\partial y} - \frac{\partial N}{\partial x}\right) = \phi(x).$$

Then

$$\mu = \pm e^{\int \phi(x)\,dx}$$

is an integrating factor. (Since a constant times an integrating factor is again one, the positive sign may be used.) The reader should determine when an integrating factor exists which is a function of y only.

Example 2–10. Solve the equation

(2–22) $$y\,dx - x\,dy = 0.$$

Solution: Here $M = -x$, $N = y$,

$$\frac{1}{N}\left(\frac{\partial M}{\partial y} - \frac{\partial N}{\partial x}\right) = -\frac{1}{x}(1 + 1),$$

so that

$$\mu = e^{-\int (2/x)\,dx} = e^{-\ln x^2} = \frac{1}{x^2}$$

is an integrating factor. (See Example 2–9.)

EXERCISES

In each of exercises 1 to 4, find an integrating factor which is a function of x alone and use it to solve the equation.

1. $(20y - 20xy^2)\,dx + (5x - 8x^2y)\,dy = 0.$
2. $(y^3 + 2xy^3 + 1)\,dx + 3xy^2\,dy = 0.$
3. $(x^3 + 2y)\,dx + (x + 1)\,dy = 0.$
4. $(2y \cos x - 1)\,dx + \sin x\,dy = 0.$

In each of exercises 5 to 8, find an integrating factor which is a function of y alone and solve the equation.

5. $(y + 6xy^3 - 4y^4) \, dx - (2x + 4xy^3) \, dy = 0.$

6. $(2xy^2 + 2x) \, dx + (6y^3 + 2y + 4x^2y) \, dy = 0.$

7. $3x^2y \ln y \, dx + [2x^3 + 2y^3 + 3y^3 \, (\ln y)^2] \, dy = 0.$

8. $(2x + 2xy^2 - y^3 - y^5) \, dx + (1 - 3xy^2 - 3xy^4) \, dy = 0.$

In each of exercises 9 to 12, determine whether there is an integrating factor of the form $x^n y^m$, and, if there is such, solve the equation.

9. $x^2 y \, dx + (x^2 - y^2) \, dy = 0.$

10. $xy^2 \, dx + (3 - 2x^2y) \, dy = 0.$

11. $(y + 2x^3) \, dx + (2x - x^4y^{-1}) \, dy = 0.$

12. $(x^3 + y^2) \, dx + (xy - 3x^2) \, dy = 0.$

2–7. LINEAR EQUATIONS

An equation of first order is called *linear* if it is of the form

$$(2\text{–}27) \qquad \frac{dy}{dx} + P(x)y = Q(x).$$

Such equations are of the utmost importance.

In Example 2–2 the case of (2–27) in which $Q = 0$ was treated fully. In this case (2–27) is called a *homogeneous linear* equation (not to be confused with the homogeneous equations of Section 2–4). The solution for the homogeneous linear case was found to be

$$y = ce^{-\int P(x)\,dx}.$$

The general case may be treated by a change of dependent variable

$$y = u(x) \cdot v,$$

where $u(x)$ is a function to be specified. Substitution yields

$$(2\text{–}28) \qquad u \frac{dv}{dx} + v \left(\frac{du}{dx} + Pu \right) = Q.$$

Variables are separable if u is chosen to satisfy

$$\frac{du}{dx} + Pu = 0 \qquad\qquad (u \neq 0),$$

for example, if $u = e^{-\int P dx}$, where the integral involved is a specific integral of $P(x)$ (see Example 2–2). Then (2–28) becomes

$$\frac{dv}{dx} = \frac{1}{u} Q,$$

whence

$$v = \int \frac{Q}{u}\, dx + c,$$

where the integral is again specific. It follows that

$$y = u \int \frac{Q}{u}\, dx + cu,$$

or, in view of the specific choice made for u,

$$(2\text{–}29) \qquad y = e^{-\int P dx} \int Q e^{\int P dx}\, dx + c e^{-\int P dx}.$$

It follows that (2–29) represents not only the general solution, but also the complete solution of (2–27).

An alternative treatment of (2–27) is the following. Multiplication of the left member of (2–27) by $e^{\int P dx}$ carries it into

$$e^{\int P dx} \frac{dy}{dx} + P y e^{\int P dx} = \frac{d}{dx}(y e^{\int P dx}).$$

Solution of (2–27) is then obtained by integrating

$$\frac{d}{dx}(y e^{\int P dx}) = Q e^{\int P dx}.$$

The result again leads to (2–29). The factor $e^{\int P dx}$ may actually be regarded as an integrating factor of the original equation if it is written in the form

$$(2\text{–}30) \qquad (Py - Q)\, dx + dy = 0.$$

Indeed, the reader may show that (2–30) meets the requirement of Section 2–6 for existence of an integrating factor which is a function of x only, and that the method of obtaining such an integrating factor leads to $e^{\int P dx}$.

Example 2-11. Solve

(2-31)
$$\frac{dy}{dx} + xy = e^{-x^2/2} \cos x.$$

Solution: An integrating factor is $e^{\int x\,dx} = e^{x^2/2}$, so that (2-31) becomes

$$e^{x^2/2} \frac{dy}{dx} + yxe^{x^2/2} = \frac{d}{dx}(ye^{x^2/2}) = \cos x.$$

The solution is

$$ye^{x^2/2} = \sin x + c,$$

or

$$y = e^{-x^2/2} \sin x + ce^{-x^2/2}.$$

Example 2-12. Solve

$$x \frac{dy}{dx} + y = x^3.$$

Solution: To apply the present theory, we must divide by x (and thus exclude $x = 0$):

$$\frac{dy}{dx} + \frac{1}{x} y = x^2.$$

Although the formula for the integrating factor

$$e^{\int P\,dx} = e^{\int (1/x)\,dx} = e^{\ln |x|} = |x|$$

is valid only for $x > 0$ (or only for $x < 0$) because of discontinuity at $x = 0$, it is nevertheless seen that $\mu = x$ is effective and defined for all values of x. Multiplication by x gives the original equation

$$\frac{d}{dx}(xy) = x^3,$$

and integration yields

$$xy = \frac{x^4}{4} + c,$$

$$y = \frac{x^3}{4} + \frac{c}{x} \qquad\qquad (x \neq 0).$$

(Of course one might avoid introducing an integrating factor by observing the exactness of the given equation.)

EXERCISES

In each of exercises 1 to 10 find the complete solution. Where an initial condition is given, find also the solution which satisfies it.

1. $y' + 3y = x + 1$.

2. $y' - 2y = \cos 3x$.

3. $y' - y = 2e^x$.

4. $y' - \dfrac{2}{x} y = 1 - x^2$ (when $x = 1$, $y = 1$).

5. $y' + x^2 y = (x^2 + 1)e^x$.

6. $y' + \dfrac{1}{x} y = \ln x - 2$.

7. $y' - (\tan x)y = \sin x$ (when $x = \pi/4$, $y = 1$).

8. $y' + \dfrac{2}{1 - x^2} y = 3$.

9. $y' \sin x - y \cos x = \cot x$.

10. $y' - xy = x^3$.

11. Show that the substitution $u = y^{-n+1}$ ($n \neq 1$) replaces the equation

$$y' + P(x)y = Q(x)y^n$$

by one of the form of (2–27) in u.

In each of exercises 12 to 15, solve by the method of exercise **11.**

12. $y' - 4y = xy^3$.

13. $y' + \dfrac{2}{x} y = x^2 y^{-2}$.

14. $y^5 y' + 5y^6 = 1$.

15. $y' + xy = xy^5$.

2–8. EQUATIONS OF HIGHER ORDER SOLVED BY FIRST-ORDER METHODS

A differential equation of order greater than 1 may, under suitable conditions, be solved by the methods already developed with the help of appropriate changes of variables. The following examples will illustrate some of the procedures.

Example 2–13. Solve $y''' = x$.

Solution: Let $p = y'$, so that $p'' = x$. Now let $q = p'$, whence $q' = x$. Integration yields

$$p' = q = \frac{x^2}{2} + c_1;$$

another integration gives

$$y' = p = \frac{x^3}{6} + c_1 x + c_2.$$

By a final integration, we have

$$y = \frac{x^4}{24} + c_1 \frac{x^2}{2} + c_2 x + c_3.$$

This method applies equally well to $y^{(n)} = f(x)$.

Example 2–14. Solve $y'' + y' = x$.

Solution: Let $p = y'$ and obtain the linear equation

$$p' + p = x.$$

Multiplication by the integrating factor $e^{\int dx} = e^x$ gives

$$\frac{d}{dx}(pe^x) = p'e^x + pe^x = xe^x,$$

so that

$$\begin{aligned}
p &= e^{-x} \int xe^x \, dx + c_1 e^{-x} \\
&= e^{-x} e^x (x - 1) + c_1 e^{-x} \\
&= x - 1 + c_1 e^{-x}.
\end{aligned}$$

It remains to solve

$$y' = (x - 1) + c_1 e^{-x};$$

the result is

$$y = \frac{x^2}{2} - x - c_1 e^{-x} + c_2.$$

The method of Example 2–14 serves in general to reduce by **1** the order of an equation involving x, y', y'', $\cdots$ but not y.

Example 2–15. Solve

$$\frac{d^2 y}{dt^2} + y = 0.$$

Solution: Substituting $p = \dfrac{dy}{dt}$, we have

$$y'' = \frac{dp}{dt} = \frac{dp}{dy}\frac{dy}{dt} = p\frac{dp}{dy}.$$

The equation becomes

$$p\frac{dp}{dy} + y = 0.$$

Integration gives

$$p^2 + y^2 = c_1^2;$$

it follows that

$$\frac{dy}{dt} = p = \pm\sqrt{c_1^2 - y^2}.$$

Separating the variables, we have

$$\frac{dy}{\sqrt{c_1^2 - y^2}} = \pm\, dt,$$

so that

(2–32)
$$\text{arc sin } \frac{y}{c_1} = \pm t + c_2.$$

Solution of (2–32) for y gives

$$\begin{aligned}
y &= c_1 \sin\left(\pm(t \pm c_2)\right) \\
&= A \sin(t + \alpha) && (A = \pm c_1,\ \alpha = \pm c_2) \\
&= A \cos\alpha \sin t + A \sin\alpha \cos t \\
&= C_1 \sin t + C_2 \cos t && (C_1 = A\cos\alpha,\ C_2 = A\sin\alpha).
\end{aligned}$$

Example 2–16. Solve $y'' - y = 0$.

Solution: Using the same substitution as in Example 2–15, we obtain

$$p\frac{dp}{dy} - y = 0,$$

$$\frac{dy}{dt} = p = \pm\sqrt{c^2 + y^2},$$

$$\ln\left| y \pm \sqrt{c^2 + y^2} \right| = t + c_2,$$

$$y \pm \sqrt{c^2 + y^2} = c_2' e^t.$$

Solving algebraically for y, we obtain

$$y = \frac{c}{2}\left(\frac{c_2'}{c} e^t - \frac{c}{c_2'} e^{-t}\right)$$

$$= C_1 e^t + C_2 e^{-t} \qquad \left(C_1 = \frac{c_2'}{2}, \; C_2 = -\frac{c^2}{2c_2'}\right).$$

Example 2–17. Solve

$$\frac{d^2y}{dt^2} \pm k^2 y = 0 \qquad\qquad (k \neq 0).$$

Solution: Let $t = \dfrac{u}{k}$. Then

$$\frac{dy}{dt} = \frac{dy}{du} \cdot \frac{du}{dt} = k\frac{dy}{du},$$

$$\frac{d^2y}{dt^2} = k\frac{d^2y}{du^2}\frac{du}{dt} = k^2 \frac{d^2y}{du^2}.$$

The given equation becomes, after division by k^2,

$$\frac{d^2y}{du^2} \pm y = 0.$$

The solution by Example 2–15 or 2–16 is

$$y = C_1 \sin u + C_2 \cos u$$

or

$$y = C_1 e^u + C_2 e^{-u};$$

that is, for the case of the positive sign,

$$y = C_1 \sin kt + C_2 \cos kt,$$

or, for the case of the negative sign,

$$y = C_1 e^{kt} + C_2 e^{-kt}.$$

Example 2–18. Solve

(2-33) $$\frac{d^2y}{dt^2} + a\frac{dy}{dt} + by = 0 \qquad (a, b \text{ constants}, a \neq 0).$$

Solution: Let $y = u(t) \cdot v$, where $u(t)$ is a function of t to be specified. Then

$$\frac{dy}{dt} = u\frac{dv}{dt} + v\frac{du}{dt},$$

$$\frac{d^2y}{dt^2} = u\frac{d^2v}{dt^2} + 2\frac{du}{dt}\frac{dv}{dt} + v\frac{d^2u}{dt^2}$$

and the equation becomes

(2–34) $uv'' + (2u' + au)v' + (u'' + au' + bu)v = 0.$

Let u be chosen so that

$$2u' + au = 0,$$

for example, $u = e^{-(a/2)t}$, whence (2–34) becomes

$$v'' + \frac{4b - a^2}{4}v = 0.$$

When $4b - a^2$ is positive or negative, we may solve for v by the method of Example 2–17 and obtain

$$y = uv = e^{-(a/2)t}\left(C_1 \sin\frac{\sqrt{4b - a^2}}{2}t + C_2 \cos\frac{\sqrt{4b - a^2}}{2}t\right),$$

or

$$y = e^{-(a/2)t}\,(C_1 e^{(\sqrt{a^2-4b}/2)t} + C_2 e^{(-\sqrt{a^2-4b}/2)t}),$$

according as $4b - a^2$ is positive or negative. When $4b - a^2 = 0$, the solution is seen to be

$$y = e^{-(a/2)t}\,(C_1 t + C_2).$$

EXERCISES

Solve the equation in each of exercises 1 to 10.

1. $(1 + 2x)y'' + y' = 0.$
2. $xy'' = 1 + x^2.$
3. $(1 + x^2)y'' + 1 + y'^2 = 0.$
4. $(x + 2)y'' - (x + 1)y' + x = 0.$
5. $y'' + 3yy' = 0.$
6. $yy'' = 1 + y'^2.$
7. $(1 - x^2)y'' + xy' = 2x.$
8. $xy'' - y' + xy'^2 = 0.$

9. $6y'' + 11y' + 4y = 2$.

10. $3y'' - 4y' + y = e^x$.

*11. Show that the complete solution of $y'' - k^2y = 0$ $(k \neq 0)$ may be written $y = c_1 \cosh kx + c_2 \sinh kx$.

*12. Show that the complete solution of $y'' + k^2y = 0$ $(k \neq 0)$ may be written $y = a \cos (kx + \phi)$, where a, ϕ are arbitrary constants. (HINT: Apply Example 2–17 and use a technique of normalization.)

2–9. SIMULTANEOUS EQUATIONS

In the theory of algebraic equations, methods of solving single equations may be applicable to the solution of simultaneous equations. Similar techniques are applicable to systems of differential equations in the simpler cases. For example, given the equations

$$\begin{cases} \dfrac{dy}{dx} = f(x, y), \\[2mm] \dfrac{dz}{dx} = g(x, y, z), \end{cases}$$

where y and z are two unknown functions of x, one solves the first for y, substitutes in the second, and then solves for z. The complete solution is so obtained.

Example 2–19. Solve

$$\begin{cases} \dfrac{dy}{dx} = y, \\[2mm] \dfrac{dz}{dx} = x + y + z. \end{cases}$$

Solution: The first equation yields $y = c_1 e^x$, whence the second becomes, after substitution,

$$\frac{dz}{dx} - z = x + c_1 e^x.$$

This linear equation is solved by the method of Section 2–7. The result is

$$\begin{aligned} z &= c_2 e^x + e^x \int (x + c_1 e^x)e^{-x} \, dx \\ &= c_2 e^x + e^x[e^{-x}(-x - 1) + c_1 x] \\ &= c_1 x e^x + c_2 e^x - x - 1. \end{aligned}$$

This, coupled with $y = c_1 e^x$, gives the solution.

EXERCISES

In each of exercises 1 to 9, solve the system of equations.

1. $\begin{cases} \dfrac{dy}{dx} = -2, \\[2mm] \dfrac{dz}{dx} = xe^{y+2x}. \end{cases}$

2. $\begin{cases} \dfrac{dy}{dx} + y = e^x, \\[2mm] \dfrac{dz}{dx} = y. \end{cases}$

3. $\begin{cases} \dfrac{dy}{dx} = z, \\[2mm] \dfrac{dz}{dx} = y. \end{cases}$

4. $\begin{cases} -x\,dx = y\,dy, \\[1mm] y\,dz = 2\,dx. \end{cases}$

5. $\dfrac{dx}{xz} = \dfrac{dy}{yz} = \dfrac{dz}{8xy^2}.$

6. $\begin{cases} \dfrac{dy}{dx} + 2z = y, \\[2mm] \dfrac{dz}{dx} + 4y = 0. \end{cases}$

7. $\begin{cases} \dfrac{dy}{dx} = x + 2z, \\[2mm] \dfrac{dz}{dx} = 3x + y - z. \end{cases}$

(HINT: Let $v = y + z$.)

8. $\begin{cases} \dfrac{dy}{dx} = x^2 + 6y + 4z, \\[2mm] \dfrac{dz}{dx} = y + 3z. \end{cases}$

[HINT: Find constants k, l, m such that $k(6y + 4z) + l(y + 3z) = m(ky + lz)$ and let $v = ky + lz$.]

9. $\begin{cases} \dfrac{dy}{dx} = x + y + z, \\[2mm] \dfrac{dz}{dx} = 1 - y - z. \end{cases}$

*10. Generalize the method of exercise 8 to the system

$$\begin{cases} \dfrac{dy}{dx} = f(x) + Ay + Bz, \\[2mm] \dfrac{dz}{dx} = g(x) + Cy + Dz, \end{cases}$$

where A, B, C, D are constants.

MISCELLANEOUS EXERCISES

In each of the following exercises, find the general solution. Where initial conditions are given, find also the particular solution satisfying them.

1. $y' = x^2 y$.

2. $(y \cos xy + y - x)\, dx + (x \cos xy + x - y)\, dy = 0$
$(x = 1, y = 1)$.

3. $y^{\mathrm{iv}} - 4y'' = 0$.

4. $(x - y + 1)\, dx + (2y - 2x + 3)\, dy = 0$.

5. $\dfrac{dx}{x} = \dfrac{dy}{y} = \dfrac{dz}{z}$ $(x = 1, y = 1, z = 2)$.

6. $x^{n-1}y^m\, dx + \dfrac{m}{n} x^n y^{m-1}\, dy = 0$.

7. $\dfrac{dy}{dx} = \dfrac{1}{x^5 + xy}$.

8. $x^2 y^5\, dx + e^{x^3}\, dy = 0$ $(x = 0, y = 2)$.

9. $(x + 2y + 2)\, dy = (3x - y - 1)\, dx$.

10. $x\sqrt{x^2 + a^2}\, dx = y\sqrt{y^2 - a^2}\, dy$.

11. $(e^x \cos y + x)\, dx - (e^x \sin y + y)\, dy = 0$.

12. $dx + (y + 1 - 3x)\, dy = 0$ $(x = 4, y = 0)$.

13. $\begin{cases} x \dfrac{dy}{dx} = y, \\[2mm] \dfrac{dz}{dx} = 3y - x. \end{cases}$

14. $y''' + 4y' = 0$ $(x = 0, y = 0, y' = 1, y'' = 0)$.

15. $\left(x + \dfrac{x}{x^2 + y^2}\right) dy + \left(y - \dfrac{y}{x^2 + y^2}\right) dx = 0$

$$(x = 1, y = \sqrt{3}).$$

16. $y'' = xy'^3$.

17. $\dfrac{dy}{dx} = \dfrac{y}{y - y^3 + 2x}$.

18. $\dfrac{dy}{dx} = \sin^3 y \cos^2 x$.

19. $(xy - x)\, dx = (xy^2 + x - y^2 - 1)\, dy$.

20. $(x^2 y + 2y^3)\, dx - (2x^3 + 3xy^2)\, dy = 0$.

21. $xy\, dy + \left(2x + \dfrac{y^2}{2}\right) dx = 0$.

22. $2xy^2\, dx + (1 - x^2 y)\, dy = 0$.

23. $x^2 \dfrac{dy}{dx} - y^2 = 2xy$.

24. $\begin{cases} \dfrac{dy}{dx} = z, \\[2mm] \dfrac{dz}{dx} = w, \\[2mm] \dfrac{dw}{dx} = y. \end{cases}$

25. $e^{2x+3y}\, dx + e^{4x-5y}\, dy = 0$.

26. $y'' \sin x = y'$.

27. $(3y^2 - 2x^2)\, dx = 2xy\, dy$.

28. $(3y + 2)y'' = y'^2$.

29. $\dfrac{dx}{y} = \dfrac{dy}{z} = \dfrac{dz}{x}$.

(HINT: Let $x + y + z = u$ and show that $x\, du = u\, dz$.)

30. $x^2 y'' - 2y = 0$.

(HINT: Let $x = e^u$.)

3

Applications

3–1. PRELIMINARIES

The reader is familiar with the fact that mathematical techniques may often be used in the solution of "applied" problems. Usually such problems occur in fields other than mathematics, such as physics, chemistry, biology, and economics. However, applications may be made also within the field of mathematics itself. A familiar example is the use of algebraic equations in the solution of geometric problems; thus formulas, like the pythagorean relationship, connecting geometric quantities provide equations which may be solved for one or more numerical "unknowns."

In much the same way fields in which numerically valued functions of numbers occur, and in which one or more derivatives of such functions have significance, may be suitable ground for the application of differential equations. For example, in the mechanics of particle motions on a line, say the x-axis, the position x of a particle is a function of time t; $v = \dfrac{dx}{dt}$ is velocity, $\dfrac{d^2x}{dt^2} = \dfrac{dv}{dt}$ is acceleration, mv is momentum (m being the mass), etc. Certain equations (mechanical laws) connecting one or more of these quantities with x or t or both appear as differential equations. Again, in plane analytic geometry, $y = f(x)$ represents a curve and $\dfrac{dy}{dx}$ is the slope of the curve; an equation connecting $\dfrac{dy}{dx}$, x, and $y\,[\,=f(x)]$ is a differential equation expressing a property of the curve.

The process of "setting up" a differential equation, or a system of such equations, for an applied problem cannot be reduced to a set of routines, because of the great variety of possible problems, even with respect to essential features. Generally speaking, one first identifies certain known, specified functions and then recognizes or introduces certain unknown or desired functions; then one translates appropriate formulas, laws, or relationships into mathematical

57

equations connecting the various functions. These equations must, of course, involve the desired functions and their derivatives in order that the theory of differential equations be applicable. In addition, the problem may contain certain numerical data, which when translated become "initial conditions" or "side conditions." In many cases, solution of the problem is achieved by finding the complete solution of the differential equations and then imposing the initial or side conditions.

The reader is warned not to rely too closely on the outline given above. Variations, both minor and major, may be required; for example, more steps may be involved, or the problem may require reformulation in a more idealized way to avoid the involvement of factors about which insufficient information exists. Occasionally the problem does not require that the solution(s) of the differential equation(s) be found; perhaps determination of certain properties of the solution(s) is all that is needed. In short, every problem must be considered by itself and must be thoroughly understood and translated into mathematical form; the mathematical problem so obtained is then solved; and the solution is finally interpreted for the original problem.

In the succeeding sections, illustrations of a few broad types of application which exhibit the most usual methods are given. No attempt is made to give all the background for the physical laws, etc., which are needed.

3–2. RATES

A familiar interpretation of the derivative $\dfrac{du}{dt}$ of a function u of t is as the "rate of change of u with respect to t." A case of particular interest is that in which t is interpreted as time. Such rates arise in many areas, and so a wide variety of applications is possible. We briefly describe a few of these.

A. Natural Growth. In biology, economics, and elsewhere a population, substance, or quantity is regarded as consisting of many units or elements. It is assumed that each unit produces new population, substance, or quantity at a constant rate. Instead of measuring the population by the number of units, we use a number u which may be any non-negative real number; for example, u may measure weight or mass of the population. Replacement of the

discrete measure by the continuous measure represents an idealization which may, in some cases, interfere with the faithfulness with
which the mathematical model represents the biological or other
applied situation. For many purposes, however, sufficient accuracy
is obtained.

Under the assumption of the law of natural growth, the quantity
u is a function of time t such that

$$(3\text{–}1) \qquad \frac{du}{dt} = ku,$$

where k is a positive constant representing the rate at which u
increases per unit time per unit of quantity u present. The constant
k has the units of the reciprocal of time, and it is often expressed in
percentage per unit time. This *unit rate* k is not to be confused with
the *rate* $\dfrac{du}{dt}$, which is measured in quantity units per unit time.

Example 3–1. A mold grows at a rate which is proportional to the
amount present. Initially the quantity is 2 ounces. In 2 days the
quantity has increased to 5 ounces. Find the quantity in 10 days.

Solution: If the quantity of mold u can be expressed as a function
of time t, this function can be evaluated for $t = 10$ to give the
result. The stated law is the law of natural growth,

$$(3\text{–}1) \qquad \frac{du}{dt} = ku,$$

where k is a constant. The linear equation (3–1) may be solved, as
in Example 2–2, to yield

$$(3\text{–}2) \qquad u = ce^{kt}.$$

The origin of time may be selected at the initial instant; the initial
condition then becomes $u(0) = 2$. Hence $2 = c$. Substitution into
(3–1) yields

$$(3\text{–}3) \qquad u = 2e^{kt}.$$

The side condition $u = 5$ when $t = 2$ may now be imposed to give

$5 = 2e^{2k}$. Rather than solve for k, we find $e^k = \left(\dfrac{5}{2}\right)^{1/2}$. Then (3–2)
becomes

$$u = 2 \cdot \left(\frac{5}{2}\right)^{t/2}.$$

When $t = 10$, $u = 2 \cdot \left(\dfrac{5}{2}\right)^{5} = 195.3$ ounces, approximately.

B. Natural Decay. The rate at which a radioactive substance loses mass is apparently proportional to the mass present. If M is the mass at time t, then

(3–4)
$$\frac{dM}{dt} = kM$$

for some negative constant k. This law of decay is the same as the law of natural growth, except that the unit rate k is negative. The time required for the mass to diminish to half its initial value is called the *half-life*.

C. Heating and Cooling. A warm (or cold) object placed in an environment where the ambient temperature remains constant loses (or gains) heat, as measured by its temperature, at a rate approximately proportional to the difference between its temperature and the ambient temperature.

D. Continuous Compounding of Interest. An amount of money P_0 drawing interest at an annual rate of i per cent compounded n times a year (in regular intervals) is increased to

$$P_1 = P_0 + \frac{i}{100n} P_0$$

at the end of one nth of a year; to

$$P_2 = P_1 + \frac{i}{100n} P_1$$

at the end of two $n$ths of a year; and so on. By induction,

$$P_k = P_{k-1} + \frac{i}{100n} P_{k-1} \qquad (k = 1, 2, \cdots),$$

so that

(3–5)
$$\frac{P_k - P_{k-1}}{1/n} = \frac{i}{100} P_{k-1} \qquad (k = 1, 2, \cdots ; n = 1, 2, \cdots).$$

Equation (3–5) shows that the ratio of the increase in principal to the length of the interval of compounding is not dependent on this length and is i per cent of the earlier of the two principals. This suggests a definition of *continuously compounded interest* by the formula

(3–6)
$$\frac{dP}{dt} = \frac{i}{100} P.$$

This law is again the same as that of natural growth. Note that, for interest compounded n times a year in the usual way, $\dfrac{dP}{dt}$ is not a useful concept; for it is zero when t is not an integral multiple of $1/n$ and does not exist when t is a multiple of $1/n$.

E. Evaporation. The rate at which water evaporates is approximately proportional to the surface area exposed, if we neglect the effects of such factors as temperature, humidity, and wind. For containers of simple shape, it is possible to express the surface area exposed in terms of the volume of the container and so obtain an equation of the form

$$(3\text{-}7) \qquad \frac{dV}{dt} = kf(V).$$

F. Mixtures. In the study of mixtures whose components are functions of time, the conditions affecting the amount of each component present may lead to one or more differential equations. One may consider what happens to each quantity between time t and time $t + \Delta t$. If u is such a quantity, then the net change in u is the amount gained G minus the amount lost L in the interval Δt. Thus we have the "equation of continuity,"

$$u(t + \Delta t) - u(t) = G - L.$$

If G and L are approximately proportional to Δt (with variable or constant factors), then

$$u(t + \Delta t) - u(t) = g\,\Delta t - l\,\Delta t.$$

Division by Δt and passage to the limit as $\Delta t \to 0$ give

$$(3\text{-}8) \qquad \frac{du}{dt} = (g - l) .$$

G. Fluid Flow. Many situations concerning flow of fluids lead to differential equations. We may consider here one simple type of problem.

The rate at which water leaves a container through a drain in the bottom of the container depends on the depth of the water as well as on the area and nature of the drain opening. Physical considerations determine that the water issues from the hole with a velocity of $\sqrt{2gh}$, where h is the depth of the water and g is the constant acceleration due to gravity, and that the cross-sectional area A should be reduced to about 0.6 that of the opening (for small openings) to account for impedance of the flow due to the edge of the hole and surface tension. That is, if V is the volume of the container, we see that

$$(3\text{–}9) \qquad \frac{dV}{dt} = -0.6\sqrt{2gh}\,A.$$

Of course, V must be expressed in terms of h or vice versa in order that (3–9) may be solved. How this is done depends on the container. Note that (3–9) provides a better approximation to reality than is obtained by assuming that water flows out of a container at a constant rate, as is done in elementary algebra problems.

H. Other Laws of Growth. When a population or substance is produced not by an internal process but by an external agency, the growth law may be quite different from the natural law. Thus, if units of one substance result from transfer from another, the rate may be proportional to those remaining in the parent source; for example,

$$(3\text{–}10) \qquad \frac{du}{dt} = k(U - u),$$

where U represents the initial measure of the parent source. Or there may be a joint effect, as in the *malthusian* law

$$(3\text{–}11) \qquad \frac{du}{dt} = ku(U - u),$$

in which the unit rate $k(U - u)$ decreases as u approaches the constant U.

In chemical reactions involving combination of two substances, the amount of compound u satisfies

$$(3\text{–}12) \qquad \frac{du}{dt} = k(U_1 - r_1 u)(U_2 - r_2 u),$$

where U_1, U_2 are initial amounts of the constituent substances, r_1 is the fraction of compound contributed by the first substance, and r_2 is the corresponding fraction contributed by the second. Of course, $r_1 + r_2 = 1$. Generalization to more components is clear.

EXERCISES

1. A radioactive substance loses mass in accordance with the law (3–4) of decay. **a.** Find M at time t and the half-life if $M = 100$ grams when $t = 0$ and $M = 98$ grams when $t = 18$ years. **b.** Find M and the half-life if it takes 10 years for M to reduce to 87 per cent of its original value.

2. The half-life of a radioactive substance is 6 hours. Write a differential equation for the mass and find how long it takes for the mass to reduce to one-tenth its original value.

3. How long will it take an initial sum of $1000 at 5 per cent (annual rate) compounded continuously to increase to $2000? Compare this with the time necessary at 5 per cent compounded quarterly.

4. Determine the simple interest for 1 year which is equivalent to 5 per cent compounded continuously.

5. Compare the value at the end of 1 year of $1000 at 5 per cent if the interest is compounded a) yearly, b) quarterly, c) monthly, d) weekly, e) daily, f) continuously.

6. An object initially at 100°F is placed in air at 60°F. If the temperature of the object drops to 90°F in the first 20 minutes of cooling, find the time required to reach a) 80°F; b) 61°F.

7. An object whose temperature is initially 30°F is placed in air at 80°F; its temperature rises 5° in the first 10 minutes. How long does it take to reach 55°F? 79°F?

8. A chemical compound is produced by uniting two substances which combine in the ratio of 5 parts of the first to 3 parts of the second. The two constituents are initially present in the amounts U_1 and U_2, respectively. Write a differential equation for the mass u of the compound.

9. In exercise 8, if $U_1 = 200$ grams and $U_2 = 180$ grams, find u after 6 hours if $u = 50$ grams after 1 hour. (Assume $u = 0$ for $t = 0$.) Show that $u(t) < 320$ grams for every $t > 0$.

10. In exercise 9, find how long it will take for 90 per cent of the 320 grams of the compound to be formed.

11. A conical glass of radius 2 inches and height 5 inches is initially full of water. The level drops 0.5 inches in the first day. **a.** Find the time required for 50 per cent of the water to evaporate. **b.** Find the time needed for all the water to evaporate.

12. Suppose that a tank contains water contaminated by the presence of some substance thoroughly mixed in the water. In order to reduce the concentration of the contaminant, pure water is poured into the tank and the mixture spills out and is drained away as fast as the pure water enters. Assume that the fluid is always thoroughly mixed. If the original mixture contained 10 pounds of the contaminant in 1000 gallons of water and if pure water enters the tank at the rate of 6 gallons per minute, how long will it take to reduce the amount of contaminant present to 5 pounds? To 1 pound?

13. A right circular cylinder of radius 3 inches is filled with water to a depth of 10 inches. The water flows out through a circular hole with diameter 1 inch. How long will it take to empty the container?

14. A tank in the form of a rectangular box with base dimensions 2 feet and 1 foot and height 1.5 feet is filled with water. A circular drain in the bottom is 1.5 inches in diameter. Find the time needed to empty.

15. The growth of a population follows the law (3–10) with $k > 0$. Find u as a function of t. Show that $U - u$ obeys the law (3–4) of decay.

16. A population grows in accordance with the malthusian law. Find u as a function of t.

17. Apply exercise 16 to the population of the United States by determining the value of the constants given that, in 1790, $u = 4 \cdot 10^6$; in 1850, $u = 23 \cdot 10^6$; in 1910, $u = 92 \cdot 10^6$.

18. Using the results of exercise 17, find the population for 1960. Then compare with the result of the 1960 census.

19. Two countries $\mathcal{U}$ and $\mathcal{S}$ are in economic competition, and the law of natural growth applies to both. The unit rate of growth of $\mathcal{S}$ is 6 per cent per year, while that of $\mathcal{U}$ is 3 per cent per year. If the economy of $\mathcal{S}$ is measured as one-half that of $\mathcal{U}$, how long will it take $\mathcal{S}$ to overtake $\mathcal{U}$?

20. In exercise 19, how long will it take $\mathcal{S}$ to overtake $\mathcal{U}$ if the rate of $\mathcal{U}$ is 5 per cent per year?

3–3. PARTICLE MOTIONS

A particle motion with *one degree of freedom* is described by specification of one coordinate describing the position of the particle as a function of time. Thus a particle motion on the x-axis is described by an equation $x = f(t)$; if the particle is constrained to move on a circle, an equation $\theta = f(t)$ describes its motion (θ is the central angle). Motions with *two* (or *three*) *degrees of freedom* are similarly described, except that two (or three) coordinates are required to specify position. Thus the history of a particle moving with two degrees of freedom might be described by equations

$$(3\text{-}13) \qquad x = f(t), \quad y = g(t),$$

so that at each time t the position in the xy-plane is known. Equations (3-13) may be regarded as parametric equations of the path.

Example 3-2. A particle moves on the x-axis with velocity equal to twice the square of its distance from the origin. At time $t = 1$, the value of x is 1. Find the motion.

Solution: From the given information, $\dfrac{dx}{dt} = 2x^2$. Separating variables and solving, we have

$$-\frac{1}{x} = 2t + c.$$

Imposing the initial condition gives $c = -3$, so that

$$x = \frac{1}{3 - 2t}.$$

Note that as t approaches $3/2$, x increases beyond all bound.

Example 3-3. A ball is caused to move vertically upward subject to constant acceleration due to gravity, $g = 32$ feet per second², directed downward. Its initial velocity is 65 feet per second. How high will it rise?

Solution: The ball is assumed to be a particle P moving on the y-axis as shown in Figure 3-1. Let the origin O be the starting point and $t = 0$ be the initial instant. Then $\dfrac{d^2y}{dt^2}$ is the acceleration, so that

$$\frac{d^2y}{dt^2} = -g,$$

the negative sign signifying the downward direction of acceleration. Let $v = \dfrac{dy}{dt}$, so that $\dfrac{dv}{dt} = -g$, and by integration,

$$\frac{dy}{dt} = v = -gt + c_1.$$

Figure 3-1

When $t = 0$, $v = 64$, whence $c_1 = 64$ and

$$\frac{dy}{dt} = 64 - gt.$$

Thus

$$y = 64t - \frac{1}{2} gt^2 + c_2.$$

But $y = 0$ when $t = 0$, so that $c_2 = 0$, and

$$y = 64t - \frac{1}{2} gt^2.$$

Now upward motion ceases when $v = 0$, that is, when $t = 64/g = 2$. But for $t = 2$,

$$y = 128 - 64 = 64,$$

and the ball rises to a height of 64 feet. (This procedure may be regarded as a determination of the maximum value of y by the usual procedure.)

Example 3–4. A particle of constant mass m moves in the xy-plane subject to a constant force directed negatively parallel to the y-axis. The particle is at the origin at time $t = 0$ and has there a velocity of magnitude v_0 and direction inclined at an angle α to the x-axis. Find the motion.

Solution: The x-component of the force vector is 0, while the y-component may be written $-mg$, where g is a positive constant. The vector *equation of motion*, force = mass · acceleration, is written in component form thus:

$$m\frac{d^2x}{dt^2} = 0, \quad m\frac{d^2y}{dt^2} = -mg.$$

These differential equations may be solved separately, since each involves only two of the quantities x, y, t. One integration applied to each yields

$$\frac{dx}{dt} = c_1, \quad \frac{dy}{dt} = -gt + c_2;$$

when $t = 0$, $\dfrac{dx}{dt} = v_0 \cos \alpha$, $\dfrac{dy}{dt} = v_0 \sin \alpha$, so that $c_1 = v_0 \cos \alpha$, $c_2 = v_0 \sin \alpha$, and

$$\frac{dx}{dt} = v_0 \cos \alpha, \quad \frac{dy}{dt} = -gt + v_0 \sin \alpha.$$

Another integration gives

$$x = v_0 t \cos \alpha + c_3, \quad y = -\frac{1}{2} g t^2 + v_0 t \sin \alpha + c_4.$$

But $t = 0$ implies $x = y = 0$, so that $c_3 = c_4 = 0$.
The motion is thus given by

$$\begin{cases} x = v_0 t \cos \alpha, \\[2mm] y = -\frac{1}{2} g t^2 + v_0 t \sin \alpha. \end{cases}$$

The reader may show that the path is a part of a parabola, by elimination of t. See Figure 3–2.

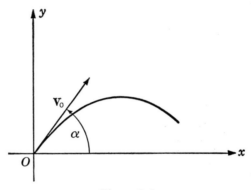

Figure 3–2

Example 3–5. A particle P moves on the x-axis in such a way that the force on P is inversely proportional to the square of its distance from the origin and is directed toward the origin. Discuss the motion.

Solution: The equation of motion is

$$\frac{d^2 x}{dt^2} = -\frac{k}{x^2}.$$

Denote $\dfrac{dx}{dt}$ by v, and note that $\dfrac{dv^2}{dt} = 2v \dfrac{dv}{dt}$. The given equation becomes, after multiplication by v,

$$v \frac{dv}{dt} = -\frac{kv}{x^2} = -\frac{k}{x^2} \cdot \frac{dx}{dt}.$$

Integration gives

$$v^2 = \frac{2k}{x} + c.$$

If, at time $t = 0$, $x = x_0 \neq 0$ and $v = v_0$, then $c = v_0^2 - 2k/x_0$, so that

$$v^2 = \frac{2k}{x} + v_0^2 - \frac{2k}{x_0}.$$

Integration of this velocity equation to yield x as a function of t is possible and may be carried out by the reader. However, much information may be obtained from the velocity equation.

Assume that $x_0 > 0$ and $v_0 > 0$. Then, if $v_0^2 < 2k/x_0$, v will decrease to zero as x increases to $2kx_0/(2k - x_0v_0^2)$. Thereafter the particle will reverse direction, since $\frac{dv}{dt}$ is negative from the given equation. It is easy to see that, if $v_0^2 \geq 2k/x_0$, the particle will never come to rest, although it moves with decreasing velocity. The critical velocity $\sqrt{2k/x_0}$ is called the *velocity of escape*.

Example 3-6. Derive the equation of the straight-line motion of a variable mass. Apply the result to the problem of rocket motion.

Solution: A particle P with variable mass may be regarded as one which is continually acquiring mass from an external source (or losing mass). The momentum of P at time t is $m(t)v(t)$. Assume that the increment of mass acquired in an interval Δt may be regarded as a particle of mass Δm with velocity $v + u$, where u is the velocity of the increment relative to P. The increment in momentum of P due to the acquisition of mass Δm is approximately $(\Delta m)(v + u)$; if an external force F acts in the direction of the motion, F produces an increment in momentum of P approximately equal to $F\,\Delta t$ by Newton's second law. Hence the total increment in momentum is given by

$$\Delta(mv) = (\Delta m)(v + u) + F\,\Delta t,$$

whence, approximately,

$$\frac{\Delta(mv)}{\Delta t} = (v + u)\frac{\Delta m}{\Delta t} + F.$$

Allowing Δt to approach zero, we obtain the exact relationship

$$\frac{d}{dt}(mv) = (v + u)\frac{dm}{dt} + F,$$

or

(3-14) $$m\frac{dv}{dt} - u\frac{dm}{dt} = F.$$

In the case of rocket motion, assume that mass in the form of combustion products is being lost at a constant rate and at a constant velocity relative to the rocket. Then $m = m_0 - kt$ and $u = u_0$, where k is a positive constant and u_0 is a constant opposite in sign to v. If $F = 0$, we have

$$(m_0 - kt)\frac{dv}{dt} + ku_0 = 0.$$

Integration yields

$$v = u_0 \ln (m_0 - kt) + c_1.$$

If we assume $v = 0$ when $t = 0$, then $c_1 = -u_0 \ln m_0$. Hence

(3-15) $$v = u_0 \ln \left(1 - \frac{k}{m_0}t\right).$$

Now $v = \dfrac{dx}{dt}$, and so

(3-16) $$x = \int u_0 \ln \left(1 - \frac{k}{m_0}t\right) dt.$$

Note from (3-15) that, as t approaches m_0/k (whence m approaches zero), v becomes infinite.

EXERCISES

1. A particle moves along the x-axis so that its velocity at any point is equal to half its abscissa minus three times the time. At time $t = 2$, $x = -4$. Find the motion. What is the maximum value (if any) that x attains?

2. Suppose that the acceleration of a particle moving on the x-axis is given by

$$\frac{d^2x}{dt^2} = 12t - 18,$$

and that, when $t = 0$, $\dfrac{dx}{dt} = 12$ and $x = 3$. Find the motion and the total distance traveled by the particle during the first three units of time.

3. Complete the solution for Example 3–4 by obtaining the cartesian equation of the path.

4. Find the motion given by

$$\frac{d^2x}{dt^2} = \cos 2t, \quad \frac{d^2y}{dt^2} = -\sin t$$

if, at $t = 0$, $\dfrac{dx}{dt} = x = y = 0$ and $\dfrac{dy}{dt} = 1$. Describe the path of the motion.

5. Find the plane motion $x = f(t)$, $y = g(t)$ which is determined by the following conditions:

$$f''(t) = -4f(t) \quad \text{and} \quad g''(t) = g'(t) - 2t \qquad \text{for all } t;$$
$$f'(0) = 3, \quad g'(0) = 0, \quad f(0) = 0, \quad g(0) = 5.$$

6. The angular velocity $\dfrac{d\theta}{dt}$ of a particle moving on a circular path is inversely proportional (with proportionality factor k) to the position angle θ. Find θ if $\theta = 3$ when $t = 0$. As t increases, does the particle approach a limiting position on the circle?

7. Suppose that the angular velocity $\dfrac{d\theta}{dt}$ of a particle moving on a circular path is related to the angular position θ and the time t by the equation

$$\frac{d\theta}{dt} \sin t = \theta \cos t.$$

Find θ as a function of t if $\theta = 1$ when $t = \pi/2$. If the initial condition is modified so that $\theta = \theta_0$ when $t = \pi/2$, find the smallest value of θ_0 for which the particle actually traverses the entire circular path. What device does this motion suggest?

8. A particle moves on a circular path. Let θ denote the position of the particle. Suppose that

$$t\frac{d\theta}{dt} + \sin 2t = \theta + 2t \cos 2t,$$

and that $\theta = \pi/2$ when $t = \pi/2$. Find θ and describe briefly the motion of the particle.

9. Apply Example 3-5 to find the velocity of escape of a particle moving on a diametral line away from the earth. First find k by noting that $\left|\dfrac{d^2x}{dt^2}\right|$ at the surface of the earth is $g = 32$ feet per second^2. Take the radius of the earth as 4000 miles.

10. Find the velocity of escape for the moon (radius = 1000 miles, acceleration = 5 feet per second^2) and Mars (radius = 2100 miles, acceleration = 12 feet per second^2).

11. Carry out the integration in (3-16), assuming $x = 0$ when $t = 0$.

12. Apply the equation (3-14) of rocket motion to the case of a vertical motion as in Figure 3-1, assuming an external force mg directed downward. Obtain the differential equation and find v, y as functions of t, assuming appropriate initial conditions.

3-4. GEOMETRIC APPLICATIONS

Inasmuch as the slope of a curve $y = f(x)$, or $F(x, y) = 0$, at the point (x, y) is $y' = \dfrac{dy}{dx}$, a statement leading to an equation connecting the coordinates x, y and the slope y' yields a differential equation $G(x, y, y') = 0$. Curves satisfying this equation will thus fulfill the stated requirement. Here an initial condition might be the specification of a point on the curve, that is, a condition giving y for some specific value of x.

A similar application may be made when polar coordinates are used; here $r \left/ \dfrac{dr}{d\theta} \right.$ is the tangent of the angle between the radius vector to the point (r, θ) and the tangent to the curve at that point.

Example 3-7. Find all curves for which the slope at (x, y) is proportional to the ordinate y.

Solution: We have as given

$$\frac{dy}{dx} = ky,$$

where k is a constant. This linear equation has as complete solution

$$y = ce^{kx};$$

there is thus a two-parameter family of curves satisfying the requirement.

Example 3-8. Find all curves for which at each point P the counterclockwise angle from the directed ray OP to the tangent line at P is 45°.

Solution: Using polar coordinates, we have

$$r \Big/ \frac{dr}{d\theta} = 1,$$

or $\dfrac{dr}{d\theta} = r$. Hence $r = ce^{\theta}$ represents the one-parameter family of curves with the stated property.

Example 3-9. Find all curves intersecting all curves of the family $y = cx^3$ orthogonally, that is, at right angles. These are called *orthogonal trajectories* of the family.

Solution: In order to relate x, y, and y' at an arbitrary point P of any one of the desired curves, it is necessary to find the corre-

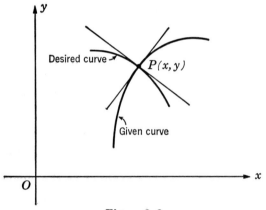

Figure 3-3

sponding relationship for the given curves. From $y = cx^3$, we have $y' = 3cx^2$; elimination of c yields

$$3y = xy',$$

or

$$y' = \frac{3y}{x},$$

if the origin is excluded. At $P(x, y)$ the slope of the cubic curve through P is $3y/x$; hence the slope of the desired curve through

P is $-\,x/3y$, since the tangents are perpendicular. This gives the differential equation

$$\frac{dy}{dx} = -\frac{x}{3y},$$

or

$$3y\,dy = -x\,dx.$$

Integration yields $x^2 + 3y^2 = c$. The desired curves are similar ellipses with axes in the ratio 1 to $1/\sqrt{3}$. (See Figure 3–4.)

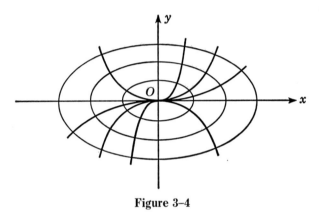

Figure 3–4

EXERCISES

In each of exercises 1 to 4, find all curves such that the slope is equal to the given function of x, y.

1. $2x - 3y$.

2. $\dfrac{y}{x^3}$ $\quad(x \neq 0)$.

3. $\dfrac{x - y + 3x^2 y}{x - x^3 + y^2}$.

4. $\dfrac{x^2 - y^2}{xy}$.

5. The slope of a curve at (x, y) is proportional to $y/(x + 1)$. The curve passes through the points $(0, 1)$ and $(1, 16)$. Find its equation.

6. Find all curves with the property that the slope of the curve at (x, y) is one unit less than the slope of the line from (x, y) to $(0, 0)$.

7. Find all curves such that at each point (x, y) the numbers x, y, and y' are, in that order, in arithmetic progression.

8. Find all curves for which x, y, and y' are, in that order, in geometric progression.

9. Find all curves such that the tangent to the curve at (x, y) intersects the x-axis at $(2x, 0)$. Show that for such curves the tangent intersects the y-axis at $(0, 2y)$.

10. Find all curves with the property that, if P is a point on the curve and O is the origin of a rectangular coordinate system, or the pole of a polar system, and P is different from O, then the counterclockwise angle from the x-axis to OP is equal to the counterclockwise angle from OP to the tangent at P.

In each of exercises 11 to 18, find the family of orthogonal trajectories of the given family.

11. $y = ax + c$, where a is a given constant.

12. $x^2 + y^2 - 2cx = 0$.

13. $y = cx^n$, where n is a given constant.

14. $x^2 + c^2y^2 = 4$.

15. $y = ce^{ax}$, where a is a given constant.

16. $y = c \sin x$.

★17. $y^2 + 4cx = 4c^2$.

★18. $\dfrac{x^2}{a^2 + c} + \dfrac{y^2}{b^2 + c} = 1$, where a, b are given constants.

3–5. CONSERVATIVE VECTOR FIELDS IN THE PLANE

If at each point $P(x, y)$ of a region of the xy-plane a vector $\mathbf{F}(x, y)$ is given, a *vector field* is said to be specified. Thus if a mass (like the sun) exerts its gravitational attraction throughout a plane region, a particle when placed at any point P of the region would be subject to a force representable by a vector $\mathbf{F}(x, y)$; the vector function $\mathbf{F}(x, y)$ thus defines a vector field, specifically called here a *force field*. Gravitational force may be replaced by electrostatic force with no change in mathematical representation, except that now repulsive as well as attractive forces are allowed. A laminar fluid motion (which may be thought of as a plane motion) may be described in part by specifying at each of its points the velocity of the fluid particle there, that is, the field of velocity vectors. Generally, a vector field $\mathbf{F}$ is represented by giving its x-component M and its y-component N as functions of x, y.

Geometrically, a vector field **F** can be regarded as a region of points (x, y) at each of which has been constructed the vector $\mathbf{F}(x, y)$ so that the initial point of $\mathbf{F}(x, y)$ is placed at (x, y). (See Figure 3–5.)

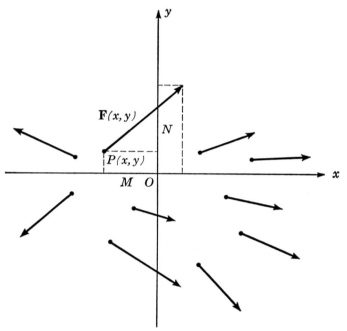

Figure 3–5

A vector field (M, N) is *conservative* if there exists a function $V(x, y)$ such that

$$(3\text{--}17) \qquad \frac{\partial V}{\partial x} = M, \quad \frac{\partial V}{\partial y} = N$$

throughout the common domain of M and N. Such a function $V(x, y)$ is called a *potential* function for the field. The theory of Section 2–5 shows that the field (M, N) is conservative if and only if $M\,dx + N\,dy$ is an exact differential, that is, if and only if

$$(3\text{--}18) \qquad \frac{\partial M}{\partial y} = \frac{\partial N}{\partial x}$$

throughout the region. It is also clear that, if V_1 and V_2 are two potential functions for the same field, then

$$dV_1 = M\,dx + N\,dy = dV_2,$$

whence $V_1 - V_2$ is a function whose differential is zero. By the mean value theorem for functions of two variables, $V_1 - V_2$ is a constant, and so all potential functions may be obtained from a given one by addition of a constant.

The problem of finding a potential function for a conservative field (M, N) is that of solving the exact differential equation

$$(3\text{–}19) \qquad\qquad M\,dx + N\,dy = 0$$

by the method of Section 2–5 or an equivalent method; for the solution was seen to be of the form $V(x, y) = c$, where V satisfies (3–17).

Example 3–10. A particle of mass m moves in the xy-plane subject to the Newtonian gravitational attraction due to a mass μ placed at the origin. Find the force field, show it to be conservative, and find a potential function.

Solution: Let the particle be placed at $P(x, y)$. The force vector

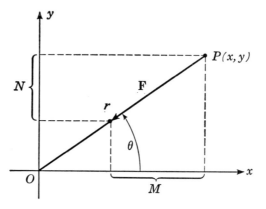

Figure 3–6

F is directed toward the origin as shown in Figure 3–6 and has magnitude

$$|\mathbf{F}| = \frac{km\mu}{r^2},$$

where k is a constant and $r = \sqrt{x^2 + y^2}$. It follows that components M, N of $\mathbf{F}$ are given by

$$M = -\frac{km\mu}{r^2}\cos\theta, \qquad N = -\frac{km\mu}{r^2}\sin\theta,$$

or

$$M = -\frac{km\mu x}{(x^2 + y^2)^{3/2}}, \qquad N = -\frac{km\mu y}{(x^2 + y^2)^{3/2}}.$$

Differentiation yields

$$\frac{\partial M}{\partial y} = \frac{3km\mu xy}{(x^2 + y^2)^{5/2}} = \frac{\partial N}{\partial x},$$

so that (M, N) is conservative. The reader may carry through the determination of $V(x, y)$ by the method of Section 2–5 to obtain

$$V = \frac{km\mu}{(x^2 + y^2)^{1/2}} + C = \frac{km\mu}{r} + C.$$

It is customary to require, for simplicity, that $\lim_{r \to \infty} V = 0$, that is, $C = 0$, and

$$(3\text{–}20) \qquad\qquad V = \frac{km\mu}{r}.$$

Note that neither V nor (M, N) is defined at the origin.

If (M, N) is a given conservative vector field with a potential V, then the curves $V(x, y) = C$, called *equipotential curves*, satisfy $dV = 0$, that is,

$$(3\text{–}19) \qquad\qquad M\,dx + N\,dy = 0.$$

At each point P, except for singular points where $M = N = 0$, the curve of the family $V = C$ through P has a tangent line at P whose direction is described by the direction numbers (dx, dy) and therefore by $(-N, M)$. Since the dot product of the vectors $(-N, M)$ and (M, N) is zero, the tangent vector is perpendicular to the vector at P of the given field. It follows that every orthogonal trajectory of the equipotential curves will at each point have a tangent with the same direction as the vector (M, N) of the field. These trajectories are called *lines of the field* (*lines of force* in the case of a force field, *lines of flow* in the case of a velocity field, etc.).

If two or more conservative vector fields (M_1, N_1), (M_2, N_2), $\cdots$, (M_k, N_k) with potentials V_1, $\cdots$, V_k are given, then the field (M, N), where

$$M = \sum_{j=1}^{k} M_j, \qquad N = \sum_{j=1}^{k} N_j,$$

is called the *sum* of the given fields. It is clear that $V = \sum\limits_{j=1}^{k} V_j$ is a potential for the sum field:

$$\frac{\partial V}{\partial x} = \sum_{j=1}^{k} \frac{\partial V_j}{\partial x} = \sum_{j=1}^{k} M_j = M,$$

and similarly $\dfrac{\partial V}{\partial y} = N$. It is often possible to study complicated fields by representing them as sums of simpler fields.

Example 3–11. Suppose two point-charges q_1, q_2 are located respectively at $P_1(-a, 0)$ and $P_2(a, 0)$. At each point $P \neq P_1, P_2$

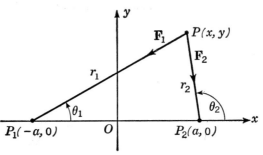

Figure 3–7

a force vector is constructed representing the resultant electrostatic force on a unit positive charge at P due to the charges at P_1 and P_2. Find this field, its potential, and the equipotential curves.

Solution: It suffices to find the separate fields due to q_1 and q_2 and form their sum. By Coulomb's law, the magnitude of the force at P due to q_1 is (see Figure 3–7)

$$|\mathbf{F}_1| = \frac{q_1 \cdot 1}{K r_1^2} = \frac{q_1}{K[(x + a)^2 + y^2]},$$

where K is the dielectric constant of the medium. The force is directed toward P_1 if $q_1 < 0$ and away from P_1 if $q_1 > 0$. Hence

(3–21) $$M_1 = -\frac{q_1}{K r_1^2} \cos \theta_1, \quad N_1 = -\frac{q_1}{K r_1^2} \sin \theta_1,$$

where M_1, N_1 are components of the force. Similarly, relative to q_2 we have

(3–22) $$M_2 = -\frac{q_2}{K r_2^2} \cos \theta_2, \quad N_2 = -\frac{q_2}{K r_2^2} \sin \theta_2.$$

Except for a constant factor, choice of coordinate system, and possibly sign, each of the fields (M_1, N_1), (M_2, N_2) agrees with that of Example 3–10. Their potentials may be obtained directly from (3–20) as

$$V_1 = \frac{q_1}{Kr_1}, \quad V_2 = \frac{q_2}{Kr_2}.$$

The resultant field is $(M_1 + M_2, N_1 + N_2)$ and its potential is

$$V_1 + V_2 = \frac{1}{K}\left(\frac{q_1}{r_1} + \frac{q_2}{r_2}\right).$$

Equipotential curves are given by $V_1 + V_2 = c$, that is, by

$$(3\text{–}23) \qquad \frac{q_1}{r_1} + \frac{q_2}{r_2} = C.$$

If (3–23) is expressed in terms of x, y, it becomes

$$q_1 \sqrt{(x - a)^2 + y^2} + q_2 \sqrt{(x + a)^2 + y^2}$$
$$= C\sqrt{(x - a)^2 + y^2} \sqrt{(x + a)^2 + y^2}.$$

Rationalization yields a family of algebraic curves of degree 8.

EXERCISES

1. Complete the work in Example 3–10 by computing V in detail.

2. In Example 3–11 express the components M_1, N_1, M_2, N_2 in (3–21) and (3–22) in terms of the coordinates x, y.

3. A vector of constant magnitude and directed toward the origin is constructed at every point (x, y). Find the field, a potential, and the equipotential curves.

4. Find the most general conservative field of the form $(0, N)$. Then express a potential in terms of N and describe the equipotential curves. (This case includes the gravitational field in a small region of a vertical plane near the earth's surface.)

5. Show that $(M(x), N(y))$ is a conservative field and express its potential.

6. Find a field of the type in exercise 5 having all lines of slope 2 as equipotential curves.

In the following exercises, $r = \sqrt{x^2 + y^2} = |OP|$, where O is the origin and P is a general point with coordinates (x, y).

7. A *central* field about the origin O is one whose magnitude at $P(x, y)$ is $f(r)$ and which is directed along OP. Find the components of such a field and show it to be conservative. (Limit consideration to a region outside a circle with O as center, and assume f to have a continuous derivative in the region.)

8. If a field has potential $V = kr^n$, where k is a constant, show that it is of the type described in exercise 7 with $f(r) = n \,|\, k \,|\, r^{n-1}$. Find the equipotential curves and the lines of the field.

9. If a field has potential $V = k \ln r$, where k is a constant, show that it is of the type described in exercise 7 with $f(r) = |\,k\,|/r$. This field, if interpreted as a velocity field, describes the plane flow of an incompressible fluid from a *source* (the origin) if $k > 0$ or to a *sink* (again the origin) if $k < 0$.

10. A field is defined by $M = -ky/r^2$, $N = kx/r^2$. Show that at each point P the vector (M, N) is perpendicular to OP. Prove the field to be conservative and find its potential and the equipotential curves. This field, if interpreted as a velocity field, describes a plane *vortex* flow about the origin.

The *conjugate* of a field (M, N) is the field $(-N, M)$. Exercises 11 to 16 concern conjugate fields.

11. Show that at every point P the vectors of two conjugate fields are perpendicular. What relationship therefore exists between the lines of the one field and those of the other?

12. Prove that the field of exercise 10 is the conjugate of that of exercise 9.

★13. Show that the potential V of a conservative field satisfies Laplace's equation $\dfrac{\partial^2 V}{\partial x^2} + \dfrac{\partial^2 V}{\partial y^2} = 0$ if and only if its conjugate is conservative too. In this case show that the potential of the conjugate field also satisfies Laplace's equation. (Assume adequate continuous differentiability of the functions involved.)

★14. For the potential V of Example 3–10 compute $\dfrac{\partial^2 V}{\partial x^2} + \dfrac{\partial^2 V}{\partial y^2}$ and hence show that V does not satisfy Laplace's equation.

★15. Determine all central fields as in exercise 7 such that their conjugates are conservative.

★16. Show that the potentials V_1, V_2 of two conjugate conservative fields satisfy the Cauchy-Riemann equations: $\dfrac{\partial V_1}{\partial x} = \dfrac{\partial V_2}{\partial y}$, $\dfrac{\partial V_1}{\partial y} = -\dfrac{\partial V_2}{\partial x}$. Conversely, show that two functions V_1, V_2 satisfying these equations are the potentials of conjugate fields.

★**17.** In Example 3–11 take $a = 1$ and find the locus of points (x, y) at which the vectors of the resultant field pass through the origin if extended.

MISCELLANEOUS EXERCISES

1. Find the orthogonal trajectories of the family $x^3 = cy^2$.

2. If the potential of a conservative vector field is $x^2 - y^2$, find the conjugate field and show it to be conservative.

3. What rate of interest per year compounded annually is equivalent to 4 per cent per year compounded continuously?

4. Find all curves all of whose normals pass through a given point (a, b).

5. A raindrop passing through a uniform fog remains spherical but expands owing to collection of water particles. Find its radius as a function of distance traveled.

6. The tangent to a curve and the coordinate axes form a triangle of given constant area A. Find the curve if it passes through $\left(\dfrac{A}{2}, 1\right)$.

7. A 50-gallon tank is initially filled with fresh water. Brine containing 1 pound of salt per gallon runs in at the rate of 4 gallons per minute, and the mixture flows out at the same rate. How much salt is in the tank at the end of 30 minutes?

8. A conservative force field has the family $x^2 - y^2 = c$ as equipotential curves. Find the lines of force.

9. Find the orthogonal trajectories of the family $y^2x = c$.

10. The air in a room containing 4000 cubic feet contains 0.10 per cent carbon dioxide. Find how many cubic feet of air (entering at a constant rate) must be admitted per minute so that 15 minutes later the air in the room contains 0.05 per cent carbon dioxide. (Assume that old air leaves the room at the same rate as new air enters.)

11. Work exercise 14 in Section 3–2 assuming that water is flowing into the tank at the rate of 0.01 cubic feet per second.

12. A long pipe is sunk vertically into an encased well. It is closed at the bottom with a foot valve and filled with water. A leak in the pipe wall develops at unknown depth. The water level, originally at the top of the pipe, is found to drop 4 inches in the first hour and 3.9 inches in the next hour. Find the depth at which the leak is located. [HINT: Apply (3–9) to a cylinder of unknown height and size of opening.]

13. After a fund drive gets under way, growth follows the law $u' = f(t)u$, where the unit rate $f(t)$ rises from zero to a maximum and then decreases asymptotically to zero. Assume $f(t) = kt/(t^4 + a^4)$. Suppose that at time $t = 0$, $u = \$1000$, and that the unit rate reaches its maximum after 1 week, at which time the amount collected is \$3000. Find the limiting value of the fund as $t \to \infty$. When will the fund reach \$9000? How long must collections continue if \$25,000 is to be collected?

14. The raindrop of exercise 5 is regarded as a particle having variable mass moving vertically downward, subject to the force mg. The mass particles collected are regarded as having velocity $u = -v$ relative to the raindrop, where v is the velocity of the raindrop. Find an equation for v as a function of distance traveled, assuming suitable initial conditions.

15. A vector field has potential $V = e^x \cos y$. Show that the conjugate field is conservative and find a potential for it.

16. A particle P moves on the x-axis subject to a retardant force along the axis whose magnitude is proportional to the speed of P. Discuss the motion.

Linear Equations

4–1. PRELIMINARIES

In this chapter we shall be concerned with *linear* differential equations, usually having constant coefficients. Although these equations are of a very special type, they represent or apply to many interesting and important natural phenomena. Our aim is to obtain explicit forms of the solutions which are useful in applications and in the studies of other types of equations. Some of the applications are discussed separately in Chapter 6.

4–2. FIRST-ORDER EQUATIONS

A linear first-order equation was defined in Section 2–7 to be an equation of the form

(4–1) $$y' + P(x)y = Q(x).$$

It was shown in Section 2–7 that the complete solution of (4–1) is given by

(4–2) $$y = e^{-\int P\,dx} \int Q\, e^{\int P\,dx}\, dx + C e^{-\int P\,dx}.$$

Here each indefinite integral is intended to represent only one (but any one) of the set of functions usually denoted by this symbol. The constant C is the parameter of the family. If $P(x)$ is a constant function, say $P(x) = a$, then (4–1) becomes

(4–3) $$y' + ay = Q(x),$$

and (4–2) can be written in the simpler form

(4–4) $$y = e^{-ax} \int Q\, e^{ax}\, dx + C e^{-ax}.$$

It should be observed that

(4–5) $$y = C e^{-\int P\,dx}$$

is the complete solution of the *homogeneous* equation

(4–6) $$y' + P(x)y = 0,$$

and that the complete solution of (4–1) consists of the functions of the family (4–5) upon which has been superposed, or to which has been added, a particular solution of (4–1). Indeed, we can easily show that if $f(x)$ is any particular solution of (4–1), then *all* solutions of (4–1) are given by

$$y = f(x) + Ce^{-\int P\,dx}.$$

Suppose $g(x)$ is a solution of (4–1). Then

$$g'(x) + P(x)g(x) = Q(x) \quad \text{and} \quad f'(x) + P(x)f(x) = Q(x),$$

so that

$$[f'(x) - g'(x)] + P(x)[f(x) - g(x)] = 0.$$

That is, $f(x) - g(x)$ is a solution of (4–6). Since (4–5) gives all solutions of (4–6), we know that

$$f(x) - g(x) = Ce^{-\int P\,dx}$$

for some choice of C, say $C = -C_1$, and hence that

$$g(x) = f(x) + C_1 e^{-\int P\,dx}.$$

The following theorem has thus been proved.

Theorem. The complete solution of a linear equation (4–1) of first order is the sum of a particular solution and the complete solution of the associated homogeneous equation (4–6).

This theorem often enables us to avoid some of the integration called for in (4–2) or (4–4). In some cases it may be possible to guess a solution of the given equation. For example, if in (4–3) $Q(x)$ is a polynomial of degree n, then $e^{-ax}\int Qe^{ax}\,dx$ is also a polynomial of degree n. Hence in (4–4) we may replace the first term by such a polynomial, whose coefficients are determined so as to make (4–3) hold. A more complete discussion of similar methods for finding particular solutions is found in Chapter 5.

Example 4–1. Find all solutions of

$$y' - 3y = x^3 - 5x + 2.$$

Solution: The complete solution of the homogeneous equation $y' - 3y = 0$ is the family Ce^{3x}. The particular solution to be added to this may be taken as a polynomial

$$y = ax^3 + bx^2 + cx + d.$$

Now we determine a, b, c, d so that this polynomial satisfies the given differential equation. Substitution yields

$$(3ax^2 + 2bx + c) - 3(ax^3 + bx^2 + cx + d) = x^3 - 5x + 2.$$

This identity in x holds if and only if the coefficients of like powers of x are the same on the two sides, that is,

$$-3a = 1, \qquad 3a - 3b = 0,$$

$$2b - 3c = -5, \qquad c - 3d = 2.$$

There result $a = -1/3$, $b = -1/3$, $c = 13/9$, $d = -5/27$. Adding the two terms as indicated in (4-4), we have the complete solution

$$y = Ce^{3x} - \frac{1}{3}x^3 - \frac{1}{3}x^2 + \frac{13}{9}x - \frac{5}{27}.$$

Note that this work is equivalent to the evaluation of $\int e^{-3x}(x^3 - 5x + 2)\, dx$ by repeated integration by parts.

Example 4-2. Find all solutions of

$$y' + 2y = \frac{1}{x} + 2\ln x \qquad\qquad (x > 0).$$

Solution: The complete solution of $y' + 2y = 0$ is $y = ce^{-2x}$. By inspection, we see that $y = \ln x$ satisfies the given equation. Hence, by the theorem, the desired complete solution is $y = Ce^{-2x} + \ln x$.

The solutions given by (4-4) are also represented in definite integral form by

(4-7) $$y = Ce^{-ax} + e^{-ax}\int_{x_0}^{x} e^{at}Q(t)\, dt.$$

Note that C is the value of y when $x = x_0$. We may also write (4-7) in the form

(4-8) $$y = Ce^{-ax} + \int_{x_0}^{x} e^{a(t-x)} Q(t)\, dt.$$

Let $Y(x) = e^{-ax}$. We see that $Y(x)$ is the unique solution of the equation $y' + ay = 0$ which has the value 1 when $x = 0$. We may now write (4–8), in the case $x_0 = 0$, in the form

$$(4\text{–}9) \qquad y = Ce^{-ax} + \int_0^x Y(x - t)Q(t)\, dt.$$

The integral in (4–9) is called a *convolution* integral.

EXERCISES

In each of the exercises 1 to 6, find the complete solution.

1. $y' - 2y = x^2 - 1$.

2. $y' + \dfrac{3}{2}y = x^4$.

3. $y' - 5y = 3x^3 + 4x$.

4. $y' - xy = x$. (HINT: Try to guess a solution.)

5. $y' - xy = 4x^3 - x^5$.

6. $y' - y = \cos x - \sin x$.

7. Solve exercise 1 by the formula (4–4).

8. Solve exercise 6 by the formula (4–4).

9. Prove that, if y_1 and y_2 are solutions of (4–6), then $y_1 + y_2$ is a solution also, and that cy_1 is a solution, where c is any constant.

10. Prove that, if y_1 is a solution of $y' + P(x)y = Q_1(x)$, and if y_2 is a solution of $y' + P(x)y = Q_2(x)$, then $y_1 + y_2$ is a solution of $y' + P(x)y = Q_1(x) + Q_2(x)$.

4–3. HOMOGENEOUS SECOND-ORDER LINEAR EQUATIONS

An equation of the form

$$(4\text{–}10) \qquad y'' + P(x)y' + Q(x)y = 0$$

is called a *homogeneous linear equation of second order*. We shall devote most of our attention to examples in which P and Q are constant functions. Since the first-order linear homogeneous equations with constant coefficients have exponential solutions, it is natural to look for exponential solutions of (4–10) when P and Q are constant. In order that $y = Ce^{mx}$ be a solution of

$$(4\text{–}11) \qquad y'' + ay' + by = 0,$$

it is necessary and sufficient that $Ce^{mx}(m^2 + am + b) = 0$. Hence if m is a real number satisfying

$$(4\text{--}12) \qquad\qquad m^2 + am + b = 0,$$

then $y = Ce^{mx}$ is a solution of (4–11) for every constant C. The algebraic equation (4–12) is called the *characteristic equation*, and $m^2 + am + b$ the *characteristic polynomial*, of the differential equation (4–11); the roots of (4–12) are called the *characteristic roots* of (4–11). In general the roots of (4–12) are complex; in treating this case at the end of the present section, we shall find it useful to give a meaning to e^{mx} when m is complex so that both real and complex cases will have similar treatments.

Suppose first that the characteristic roots m_1 and m_2 are real. Let y be a solution of (4–11). Then

$$(4\text{--}13) \qquad\qquad z = y' - m_1 y$$

is a solution of

$$(4\text{--}14) \qquad\qquad z' - m_2 z = 0,$$

since, by (4–13),

$$z' - m_2 z = y'' - m_1 y' - m_2 y' + m_1 m_2 y$$
$$= y'' + ay' + by = 0.$$

From Section 4–2 it follows that z, being a solution of (4–14), must be of the form $z = C_3 e^{m_2 x}$. Then (4–13) states that y satisfies

$$y' - m_1 y = C_3 e^{m_2 x}.$$

Using (4–7), we obtain

$$(4\text{--}15) \qquad y = C_4 e^{m_1 x} + e^{m_1 x} \int_0^x e^{-m_1 t} C_3 e^{m_2 t} \, dt.$$

If $m_1 \neq m_2$, (4–15) becomes

$$(4\text{--}16) \qquad\qquad y = C_1 e^{m_1 x} + C_2 e^{m_2 x},$$

where

$$C_1 = C_4 - \frac{C_3}{m_2 - m_1}, \qquad C_2 = \frac{C_3}{m_2 - m_1}.$$

If $m_1 = m_2$, (4–15) becomes

$$(4\text{--}17) \qquad\qquad y = C_1 e^{m_1 x} + C_2 x e^{m_1 x},$$

where we have written C_1 for C_4 and C_2 for C_3.

Direct substitution of (4–16) or (4–17) into (4–11) shows that, for all values of C_1 and C_2, the family of functions given by (4–16) or (4–17) actually satisfies (4–11). This completes the proof of the following theorem.

Theorem. If the characteristic roots m_1 and m_2 of (4–11) are real, then the complete solution of (4–11) is given by (4–16) when $m_1 \neq m_2$ and by (4–17) when $m_1 = m_2$.

Example 4–3. Find the complete solution of

$$y'' + 3y' + 2y = 0.$$

Solution: The characteristic equation is $m^2 + 3m + 2 = 0$; the roots are $m_1 = -1$ and $m_2 = -2$. Then (4–16) applies and gives as the complete solution

$$y = C_1 e^{-x} + C_2 e^{-2x}.$$

Example 4–4. Find all solutions of

$$y'' - 2y' + y = 0.$$

Solution: The characteristic equation, $m^2 - 2m + 1 = 0$, has coincident roots $m_1 = m_2 = 1$. The complete solution by (4–17) is

$$y = C_1 e^x + C_2 x e^x.$$

The solutions of the second-order equations just given have been obtained in each case by solving successively two first-order equations. This procedure corresponds to a factorization of the characteristic polynomial and to a sort of "factorization" of the differential equation. This may be regarded from a slightly different point of view (see exercise 7 of Section 2–8). If there exist real numbers g and k such that $y'' + ay' + by = (y'' + ky') + g(y' + ky)$, then the substitution $u = y' + ky$ reduces the problem of solving (4–11) to that of solving successively the first-order equations $u' + gu = 0$ and $y' + ky = u$. Since $k + g = a$ and $kg = b$, k and g are the roots of the characteristic equation. This "factorization" of the differential equation is formalized with the help of the concept of operators and is discussed in Section 4–6. In Section 4–7 we shall generalize these methods to solve linear equations of higher order.

Finally, suppose the roots of the characteristic equation are non-real complex numbers, whence they are distinct and conjugate:

$m_1 = \alpha + \beta i$, $m_2 = \alpha - \beta i$, where α, β are real and $\beta \neq 0$. The treatment in Example 2–18 shows that the complete solution of (4–11) is

$$(4\text{–}18) \qquad y = e^{\alpha x} (C_1 \sin \beta x + C_2 \cos \beta x).$$

We shall show now that this solution agrees with that given for the real case (4–16), provided complex powers are suitably defined.

In complex analysis, if $z = x + iy$, where x and y are real, e^z is defined by

$$(4\text{–}19) \qquad e^z = e^x (\cos y + i \sin y).$$

One readily verifies that the usual laws of exponents hold under this definition. Thus, for example, if $w = u + iv$, then

$$
\begin{aligned}
e^z e^w &= e^x e^u (\cos y + i \sin y)(\cos v + i \sin v) \\
&= e^{x+u} [(\cos y \cos v - \sin y \sin v) + i(\sin y \cos v + \cos y \sin v)] \\
&= e^{x+u} [\cos (y + v) + i \sin (y + v)] \\
&= e^{z+w}.
\end{aligned}
$$

For a more complete discussion, see pages 91 and 92.

To return to the main problem, let us show that if $m_1 = \alpha + \beta i$, $m_2 = \alpha - \beta i$, then (4–18) is equivalent to (4–16), provided the constants appearing in (4–16) are suitably restricted. From (4–19) we have

$$
\begin{aligned}
e^{m_1 x} &= e^{\alpha x} (\cos \beta x + i \sin \beta x), \\
e^{m_2 x} &= e^{\alpha x} (\cos \beta x - i \sin \beta x),
\end{aligned}
$$

so that (4–16) becomes

$$C_1 e^{m_1 x} + C_2 e^{m_2 x} = e^{\alpha x} [(C_1 + C_2) \cos \beta x + (C_1 - C_2) i \sin \beta x]$$

$$= e^{\alpha x}(C_1' \cos \beta x + C_2' \sin \beta x).$$

This agrees with (4–18), provided it is understood that C_1' and C_2', where

$$C_1' = C_1 + C_2, \quad C_2' = (C_1 - C_2)i,$$

are allowed to take on independently all real values. This reality requirement is clearly met if and only if, in (4–16), C_1 and C_2 are restricted to be any complex numbers conjugate to each other.

It is important to note that, even in the case where m_1 and m_2 are complex,

$$(4\text{–}16) \qquad y = C_1 e^{m_1 x} + C_2 e^{m_2 x}$$

by direct verification may be seen to satisfy the equation

(4–11) $$y'' + ay' + b = 0.$$

That this is true depends on the fact that

$$\frac{d}{dx}(e^{mx}) = me^{mx},$$

even if m is complex, and that other general rules for differentiation hold for complex-valued as well as real-valued functions of the real variable x (see pages 91 and 92). For differentiation of (4–16) gives

$$y' = C_1 m_1 e^{m_1 x} + C_2 m_2 e^{m_2 x},$$

$$y'' = C_1 m_1^2 e^{m_1 x} + C_2 m_2^2 e^{m_2 x};$$

substitution into the left side of (4–11) yields

$$C_1(m_1^2 + am_1 + b)e^{m_1 x} + C_2(m_2^2 + am_2 + b)e^{m_2 x},$$

which is equal to zero, since m_1 and m_2 are roots of the characteristic equation.

It is possible now to strengthen the theorem on the solution of (4–11).

Theorem. If the characteristic roots of (4–11) are distinct, whether real or complex, the complete solution of (4–11) is given by (4–16). In the complex case, C_1 and C_2 in (4–16) are any conjugate complex numbers. If the roots are coincident, the solution is given by (4–17).

Example 4–5. Solve $y'' + y' + y = 0$.

Solution: The characteristic roots are the solutions of $m^2 + m + 1 = 0$, and are therefore given by

$$m_1 = \frac{-1 + \sqrt{3}\,i}{2}, \quad m_2 = \frac{-1 - \sqrt{3}\,i}{2}.$$

Hence, by (4–16), the complete solution is

$$y = C_1 e^{m_1 x} + C_2 e^{m_2 x},$$

with C_1, C_2 arbitrary complex conjugates; equivalently, the solution is

$$y = e^{-x/2}\left(C_1 \cos \frac{\sqrt{3}}{2}x + C_2 \sin \frac{\sqrt{3}}{2}x\right),$$

with C_1, C_2 arbitrary real numbers.

Use of complex functions has provided a notational unification for the solutions in real and complex cases. Actually, the advantages in using complex rather than real functions are more than notational, as will be seen in Section 4–7 and Chapter 6. The situation for linear differential equations is analogous to that for polynomial equations in elementary algebra, where a unified theory does not exist in the real domain.

*More on Complex Functions. Let us examine more closely the theory of complex-valued functions. If $z = x + iy$, define a complex-valued function $f(z)$, where z is restricted to a certain complex domain A, by

$$f(z) = g(x, y) + ih(x, y),$$

in which g and h are real-valued functions of (x, y) defined for all (x, y) in A (in the sense that $z = x + iy$ is in A).

Algebraic operations on such functions are performed in the natural way. For example, if $f_1 = g_1 + ih_1$, $f_2 = g_2 + ih_2$, then

$$f_1 g_1 = (g_1 g_2 - h_1 h_2) + i(g_1 h_2 + h_1 g_2).$$

We say that $f(z)$ is *continuous* if g and h are continuous. If $\dfrac{\partial g}{\partial x}$ and $\dfrac{\partial h}{\partial x}$ exist, then

$$\frac{\partial f}{\partial x} = \frac{\partial g}{\partial x} + i\frac{\partial h}{\partial x};$$

similarly for differentiation with respect to y. If x and y are functions of a single real variable t, then

$$\frac{df}{dt} = \frac{dg}{dt} + i\frac{dh}{dt},$$

where the total derivatives on the right are assumed to exist, and, for example,

$$\frac{dg}{dt} = \frac{\partial g}{\partial x}\frac{dx}{dt} + \frac{\partial g}{\partial y}\frac{dy}{dt}.$$

There are many ways of motivating the definition (4–19). It is natural to define complex exponents so that, among other things, the basic law $e^z e^w = e^{z+w}$ holds. On this basis, it is reasonable to demand that $e^{x+iy} = e^x e^{iy}$. Now denote the second factor e^{iy} by $k(y)$, so that

$$k(y) = e^{iy} = g(y) + ih(y).$$

The law $e^z e^w = e^{z+w}$ with $w = 0$ gives $e^z e^0 = e^z$, so that, if it is assumed that e^z is not 0 for every z, e^0 must be 1.

Let us now demand that the rules of real calculus apply to the function e^{iy} as a function of y, specifically, that $\dfrac{d}{dy} e^{iy} = ie^{iy}$.

This leads to

$$g'(y) + ih'(y) = i(g(y) + ih(y)),$$

or to

$$g'(y) = -h(y),$$
$$h'(y) = g(y).$$

Hence

$$g''(y) = -g(y),$$

and application of (4–18) gives

$$g(y) = c_1 \sin y + c_2 \cos y,$$

whence

$$h(y) = g'(y) = c_1 \cos y - c_2 \sin y.$$

Finally, $1 = e^{i0} = g(0) + ih(0)$, whence $g(0) = 1$, $h(0) = 0$; therefore $c_1 = 0$, $c_2 = 1$, and it follows that

$$k(y) = \cos y + i \sin y.$$

Throughout the theory of linear differential equations, we shall find it convenient to deal with functions e^w, where w is a complex-valued function of one real variable t. It is important to see that the rules of real calculus apply to complex-valued functions of t. If

$$F(t) = g(t) + ih(t),$$

then, by the definition given earlier,

$$F'(t) = g'(t) + ih'(t).$$

Moreover, if $G(t)$ is another such function, then

$$(F + G)' = F' + G',$$
$$(FG)' = FG' + F'G,$$
$$(F^n)' = nF^{n-1}F' \qquad (n = 1, 2, \cdots),$$

and so on.

Also, after defining

$$\int_a^b F(t)\, dt = \int_a^b g(t)\, dt + i\int_a^b h(t)\, dt,$$

we may prove the standard properties of integrals, including the fundamental theorem of integral calculus.

EXERCISES

In each of exercises 1 to 8, find the complete solution. Where initial conditions are given, find also the solution which satisfies them.

1. $y'' - 5y' - y = 0.$

2. $y'' + 4y' + 4y = 0.$

3. $y'' - 2y' - 4y = 0.$

4. $y'' - y = 0$ $[y(0) = 1,\ y'(0) = -1].$

5. $y'' + y = 0.$

6. $y'' + y' - y = 0$ $[y(0) = 2,\ y'(0) = 0].$

7. $y'' + ky' + ly = 0$ (k, l are real numbers).

8. $y'' + 3.27y' - 0.42y = 0.$

9. Prove by direct substitution that (4–16) satisfies (4–11) if $m_1 \neq m_2$, as stated in the text.

10. Prove by direct substitution that (4–17) satisfies (4–11) if $m_1 = m_2$, as stated in the text.

11. Prove that, if y_1 and y_2 are solutions of (4–11), then $y_1 + y_2$ and Cy_1 are also solutions, where C is any constant.

★12. If $F(t) = g(t) + ih(t)$ and $G(t) = k(t) + il(t)$, prove that $(F + G)' = F' + G'$, $(FG)' = FG' + F'G$, $(F^n)' = nF^{n-1}F'$ $(n = 1, 2, \cdots)$, $\left(\dfrac{F}{G}\right)' = \dfrac{GF' - G'F}{G^2}$ if $G \neq 0$. (Assume the derivatives of F and G exist.)

★13. If $F(t) = g(t) + ih(t)$, and if $t = \phi(u)$, where ϕ is a real function of the real variable u, prove that $\dfrac{dF}{du} = \dfrac{dF}{dt} \cdot \dfrac{dt}{du}$. (Assume that $\dfrac{dF}{dt}$ and $\dfrac{dt}{du}$ exist.)

★14. For a function $F(t) = g(t) + ih(t)$, state and prove the fundamental theorem of integral calculus, using the corresponding theorem for real functions.

⋆15. Prove that $\int_a^b e^{mx}\, dx = \dfrac{1}{m}\,(e^{mb} - e^{ma})$ for real a, b and complex m.

⋆16. Prove the assertion in the text relative to the equations

$$C_1' = C_1 + C_2, \quad C_2' = (C_1 - C_2)i$$

connecting complex constants C_1, C_2, C_1', C_2'. That is, prove the following four assertions:

    (a) if C_1, C_2 are complex conjugates, then C_1' and C_2' are real;

    (b) if C_1' and C_2' are real, then C_1, C_2 are complex conjugates;

    (c) if C_1' and C_2' are real, then there exist complex conjugates C_1, C_2 such that the equations are true;

    (d) if C_1, C_2 are complex conjugates, then there exist real numbers C_1' and C_2' such that the equations are true.

4–4. NON-HOMOGENEOUS SECOND-ORDER LINEAR EQUATIONS

Consider the non-homogeneous linear equation

$$(4\text{–}20) \qquad\qquad y'' + ay' + by = f(x),$$

where $f(x)$ is a given continuous function, and a and b are constants. The *characteristic equation* of (4–20) is defined to be $m^2 + am + b = 0$, as for the homogeneous equation (4–11). Denote the characteristic roots by m_1 and m_2.

Suppose that the solution of the associated homogeneous equation

$$(4\text{–}11) \qquad\qquad y'' + ay' + by = 0$$

has been obtained as $C_1 e^{m_1 x} + C_2 e^{m_2 x}$ or $C_1 e^{m_1 x} + C_2 xe^{m_1 x}$. This solution is called the *complementary function*[1] for (4–20). We shall show first that the complete solution of (4–20) is the sum of a particular solution of (4–20) plus the complementary function, as was the case for first-order equations.

Let y_f be a particular solution of (4–20) and let y be any solution. Then from

$$y'' + ay' + by = f \quad \text{and} \quad y_f'' + ay_f' + by_f = f$$

---

[1]This is not a completely satisfactory term, since what is referred to is a set of functions. However, it is a traditional term, and so will be used here.

it follows, by subtraction, that

$$(y - y_f)'' + a(y - y_f)' + b(y - y_f) = 0.$$

Hence $y - y_f$ satisfies (4–11), whence we have, according as $m_1 \neq m_2$ or $m_1 = m_2$,

$$y - y_f = C_1 e^{m_1 x} + C_2 e^{m_2 x} \quad \text{or} \quad y - y_f = C_1 e^{m_1 x} + C_2 x e^{m_1 x}$$

for some choice of C_1, C_2. Conversely, $y_f +$ the complementary function satisfies (4–20), as direct substitution shows. This completes the proof.

More specific formulas for y may be obtained by the following derivation, which is restricted to the case in which m_1 and m_2 are real, although the result is valid also when m_1 and m_2 are complex. Again let y be any solution of (4–20), and let

(4–21) $$z = y' - m_1 y;$$

then (4–20) is equivalent to (4–21) together with

(4–22) $$z' - m_2 z = f(x).$$

Thus, by (4–7),

(4–23) $$z = C_2' e^{m_2 x} + e^{m_2 x} \int_{x_0}^{x} e^{-m_2 u} f(u) \, du,$$

and so, again by (4–7),

$$y = C_1 e^{m_1 x} + e^{m_1 x} \int_{x_0}^{x} \left[C_2' e^{m_2 t} + e^{m_2 t} \int_{t_0}^{t} e^{-m_2 u} f(u) \, du \right] e^{-m_1 t} \, dt.$$

By considering the cases $m_1 \neq m_2$ and $m_1 = m_2$ separately and suitably changing the form of the constants, we obtain, respectively,

(4–24) $$y = C_1 e^{m_1 x} + C_2 e^{m_2 x} + e^{m_1 x} \int_{x_0}^{x} e^{(m_2 - m_1) t} \left[\int_{t_0}^{t} e^{-m_2 u} f(u) \, du \right] dt,$$

and

(4–25) $$y = C_1 e^{m_1 x} + C_2 x e^{m_1 x} + e^{m_1 x} \int_{x_0}^{x} e^{(m_2 - m_1) t} \left[\int_{t_0}^{t} e^{-m_2 u} f(u) \, du \right] dt.$$

Direct substitution of (4–24) or (4–25) into (4–20) shows that the family of functions actually satisfies (4–20). The following theorem is thus verified.

Theorem. The complete solution of the general second-order equation (4–20) with constant coefficients is obtained through (4–24) or (4–25) as the sum of a particular solution and the complementary function.

Denote by $F(x, C_2')$ the family of functions given by (4–23):

$$(4\text{–}26) \qquad z = F(x, C_2') = C_2' e^{m_2 x} + e^{m_2 x} \int_{x_0}^{x} e^{-m_2 u} f(u)\, du.$$

Then the solution of (4–20) may be expressed as

$$(4\text{–}27) \qquad y = C_1 e^{m_1 x} + e^{m_1 x} \int_{x_0}^{x} e^{-m_1 t} F(t, C_2')\, dt.$$

The solution (4–24) or (4–25) is obtained by combining (4–26) and (4–27). We include a remark about the constants of integration, C_1 and C_2'. Assume for simplicity that $x_0 = 0$. Then C is the value $y(0)$. Similarly, C_2' is the value $z(0)$. Since $z = y' - m_1 y$, $C_2' = y'(0) - m_1 y(0)$.

While it is true that the general solution of (4–20) is given in every case by (4–26) and (4–27), the use of these formulas is very often not the quickest way to obtain a simple form of the complete solution. Inasmuch as it is known that (4–24) or (4–25) gives all solutions, the only problem of consequence is that of determining a single particular solution, by any method which may present itself. For the characteristic roots are always easily obtained; the complementary function constructed from them plus the particular solution found will thus give the desired complete solution.

Example 4–6. Solve $y'' - 8y' + 17y = 5$.

Solution: The characteristic roots are $4 \pm i$. By inspection we see that $y = 5/17$ is a particular solution. Hence the desired solution is

$$y = e^{4x}(C_1 \sin x + C_2 \cos x) + \frac{5}{17},$$

in view of (4–18) and the remarks above.

Example 4–7. Solve $y'' + 6y' + 9y = x^2$.

Solution: The characteristic roots are both equal to -3, so that the complementary function is, by (4–17), $C_1 e^{-2x} + C_2 x e^{-2x}$. Two methods suggest themselves for the determination of a particular solution and hence the completion of the work.

Method 1. The part of (4–25) representing a particular solution becomes, if we let $t_0 = x_0 = 0$,

$$e^{-3x} \int_0^x \left(\int_0^t e^{3u} u^2 \, du \right) dt = e^{-3x} \int_0^x \left[e^{3t} \left(\frac{t^2}{3} - \frac{2t}{9} + \frac{2}{27} \right) - \frac{2}{27} \right] dt$$

$$= \frac{1}{9} x^2 - \frac{4}{27} x + \frac{2}{27} - \frac{2}{27} e^{-3x} - \frac{2}{27} x e^{-3x}.$$

The complete solution is

$$y = C_1' e^{-3x} + C_2' x e^{-3x} + \frac{1}{9} x^2 - \frac{4}{27} x + \frac{2}{27},$$

where the last two terms in the particular solution have been "absorbed" by the complementary function.

Method 2. Since the right side of the given equation is a polynomial of degree 2, we might try to find a solution of the form $Ax^2 + Bx + C$. Substituting into the equation and equating coefficients of like powers of x yield

$$A = \frac{1}{9}, \quad B = -\frac{4}{27}, \quad C = \frac{2}{27}.$$

The complete solution is thus again

$$y = C_1 e^{-3x} + C_2 x e^{-3x} + \frac{1}{9} x^2 - \frac{4}{27} x + \frac{2}{27}.$$

EXERCISES

In each of exercises 1 to 8, find the complete solution. Where possible, avoid the use of the formulas (4–24) and (4–25). If initial conditions are given, find also the solution which satisfies them.

1. $y'' + 5y' - 6y = x^3$.
2. $y'' + 4y' + 4y = x^2 - 2x + 1$.
3. $y'' + 4y = 1 - x$ $[y(0) = y'(0) = 0]$.
4. $y'' + y' = 4$.
5. $y'' + y' + y = e^x$. (HINT: Try an exponential solution as a particular solution.)
6. $y'' + y' - 2y = 2e^x$ $[y(0) = y'(0) = 1]$.
7. $y'' - 9y = e^x + 3e^{-3x}$.
8. $y'' - 2y' + y = 1 + 2x + 3e^x$.

9. Assume that y_1 is a solution of $y'' + ay' + by = f_1(x)$ and y_2 is a solution of $y'' + ay' + b = f_2(x)$. Then prove that $C_1 y_1 + C_2 y_2$ is a solution of $y'' + ay' + by = C_1 f_1(x) + C_2 f_2(x)$, where C_1 and C_2 are constants.

10. Using exercise 9, solve exercise 8.

11. Solve $y'' - (m_1 + m_2)y' + m_1 m_2 y = e^{mx}$, treating all cases.

12. Prove that, as claimed in the text, the functions given by (4–24) satisfy (4–20).

★13. Derive an analog of (4–9) for second-order equations thus: Let $Y(x)$ be the unique solution of (4–11) for which $y(0) = 0$, $y'(0) = 1$. Then the complete solution of (4–20) is

$$y = \text{complementary function} + \int_0^x Y(x - t)f(t)\, dt.$$

4–5. OPERATORS

It is our objective now to generalize the results and methods of Sections 4–3 and 4–4 to linear equations of higher order. While the "factorization" procedure can be generalized directly, it is more convenient to do this with the help of a notational tool provided by the theory of *operators*. Accordingly, this section is devoted to a survey of this theory, including a minimal list of definitions and theorems needed to provide a working knowledge of this subject in its formal aspects.

Let us recall that an ordinary function, even one that is multiple-valued (sometimes called a *binary relation*), may be regarded as a set of ordered pairs of numbers (x, y). If f is the function, and if (x, y) belongs to f, we write $y = f(x)$. The set of all first entries in the pairs constituting f is the *domain* of f, while the set of all second entries in the pairs constituting f is the *range* of f. The function is *single-valued* in case

if (x, y_1) and (x, y_2) are in f, then $y_1 = y_2$.

In this book we have been restricting our attention to functions which are single-valued; this we shall continue to do. Also, we shall consider only functions whose domains are *intervals* of the form

all real numbers x such that $a \leqq x \leqq b$,

or

all real numbers x such that $a \leqq x$,

or

all real numbers x such that $x \leqq b$,

or

all real numbers x.

This assumption was stated in Section 1–1 and has been implicit in our preceding work.

Note. While more often than not the values of functions under consideration are to be real numbers, it is necessary also to include the case when the values are complex. (However, the domain is always a real interval.) Complex-valued functions are expressed in the form $f_1(x) + if_2(x)$. Thus, if $f = f_1 + if_2, g = g_1 + ig_2$, then, for example,

$$f + g = (f_1 + g_1) + i(f_2 + g_2),$$
$$fg = (f_1g_1 - f_2g_2) + i(f_1g_2 + f_2g_1),$$
$$f' = f_1' + if_2',$$

and the algebra and calculus of such complex-valued functions follow along natural and expected lines. (See pages 91 to 93.)

In similar fashion, we define an *operator* as a set of ordered pairs of functions (of the sort described in the last three paragraphs). If A is an operator, and if (f, g) is a pair of functions in it, we write $g = Af$. The symbol Af alone is used to designate the set of all functions g such that (f, g) belongs to A; however, when there is only one such function g, then Af represents that function.[2] If Af consists of only real-valued functions whenever f is real, then A is called a *real* operator. Otherwise it is called a *non-real complex* operator.

The set of all first entries in the pairs constituting the operator A is the *domain* of A; the set of all second entries in these pairs is the *range* of A. The operator A is *single-valued* in case

if (f, g_1) and (f, g_2) are in A, then $g_1 = g_2$.

Operators A and B are equal when they consist of the same pairs. It follows that $A = B$ if and only if A and B have the same domain and $Af = Bf$ for every function f in that domain. Note that the condition $Af = Bf$ means that every function g in the set Af is also in Bf and conversely; that is, $Af = Bf$ means

g is in Af if and only if g is in Bf.

As is the case with functions, it is possible to apply certain operations to operators to obtain new operators. Specifically, we define three operations as follows.

[2]Custom dictates the unfortunate use of the symbol Af in three distinct ways: notation for a set, notation for a single function, and part of the complete notation $g = Af$. In the last of these, Af has no meaning by itself; only the entire symbol $g = Af$ has meaning, standing for the sentence, "(f, g) is a member of A." The context should always make clear which usage is intended.

Definition. If A and B are operators, then $A + B$ is the operator having as domain those functions f in both domains of A and B, and having the property that, for every such f,

$$(4\text{–}28) \qquad\qquad (A + B)f = Af + Bf.$$

Note. In (4–28), $Af + Bf$ means the set of all functions obtained by adding any function in Af to any function in Bf. When Af and Bf represent single functions, then $Af + Bf$ is their sum.

Definition. If A and B are operators, then the product AB is the operator having domain consisting of those functions f in the domain of B for which some member of Bf is in the domain of A and having the property that, for every such f,

$$(4\text{–}29) \qquad\qquad (AB)f = A(Bf).$$

Note. In (4–29), $A(Bf)$ is the set of all functions belonging to some set Ag, where g is some function in Bf. When Bf represents a single function g, then $A(Bf)$ is Ag.

Definition. If A is an operator and g is a function, gA is the operator having the same domain as A and having the property that, for every function f in that domain,

$$(4\text{–}30) \qquad\qquad (gA)f = g(Af).$$

Note. In (4–30), $g(Af)$ means the set of all products of g and the various functions in Af. When Af represents a single function h, then $g(Af)$ is gh.

Important special operators are the *zero operator* θ for which $\theta f = 0$ for all functions f, 0 being the zero function; the *identity operator* I, where $If = f$ for all functions f; and the *derivative operator* D, where $Df = g$ means that $g = f'$. The domain of D consists of those functions f (real- or complex-valued) possessing derivatives at points x constituting one of the sets admissible as domains for our functions. All these operators are single-valued and real.

Powers of operators are defined in a natural way: $A^1 = A$, $A^2 = AA$, $A^3 = A^2A$, $\cdots$, $A^n = A^{n-1}A$. Also, $A^0 = I$; and A^{-1}, called the *inverse* of A, consists of those pairs of functions (g, f) for which (f, g) is in A. Finally, A^{-n} is defined as $(A^{-1})^n$ for $n = 1, 2, \cdots$.

Example 4–8. Interpret $D^2, \cdots, D^n, D^{-1}$.

Solution: We have that (f, g) is in D^2 if and only if $g = Dh$ for some function h in Df. But Df is the one function f'; also $Dh = h'$. Hence $g = h' = (f')' = f''$. Similarly, (f, g) is in D^3 if and only if $g = f'''$; (f, g) is in D^n if and only if $g = f^{(n)}$. Finally, (g, f) is in D^{-1} when (f, g) is in D, that is, when $g = f'$. Hence $D^{-1}g$ is the set of all functions f such that $g = f'$; that is, the set of all antiderivatives of g. When g is continuous,

$$f = D^{-1}g \text{ if and only if } f = \int g(x)\, dx.$$

Note that, although $D, D^2, \cdots$ are single-valued, D^{-1} is not. For example,

$$D^{-1}(2x - 1) = \int (2x - 1)\, dx = x^2 - x + C,$$

the various functions in $D^{-1}(2x - 1)$ being obtained by assigning all numerical values to the parameter C.

While many algebraic properties of the operations of addition and multiplication of operators are similar to those of the corresponding operations for numbers, there are some important differences. For example, it is not generally true that $AB = BA$. If it happens that two particular operators do have this property, they are said to *commute*. A few results from the algebra of operators are stated here without proof. More details concerning these results are found on pages 102 and 103.

Theorem. If A, B, and C are operators, and if f and g are functions, then

(a) $(A + B) + C = A + (B + C)$;
(b) $(AB)C = A(BC)$;
(c) $A + B = B + A$;
(d) $A + \theta = A$;
(e) $AI = IA = A$;
(f) $(AB)^{-1} = B^{-1}A^{-1}$;
(g) $(A^{-1})^{-1} = A$;
(h)   if A or A^{-1} is single-valued, then
          $AA^{-1}A = A$ and $A^{-1}AA^{-1} = A^{-1}$;
(i)   if A is single-valued, then AA^{-1} is single-valued, and
          $f = (AA^{-1})f$ for every f in the domain of A^{-1};
(j) $f(A + B) = fA + fB$;
(k) $(fA)B = f(AB)$;
(l) $f(gA) = (f \cdot g)A$, where $f \cdot g$ is the product of f and g.

In the following sections we shall be concerned only with operators having a special property called *linearity*.

Definition. An operator A is *linear* if, whenever f_1 and f_2 are in the domain of A, and c_1, c_2 are complex numbers, $c_1 f_1 + c_2 f_2$ is in that domain and

$$(4\text{–}31) \qquad A(c_1 f_1 + c_2 f_2) = c_1 A f_1 + c_2 A f_2.$$

It may be shown that the sum, product and inverses of linear operators are again linear; also, if A is linear, so is fA for any function f.

*More on Operators. The reader who wishes to gain more insight into the theory of operators would do well to study the theorem of this section carefully, working out proofs of the various parts. Let us carry out proofs of two of these properties to indicate the method.

Proof of $A + \theta = A$. Let (f, g) be in $A + \theta$. Then $g = (A + \theta)f$, that is, g is the sum of functions g_1 and g_2 such that $g_1 = Af$ and $g_2 = \theta f$. Hence $g_2 = 0$ and $g = g_1$, so that (f, g) is in A [since (f, g_1) is in A]. This proves that every pair (f, g) in $A + \theta$ is in A. Conversely, if (f, g) is in A, that is, $g = Af$, then clearly $g = g + 0$, whence g is in Af and 0 is in θf. This proves that g is in $(A + \theta)f$, whence (f, g) is in $A + \theta$. The proof is complete.

Proof of $(AB)^{-1} = B^{-1}A^{-1}$. Let (f, g) be in $(AB)^{-1}$. Then (g, f) is in AB, that is, $f = (AB)g$. But this means that there exists a function h such that $f = Ah$, $h = Bg$. It follows that $g = B^{-1}h$, $h = A^{-1}f$, so that $g = B^{-1}A^{-1}f$. Hence (f, g) is in $B^{-1}A^{-1}$. The converse, that every pair (f, g) in $B^{-1}A^{-1}$ is in $(AB)^{-1}$, is shown in like manner. The proof is complete.

It has been remarked after the definition of linearity that the set of linear operators is closed with respect to addition, multiplication, multiplication (on the left) by functions, and the process of taking inverses. Let us prove the last of these closure properties. Suppose A is linear, and let f_1, f_2 be functions in the domain of A^{-1}. Then there exist g_1, g_2 such that $g_1 = A^{-1}f_1$, $g_2 = A^{-1}f_2$. It follows that $f_1 = Ag_1$, $f_2 = Ag_2$. Since A is linear, $c_1 g_1 + c_2 g_2$ is in the domain of A (where c_1, c_2 are any constants), and

$$A(c_1 g_1 + c_2 g_2) = c_1 A g_1 + c_2 A g_2 = c_1 f_1 + c_2 f_2.$$

Thus

$$c_1 A^{-1}f_1 + c_2 A^{-1}f_2 = c_1 g_1 + c_2 g_2 = A^{-1}(c_1 f_1 + c_2 f_2),$$

and the condition (4–31) is verified for A^{-1}.

Properties (h) and (i) of the theorem are weaker than what might be expected from ordinary algebra, namely, $AA^{-1} = A^{-1}A = I$. This last statement cannot be true, since the domain of AA^{-1} is possibly a very limited set of functions (it is contained in the domain of A^{-1}), while the domain of I is the set of all functions. However, it is not true even that A and A^{-1} commute. For, if $f(x) = x$, then

$$DD^{-1}f = D\left(\frac{x^2}{2} + C\right) = f,$$

while

$$D^{-1}Df = D^{-1}(1) = f + C.$$

Hence DD^{-1} is single-valued, while $D^{-1}D$ is not.

To prove part (i), note that, if f is in the domain of A^{-1}, then there exists g such that $g = A^{-1}f$. Thus also $f = Ag$. By the definition of product, $f = AA^{-1}f$. Moreover, if $h = AA^{-1}f$, then $h = Ak$, $k = A^{-1}f$ for some k. But the last statement yields $f = Ak$, so that $h = f$ in view of the single-valuedness of A. This proves that AA^{-1} is single-valued.

Finally, it should be noted that the distributive laws,

$$(A + B)C = AC + BC, \quad C(A + B) = CA + CB,$$

do not appear, since they are not generally true. The first of these may be proved for the case in which C is single-valued, and the second is true when C is linear and its domain contains the range of A or the range of B, or when C is linear and A, B are single-valued.

EXERCISES

1. Let $g(x) = x$ and define the operator A as gD. Then show that $AD \neq DA$. [HINT: Show that $(AD)g \neq (DA)g$.]

2. Prove that θ and I are single-valued and linear.

3. Prove that the operator kI, where k is any constant function, is single-valued and linear.

4. Prove that, if A is single-valued and f is any function, then fA is single-valued. Also prove that, if A is linear, so is fA.

5. Let A be defined so that $Af = f^2$. Then show that A is not linear.

6. Prove that an operator A is linear if and only if $A\left(\sum_{k=1}^{n} c_k f_k\right)$
$= \sum_{k=1}^{n} c_k A f_k$ for every $n = 1, 2, \cdots$ and for every choice of constants $c_1, \cdots, c_n$.

★**7.** Show that it is not necessarily true that $(f + g)A = fA + gA$. [HINT: Let $f(x) = 1$, $g(x) = x$, and $A = D^{-1}$. Then show that $(f + g)Af$ is a one-parameter family of functions, while $(fA + gA)f$ is a two-parameter family.]

★**8.** Prove parts (a), (b), (c), (e), (g), (h), (j), (k), (l) of the theorem.

★**9.** Let A and B be linear operators and f a function. Prove that $A + B$, AB, and fA are linear.

★**10.** If A is a single-valued operator, prove that

$$\left(\sum_{k=1}^{n} f_k\right) A = \sum_{k=1}^{n} (f_k A) \text{ for every } n = 1, 2, \cdots .$$

★**11.** Prove that, for operators A, B, C, if C is single-valued, then $(A + B)C = AC + BC$.

★**12.** Prove that, for operators A, B, C, if C is linear and has domain containing the range of A or the range of B, then $C(A + B) = CA + CB$.

4–6. THE OPERATOR D

Some results concerning the operator D and certain operators associated with D are developed in this section. It has already been noted that D is real and single-valued. Let us now verify that D is linear. If f_1 and f_2 are differentiable functions, then $c_1 f_1 + c_2 f_2$ is differentiable and

$$(c_1 f_1 + c_2 f_2)' = c_1 f_1' + c_2 f_2',$$

where c_1 and c_2 are constants, by elementary calculus. But this means that

$$D(c_1 f_1 + c_2 f_2) = c_1 D f_1 + c_2 D f_2,$$

and hence that D satisfies the requirement of linearity.

It follows from Section 4–5 (see in particular page 102) that D^{-1} and all integral powers of D are linear. Since I is linear, so is $-rI$, where r is a constant; hence $G_r = D - rI$ is also linear. If $g = G_r f = (D - rI)f$, then $g = f' - rf$, and so G_r is single-valued.

It is clear that any operator A commutes with its positive integral powers. Thus A commutes with itself: $AA = AA$; A commutes with its square:

$$AA^2 = A(AA) = (AA)A = A^2A,$$

by the associative property; and so on. Moreover, if A commutes with B, then A commutes with B^n for $n = 1, 2, \cdots$. For

$$AB^n = A(BB^{n-1}) = (AB)B^{n-1} = B(AB^{n-1})$$
$$= B(BAB^{n-2}) = B^2AB^{n-2} = \cdots = B^nA.$$

Application of this result to the commuting operators B^n and A shows that B^n commutes with A^m for $m = 1, 2, \cdots$. In particular, D commutes with its powers D^n, $n = 1, 2, \cdots$.

Let us now show that two operators G_r and G_s, where r and s are constants, commute. We have, for any twice-differentiable function f,

$$\begin{aligned}
G_rG_sf &= (D - rI)((D - sI)f) \\
&= (D - rI)(f' - sf) \\
&= D(f' - sf) - r(f' - sf) \\
&= f'' - sf' - rf' + rsf \\
&= D^2f - (r + s)Df + rsIf;
\end{aligned}$$

hence

(4–32) $$G_rG_s = D^2 - (r + s)D + rsI.$$

Interchanging r and s in (4–32) yields

$$G_sG_r = D^2 - (r + s)D + rsI.$$

Thus $G_rG_s = G_sG_r$. It follows then that G_r^m commutes with G_s^n for $m = 1, 2, \cdots$ and $n = 1, 2, \cdots$.

We are now in a position to study *polynomials* in D, that is, operators of the form

(4–33) $$p(D) = D^n + a_1(x)D^{n-1} + a_2(x)D^{n-2}$$
$$+ \cdots + a_{n-1}(x)D + a_n(x)I,$$

where the coefficients $a_1(x), \cdots, a_n(x)$ are given real- or complex-valued functions of x. Each term in $p(D)$ is single-valued and linear, and so $p(D)$ is also single-valued and linear. In what follows we shall usually limit attention to polynomials having constant coefficients.

Consider now a polynomial (4–33) in which $a_1(x)$, $\cdots$, $a_n(x)$ are constants. For simplicity, let us limit our attention to the case $n = 2$ and write

$$p(D) = D^2 + aD + bI.$$

If m_1 and m_2 are the roots of the equation

$$m^2 + am + b = 0,$$

we call m_1 and m_2 the *characteristic roots* of $p(D)$. It follows that

$$(4\text{–}34) \qquad a = -(m_1 + m_2), \quad b = m_1 m_2.$$

Then

$$\begin{aligned}
G_{m_1} G_{m_2} &= D^2 - (m_1 + m_2)D + m_1 m_2 I \qquad &&\text{[by (4–32)]} \\
&= D^2 + aD + bI \qquad &&\text{[by (4–34)]} \\
&= p(D).
\end{aligned}$$

Generalization of this argument establishes the following theorem, yielding *factorizations* of polynomials in D.

Theorem. Every polynomial $p(D)$ in D of degree n and having constant coefficients has a factorization into *linear* factors,

$$p(D) = (D - m_1 I)(D - m_2 I) \cdots (D - m_n I),$$

where m_1, $\cdots$, m_n are the characteristic roots of $p(D)$, that is, are the roots of the *characteristic equation*

$$(4\text{–}35) \qquad m^n + a_1 m^{n-1} + \cdots + a_{n-1} m + a_n = 0.$$

Note. When a root, say m_k, of the characteristic equation (4–35) is real, then the corresponding factor $D - m_k I$ is evidently a real operator. But if m_k is a non-real complex number, then $D - m_k I$ is a non-real complex operator. If the coefficients a_1, $\cdots$, a_n in (4–33) are all real, then $p(D)$ is a real operator.

Example 4–9. Factor each of the operators $D^2 - 7D + 6I$ and $D^3 - I$ into linear (that is, first-degree) factors.

Solution: The characteristic roots of $D^2 - 7D + 6I$ are the solutions of $m^2 - 7m + 6 = 0$; they are $m_1 = 1$, $m_2 = 6$. Hence $D - m_1 I = D - I$ and $D - m_2 I = D - 6I$. It follows that

$$D^2 - 7D + 6I = (D - I)(D - 6I).$$

The characteristic equation of $D^3 - I$ is $m^3 - 1 = 0$, whose roots are

$$m_1 = 1, \quad m_2 = \frac{-1 + i\sqrt{3}}{2}, \quad m_3 = \frac{-1 - i\sqrt{3}}{2}.$$

It follows that

$$D^3 - I = (D - I)\left(D - \frac{-1 + i\sqrt{3}}{2}I\right)\left(D - \frac{-1 - i\sqrt{3}}{2}I\right).$$

It should be noted here that while the linear factors are non-real operators, a factorization into real factors is possible, provided that one allows quadratic as well as linear polynomials. Thus

$$D^3 - I = (D - I)(D^2 + D + I).$$

More on the Operator D. The algebra of operators which are polynomials in D with constant coefficients is much richer than the algebra of operators in general. This is true because these operators are linear and single-valued. Thus (as was proved for the first-degree case) two such polynomials always commute. Also, they satisfy both distributivity conditions (see Section 4–5, exercises 11 and 12). Indeed, these operators correspond in one-to-one fashion with numerical polynomials $p(m)$, where corresponding polynomials have the same coefficients. And all algebraic properties of numerical polynomials $p(m)$ imply, through the correspondence, substantially the same algebraic properties for the operators $p(D)$.

Unfortunately, the algebra of *rational forms*, that is, quotients $p(m)/q(m)$ $[q(m) \neq 0]$ of polynomials, does not carry over to operators. Thus, it would be natural to make correspond to $1/m$ the operator D^{-1}. But the property $(1/m)m = 1$ does not lead to $D^{-1}D = I$, since the latter is not true, as we have seen in Section 4–5 (page 103).

EXERCISES

In each of exercises 1 to 4, factor the given operator into linear polynomial operators.

1. $D^2 + 2D - 4I$.
2. $D^3 - 8I$.
3. $D^3 - 6D^2 + 7D + 6I$.
4. $D^2 - 4D + 4I$.

In each of exercises 5 to 8, factor into real polynomial operators each having degree one or two.

5. $D^2 + 2D + 4I$.

6. $D^3 - 3D^2 + D + I$.

7. $D^6 - I$.

8. $D^4 + D^2 + I$.

⋆**9.** Let $p(D)$ and $q(D)$ be polynomials with constant coefficients. Prove that $p(D)$ and $q(D)$ commute.

⋆**10.** Let $p(m)$, $q(m)$, $r(m)$ be numerical non-zero polynomials. Prove that, if $r(m) = p(m) + q(m)$, then $r(D) = p(D) + q(D)$, provided that $p(m)$ and $q(m)$ have different degrees or that $p(m)$, $q(m)$, $r(m)$ all have the same degree. Prove also that, if $r(m) = p(m)q(m)$, then $r(D) = p(D)q(D)$.

⋆**11.** Prove that the correspondence $p(m) \leftrightarrow p(D)$ is one-to-one. [HINT: Show that, if $p(m)$, $q(m)$ are different polynomials, then $p(D)$, $q(D)$ are different operators.]

4–7. LINEAR EQUATIONS OF HIGHER ORDER

A linear differential equation of order n is one of the form

$$(4\text{--}36) \qquad y^{(n)} + a_1(x)y^{(n-1)} + \cdots + a_{n-1}(x)y' + a_n(x)y = f(x),$$

where the coefficients and $f(x)$ are continuous functions. It is possible to write (4–36) in the form

$$(4\text{--}37) \qquad\qquad p(D)y = f(x),$$

where

$$p(D) = D^n + a_1(x)D^{n-1} + \cdots + a_{n-1}(x)D + a_n(x)I.$$

When $f(x) = 0$, equation (4–37) is called *homogeneous*.

The methods and theorem of Section 4–4 concerning the case $n = 2$ can now be extended to yield the solution of (4–37) in general.

Suppose y_f is a particular solution of (4–37). First let y_0 satisfy the associated homogeneous equation

$$(4\text{--}38) \qquad\qquad p(D)y = 0.$$

Then, since $p(D)$ is a linear operator,

$$p(D)(y_0 + y_f) = p(D)y_0 + p(D)y_f = 0 + f(x) = f(x).$$

Conversely, let y be any solution of (4–37). Hence, from

$p(D)y = p(D)y_f = f(x)$ it follows that $p(D)(y - y_f) = 0$, so that $y - y_f$ is a solution y_0 of (4–38). Thus $y = y_0 + y_f$. The following result is thus obtained.

Theorem. The complete solution of the general linear equation (4–37) is obtained by adding a particular solution y_f of (4–37) to the complete solution y_0 of the associated homogeneous equation (4–38).

It should be noted that the present theorem applies whether the coefficients in (4–37) are constants or not, in contrast to the theorem of Section 4–4. However, no explicit formula is available for the general case, except when the coefficients are constants. Throughout the remainder of this section, it is assumed that $a_1, \cdots, a_n$ are constants.

The principal tool for obtaining explicitly the complete solution of (4–37) is the factorization theorem of Section 4–6. Let $m_1, \cdots, m_n$ be the characteristic roots of $p(D)$, so that

$$(4\text{--}39) \qquad p(D) = (D - m_1 I)(D - m_2 I) \cdots (D - m_n I).$$

Now (4–37) may be written as

$$(4\text{--}40) \qquad y = p(D)^{-1}f.$$

But the inverse of a product is the product of the inverses of the factors in the reverse order (by the theorem in Section 4–5). Hence (4–40) becomes

$$(4\text{--}41) \qquad y = (D - m_n I)^{-1} (D - m_{n-1} I)^{-1} \cdots (D - m_1 I)^{-1}f.$$

By the definition of the product of operators, (4–41) is equivalent to the existence of functions $u_1, \cdots, u_{n-1}$ such that

$$(4\text{--}42) \qquad \left\{ \begin{aligned} u_1 &= (D - m_1 I)^{-1}f, \\ u_2 &= (D - m_2 I)^{-1}u_1, \\ &\cdot \quad \cdot \quad \cdot \quad \cdot \quad \cdot \quad \cdot \\ u_{n-1} &= (D - m_{n-1} I)^{-1}u_{n-2}, \\ y &= (D - m_n I)^{-1}u_{n-1}. \end{aligned} \right.$$

If we write u_0 for f and u_n for y, (4–42) may be written compactly as

$$(4\text{--}43) \qquad u_k = (D - m_k I)^{-1}u_{k-1} \qquad (k = 1, \cdots, n),$$

or as

$$(4\text{--}44) \qquad u_k' - m_k u_k = u_{k-1} \qquad (k = 1, \cdots, n).$$

Successive solutions of the first-order equations in (4–44) by the methods of Section 4–2 leads to a determination of $u_n = y$. If the complete solution for each first-order equation is obtained and inserted in the next, y will be the complete solution of (4–37).

Example 4-10. Solve $y''' - 2y'' - y' + 2y = x$.

Solution: The characteristic equation is $m^3 - 2m^2 - m + 2 = 0$, and the roots are $m_1 = 1$, $m_2 = -1$, $m_3 = 2$. Equations (4–44) become

$$u_1' - u_1 = x,$$

$$u_2' + u_2 = u_1,$$

$$y' - 2y = u_2.$$

From the first of these,

$$u_1 = c_1 e^x - x - 1;$$

the second yields

$$u_2 = c_2 e^{-x} + e^{-x} \int_0^x e^t(c_1 e^t - t - 1)\, dt$$

$$= c_1' e^x + c_2 e^{-x} - x.$$

Finally,

$$y = c_3 e^{2x} + e^{2x} \int_0^x e^{-2t}(c_1' e^t + c_2 e^{-t} - t)\, dt$$

$$= C_1 e^x + C_2 e^{-x} + C_3 e^{2x} + \frac{2x + 1}{4}.$$

Note that the first three terms constitute the complete solution y_0 of the associated homogeneous equation, while the last is a particular solution y_f, in accordance with the theorem.

The method illustrated in Example 4–10 is perfectly general, applying whether or not the characteristic roots are all distinct and whether or not they are all real. However, a general formula, which would include (4–24) and (4–25) when $n = 2$, is cumbersome to write. (See page 115.) In practice, it is best to use a step-by-step procedure.

Some simplification is suggested by Example 4–10. The procedure may be separated into two parts: first, the determination of the complete solution y_0 of the homogeneous equation, and, secondly, the determination of a particular solution y_f. Frequently y_f may be found by inspection or a method of undetermined coefficients as in Section 4–4 (see Example 4–7). Also, it is reasonable to expect that a general formula for y_0 can be given. We shall consider two extreme cases and then state the general result without proof.

Case 1. Solution of $p(D)y = 0$ when the characteristic roots are all distinct.

In (4–44), we have $u_0 = 0$. Then solution of $u_1' - m_1 u_1 = 0$ gives $u_1 = c_1' e^{m_1 x}$. The next equation is $u_2' - m_2 u_2 = c_1' e^{m_1 x}$, and the solution is $u_2 = c_1 e^{m_1 x} + c_2 e^{m_2 x}$ from (4–7). Assume that a similar formula holds for $u_1, u_2, \cdots, u_{k-1}$, where $k \leq n$. Then the kth equation in (4–44) is

$$u_k' - m_k u_k = c_1 e^{m_1 x} + c_2 e^{m_2 x} + \cdots + c_{k-1} e^{m_{k-1} x}.$$

There results

$$u_k = c_k e^{m_k x} + e^{m_k x} \int_0^x e^{-m_k t} \sum_{j=1}^{k-1} c_j e^{m_j t} \, dt$$

$$= c_k e^{m_k x} + e^{m_k x} \sum_{j=1}^{k-1} c_j \int_0^x e^{(m_j - m_k) t} \, dt$$

$$= C_k e^{m_k x} + e^{m_k x} \sum_{j=1}^{k-1} \frac{c_j}{m_j - m_k} e^{(m_j - m_k) x}$$

$$= C_k e^{m_k x} + \sum_{j=1}^{k-1} C_j e^{m_j x}$$

$$= C_1 e^{m_1 x} + C_2 e^{m_2 x} + \cdots + C_k e^{m_k x}.$$

The same formula thus holds for u_k. By induction, the result holds for all $k \leq n$; in particular, we have that

(4–45) $$y = \sum_{j=1}^{n} C_j e^{m_j x}$$

is the complete solution of (4–37).

Case 2. Solution of $p(D)y = 0$ when the characteristic roots are all equal.

In (4–44), solution of $u_1' - m_1 u_1 = 0$ again gives $u_1 = c_1' e^{m_1 x}$. The next equation is $u_2' - m_1 u_2 = c_1' e^{m_1 x}$, and the solution from (4–7) is

$$u_2 = c_2' e^{m_1 x} + e^{m_1 x} \int_0^x c_1' \, dt = c_1 e^{m_1 x} + c_2 x e^{m_1 x}.$$

Assume that a similar formula holds for u_1, u_2, $\cdots$, u_{k-1}, where $k \leq n$. Then the kth equation in (4–44) is

$$u_k' - m_1 u_k = c_1 e^{m_1 x} + c_2 x e^{m_1 x} + \cdots + c_{k-1} x^{k-2} e^{m_1 x}.$$

There results

$$u_k = c_k e^{m_1 x} + e^{m_1 x} \int_0^x (c_1 + c_2 t + \cdots + c_{k-1} t^{k-2})\, dt$$

$$= C_1 e^{m_1 x} + C_2 x e^{m_1 x} + \cdots + C_k x^{k-1} e^{m_1 x},$$

and the same formula holds for u_k. By induction, the result holds for all $k \leq n$; in particular,

$$(4\text{–}46) \qquad\qquad y = e^{m_1 x} \sum_{j=0}^{n-1} C_j x^j.$$

The next theorem extends (4–45) and (4–46) to the general situation with respect to the characteristic roots.

Theorem. Let $p(D)$ be a polynomial in D with constant coefficients. Let the *distinct* characteristic roots of $p(D)$ be m_1, $\cdots$, m_k, where m_j has the multiplicity r_j, for $j = 1, \cdots, k$, and $\sum_{j=1}^{k} r_j = n$. The complete solution of the homogeneous equation $p(D)y = 0$ is given by

$$(4\text{–}47) \qquad y = \sum_{i=1}^{k} e^{m_i x} \left(c_{i1} + c_{i2}\, x + \cdots + c_{i, r_i - 1}\, x^{r_k - 1} \right).$$

In solving a linear equation (4–37) it is wise to combine the two theorems of this section. Thus by the first theorem, $y = y_0 + y_f$, where y_0 is the complete solution of $p(D)y = 0$, and y_f is a particular solution of (4–37). Now y_0 is given by (4–47). To obtain y_f, if it cannot be found by inspection, one may use (4–44), retaining at each stage for each u_k only a convenient particular solution. In this way a desired particular solution y_f of (4–37) results as u_n.

Example 4–11. Solve $y^{\text{iv}} - 2y'' + y = e^x$.

Solution: The characteristic equation is

$$(m^2 - 2m + 1)(m^2 + 2m + 1) = 0.$$

Distinct characteristic roots are $m_1 = 1$ and $m_2 = -1$, each having multiplicity 2. By (4–47), we obtain

$$y_0 = e^x(c_{11} + c_{12}\,x) + e^{-x}(c_{21} + c_{22}\,x).$$

Equations (4–44) become

$$\begin{cases} u_1' - u_1 = e^x, \\ u_2' - u_2 = u_1, \\ u_3' + u_3 = u_2, \\ u_4' + u_4 = u_3. \end{cases}$$

A particular value of u_1 is given by (4–4) in the form

$$u_1 = e^x \int e^{-x}(e^x)\, dx = xe^x,$$

in which a particular convenient choice has been made for the integral appearing. Next, we have

$$u_2 = e^x \int e^{-x}(xe^x)\, dx = \frac{x^2}{2}\, e^x.$$

Then

$$u_3 = e^{-x} \int e^x \left(\frac{x^2}{2}\, e^x \right) dx = \left(\frac{1}{4}x^2 - \frac{1}{4}x + \frac{1}{8} \right) e^x.$$

Finally,

$$y_f = u_4 = e^{-x} \int e^x \left(\frac{1}{4}x^2 - \frac{1}{4}x + \frac{1}{8} \right) e^x\, dx$$

$$= \left(\frac{1}{8}x^2 - \frac{1}{4}x + \frac{3}{16} \right) e^x.$$

The desired solution is

$$y = y_0 + y_f = e^x(C_1 + C_2 x) + e^{-x}(C_3 + C_4 x) + \frac{1}{8}x^2 e^x.$$

Note that the terms $\left(-\frac{1}{4}x + \frac{3}{16} \right) e^x$ in y_f have been absorbed in similar terms of y_0.

Example 4–12. Solve $y''' - y'' + y' - y = 4 \cos x \sin x$.

Solution: The characteristic roots are $m_1 = i, m_2 = -i, m_3 = 1$. The solution of the homogeneous equation is

$$y_0 = c_1 e^{ix} + c_2 e^{-ix} + c_3 e^x,$$

or

$$y_0 = C_1 \cos x + C_2 \sin x + C_3 e^x.$$

Equations (4–44) become

$$\begin{cases} u_1' - iu_1 = 4\cos x \sin x, \\ u_2' + iu_2 = u_1, \\ u_3' - u_3 = u_2. \end{cases}$$

It is convenient here to transform $\cos x$ and $\sin x$ to exponential form. Using (4–19), we have

$$e^{ix} = \cos x + i \sin x,$$
$$e^{-ix} = \cos x - i \sin x,$$

from which it follows that

$$\cos x = \frac{e^{ix} + e^{-ix}}{2}, \quad \sin x = \frac{e^{ix} - e^{-ix}}{2i},$$

$$4\cos x \sin x = \frac{e^{2ix} - e^{-2ix}}{i} = i(e^{-2ix} - e^{2ix}).$$

The procedure of Example 4–11 now applies readily. The results are

$$u_1 = e^{ix} \int e^{-ix} (e^{-2ix} - e^{2ix})\, dx = -\frac{e^{-2ix}}{3} - e^{2ix},$$

$$u_2 = e^{-ix} \int e^{ix} \left(-\frac{e^{-2ix}}{3} - e^{2ix} \right) dx = \frac{e^{-2ix} - e^{2ix}}{3i},$$

$$y_f = u_3 = e^{x} \int e^{-x} \left(\frac{e^{-2ix} - e^{2ix}}{3i} \right) dx$$

$$= -\frac{1}{15} [-2(e^{-2ix} + e^{2ix}) + i(e^{2ix} - e^{-2ix})]$$

$$= \frac{4}{15} \cos 2x + \frac{2}{15} \sin 2x.$$

Finally,

$$y = y_0 + y_f = C_1 \cos x + C_2 \sin x + C_3 e^{x} + \frac{4}{15} \cos 2x + \frac{2}{15} \sin 2x.$$

Example 4–13. Let $p(m)$ be a polynomial in m (with constant coefficients). Suppose $p(m) = q(m)r(m)$, where q and r are polynomials without common linear factors. Prove that the complete solution of $p(D)y = 0$ is the sum of the complete solution of $q(D)y = 0$ and the complete solution of $r(D)y = 0$.

Solution: The characteristic equation of $p(D)y = 0$ is

$$p(m) = q(m)r(m) = 0.$$

The distinct roots of $p(m) = 0$ are $m_1, \cdots, m_k$, which satisfy $q(m) = 0$, together with $m_1', \cdots, m_l'$, which satisfy $r(m) = 0$. No root m_i is equal to any root m_j'. Hence the formula (4–47) applied to $p(D)y = 0$ splits into two parts, one containing terms $x^j e^{m_i x}$ ($i = 1, \cdots, k; j < r_i$) and the other containing terms $x^j e^{m_i x}$ ($i = 1, \cdots, l; j < r_i'$). These two parts are the complete solutions of $q(D)y = 0$ and $r(D)y = 0$, respectively.

*A Formula for a Particular Solution. It has been seen that a particular solution y_f of (4–37), where the coefficients are constants, may be obtained by solving the system (4–44) *seriatim*, employing at each stage a particular solution. This process leads to a general formula as follows.

Define

$$u_1(x) = e^{m_1 x} \int_{x_0}^{x} e^{-m_1 t_1} f(t_1) \, dt_1,$$

whence u_1 satisfies the first equation in (4–44). Similarly, define

$$u_2(x) = e^{m_2 x} \int_{x_1}^{x} e^{(m_1 - m_2) t_2} \int_{x_0}^{t_2} e^{-m_1 t_1} f(t_1) \, dt_1 \, dt_2.$$

Suppose that u_k has been similarly defined so that

$$u_k(x) = e^{m_k x} \int_{x_{k-1}}^{x} e^{(m_{k-1} - m_k) t_k} \int_{x_{k-2}}^{t_k} e^{(m_{k-2} - m_{k-1}) t_{k-1}} \int_{x_{k-3}}^{t_{k-1}} $$
$$\cdots \int_{x_0}^{t_2} e^{-m_1 t_1} f(t_1) \, dt_1 \cdots dt_k.$$

Substitution in

$$u_{k+1}(x) = e^{m_{k+1} x} \int_{x_k}^{x} e^{-m_{k+1} t_{k+1}} u_k(t_{k+1}) \, dt_{k+1}$$

yields that u_{k+1} is what is obtained from the formula for u_k by replacing k by $k + 1$. By induction the formula for u_k is true for all values of $k = 1, \cdots, n$. Since $y_f = u_n$, the desired result is obtained by setting $k = n$ in the formula for u_k. The lower limits may be chosen as convenient, so long as all limits lie in an interval in which $f(x)$ is continuous.

EXERCISES

In exercises 1 to 6, find the complete solution by using the theorems and methods of this section.

1. $y^{\text{iv}} - y = 0$.

2. $y^{(8)} - y = 0$.

3. $y''' - y = 1$.

4. $y'' - 2y - 3y = e^{-2x}$.

5. $y^{\text{iv}} - y'' = x^3$.

6. $y'' - 4y' + 4y = x + e^{2x}$.

7. Carry out in detail the work of Example 4–12.

8. Solve $y''' - y = \sin x$.

9. Given an equation $(D - mI)^3 y = e^{ax}$, where m is real. Prove that, if $a \neq m$, a particular solution of the form Ae^{ax} exists. Also prove that, if $a = m$, a particular solution of the form $Ax^3 e^{ax}$ exists.

10. Solve $y'' + k^2 y = A \sin kx + B \cos kx$.

11. Let $p(D)$ be a polynomial in D whose coefficients are not necessarily constants. If y_1 satisfies $p(D)y = f_1(x)$ and if y_2 satisfies $p(D)y = f_2(x)$, show that $C_1 y_1 + C_2 y_2$ satisfies $p(D)y = C_1 f_1(x) + C_2 f_2(x)$, where C_1 and C_2 are constants. (See Section 4–4, exercise 9.)

★12. By the formula of the starred subsection of this section (page 115) find a particular solution of $(D^3 + D^2 - D - I)y = 1$. Then write the complete solution.

4–8. LINEAR INDEPENDENCE

It has been seen that the complete solution of a linear homogeneous differential equation

$$(4\text{–}38) \qquad\qquad p(D)y = 0$$

of order n is a *linear combination* with constant coefficients,

$$(4\text{–}48) \qquad\qquad c_1 y_1 + c_2 y_2 + \cdots + c_n y_n,$$

of n particular solutions $y_1, \cdots, y_n$ of the equation. In all cases, the functions $y_1, \cdots, y_n$ are distinct, as is clear from the second theorem in Section 4–7. Actually, much more can be said.

For example, consider the case in which the characteristic roots are all distinct. Here $y_k = e^{m_k x}$ $(k = 1, \cdots, n)$. It is clear that a linear combination (4–48) is the zero function when $c_1 = c_2 = \cdots = c_n = 0$. This gives what is called the *trivial* solution of

$$(4\text{–}49) \qquad\qquad c_1 y_1 + c_2 y_2 + \cdots + c_n y_n = 0.$$

We shall now show that (4–49) has no other solutions for $c_1, \cdots, c_n$ than the trivial one. If (4–49) holds, then

(4–50)
$$\begin{cases} c_1 y_1 + \cdots + c_n y_n = 0, \\ c_1 y_1' + \cdots + c_n y_n' = 0, \\ \cdots \cdots \cdots \cdots \cdots \cdots \cdots \\ c_1 y_1^{(n-1)} + \cdots + c_n y_n^{(n-1)} = 0, \end{cases}$$

where each equation after the first is obtained from the preceding one by differentiation. The determinant W of the system (4–50) of n linear equations,

(4–51)
$$W = \begin{vmatrix} y_1 & y_2 & \cdots & y_n \\ y_1' & y_2' & \cdots & y_n' \\ \cdots & \cdots & \cdots & \cdots \\ y_1^{(n-1)} & y_2^{(n-1)} & \cdots & y_n^{(n-1)} \end{vmatrix},$$

is called the *wronskian* of the functions $y_1, \cdots, y_n$. Writing $y_k = e^{m_k x}$, $y_k' = m_k e^{m_k x}$, and so on, we have, after simplification,

(4–52) $\quad W = e^{(m_1 + \cdots + m_n)x}$
$$\begin{vmatrix} 1 & 1 & \cdots 1 \\ m_1 & m_2 & \cdots m_n \\ m_1^2 & m_2^2 & \cdots m_n^2 \\ \cdots & \cdots & \cdots \cdots \\ m_1^{n-1} & m_2^{n-1} & \cdots m_n^{n-1} \end{vmatrix}.$$

The determinant in (4–52) is called the *determinant of van der Monde* and is shown in algebra to be the product of all factors $(m_k - m_l)$, where $k > l$. Thus $W \neq 0$, since the characteristic roots are all distinct. If the system (4–50) is solved for the c_k by Cramer's rule, it is found that $c_k = 0/W = 0$ $(k = 1, \cdots, n)$. Thus the only solution of (4–49) is the trivial one.

In general, let $y_1, \cdots, y_n$ be any given functions. These functions are called *linearly independent* relative to a common domain A if

(4–53) $\qquad c_1 y_1(x) + \cdots + c_k y_k(x) = 0 \qquad$ (for every x in A)

implies $c_1 = c_2 = \cdots = c_n = 0$. The functions are called *linearly dependent* relative to A if they are not linearly independent, that is, if (4–53) has a non-trivial solution.

If each function $y_1, \cdots, y_n$ is $n-1$ times differentiable in A, the wronskian $W = W(x)$ of these functions, computed as in (4–51), is defined as a function of x in A. Suppose there exists a number x_0 in A for which $W(x_0) \neq 0$. Then the system (4–50), with each function evaluated at $x = x_0$, is a numerical system of equations whose determinant is $W(x_0) \neq 0$. This system thus has only the trivial solution, and it follows that the given functions $y_1, \cdots, y_n$ are linearly independent over A.

If the functions $y_1, \cdots, y_n$ are linearly dependent over A, then $W(x) = 0$ for every x in A, since otherwise $y_1, \cdots, y_n$ would be linearly independent in accordance with the last paragraph.

It is important to note that it is *not* true that if functions are linearly independent, then $W \neq 0$; and it is *not* true that if $W = 0$, then the functions are linearly dependent.

It may be shown that every homogeneous linear differential equation (4–38) has n linearly independent solutions (over the reals), provided the coefficients satisfy certain smoothness conditions. In the case of constant coefficients, this was shown to be true when the characteristic roots were distinct; a similar proof applies even when the roots are not all distinct by merely showing that the wronskian of the solutions appearing in (4–47) is not zero. (See Example 4–15.)

Example 4–14. Prove that $\cos mx$, $\sin mx$ are linearly independent over the reals, if m is a constant $\neq 0$.

Solution: The wronskian is

$$\begin{vmatrix} \cos mx & \sin mx \\ -m \sin mx & m \cos mx \end{vmatrix} = m \neq 0.$$

Example 4–15. Prove that the differential equation $y^{iv} - 2y'' + y = 0$ has four linearly independent solutions (over the reals).

Solution: The solution was found in Example 4–11 to be

$$c_1 e^x + c_2 x e^x + c_3 e^{-x} + c_4 x e^{-x}.$$

The wronskian of the four special solutions e^x, xe^x, e^{-x}, xe^{-x} is given by

$$W = \begin{vmatrix} e^x & e^x x & e^{-x} & e^{-x}x \\ e^x & e^x(x+1) & -e^{-x} & e^{-x}(-x+1) \\ e^x & e^x(x+2) & e^{-x} & e^{-x}(x-2) \\ e^x & e^x(x+3) & -e^{-x} & e^{-x}(-x+3) \end{vmatrix}.$$

Removal of the column factors e^x and e^{-x} and subsequent expansion yield $W = 16 \neq 0$.

Example 4–16. Show that functions may be linearly independent while the wronskian is zero.

Solution: Define functions y_1, y_2 for $-1 \leqq x \leqq 1$ as follows:

$$y_1(x) = \begin{cases} x^3 & (0 \leqq x \leqq 1) \\ 2x^3 & (-1 \leqq x < 0), \end{cases}$$

$$y_2(x) = \begin{cases} 2x^3 & (0 \leqq x \leqq 1) \\ x^3 & (-1 \leqq x < 0). \end{cases}$$

It is easy to see that y_1' and y_2' exist throughout the interval $-1 \leqq x \leqq 1$, and indeed that

$$y_1'(x) = \begin{cases} 3x^2 & (0 \leqq x \leqq 1) \\ 6x^2 & (-1 \leqq x < 0), \end{cases}$$

$$y_2'(x) = \begin{cases} 6x^2 & (0 \leqq x \leqq 1) \\ 3x^2 & (-1 \leqq x < 0). \end{cases}$$

For $0 \leqq x \leqq 1$,

$$W(x) = \begin{vmatrix} x^3 & 2x^3 \\ 3x^2 & 6x^2 \end{vmatrix} = 0;$$

for $-1 \leqq x < 0$,

$$W(x) = \begin{vmatrix} 2x^3 & x^3 \\ 6x^2 & 3x^2 \end{vmatrix} = 0.$$

That y_1 and y_2 are linearly independent over the interval $-1 \leqq x \leqq 1$ is seen as follows. If $c_1 y_1 + c_2 y_2 = 0$, then we have

$$\begin{cases} 0 = c_1 y_1(1) + c_2 y_2(1) = c_1 + 2c_2, \\ 0 = c_1 y_1(-1) + c_2 y_2(-1) = 2c_1 + c_2. \end{cases}$$

It follows that $c_1 = c_2 = 0$.

Note that y_1, y_2 are linearly dependent over the interval $0 \leqq x \leqq 1$ and over the interval $-1 \leqq x \leqq 0$, although they are independent over the total given interval.

The Existence Question. The linear equation $p(D)y = f(x)$, where $f(x)$ is continuous, has been fully treated in case the coefficients are constants. Thus, the complete solution is of the form $y_0 + y_f$, where y_0 is a linear combination of linearly independent solutions of $p(D)y = 0$ and y_f is a particular solution of the given equation, for example, as determined in Section 4–7 (page 115).

Let us consider now the general case,

$$p(D)y = \left(\sum_{k=0}^{n} a_{n-k}(x)D^k \right)y = f(x),$$

where $a_0, \cdots, a_n, f$ are continuous functions of x over a suitable interval $|x - a| \leq b$, and $a_0 = 1$. It has been shown that again the complete solution is of the form $y_0 + y_f$, where y_f is a particular solution (if one exists) and y_0 is the complete solution of $p(D)y = 0$. We shall now outline a proof that there exist n linearly independent solutions $y_1, \cdots, y_n$ of the homogeneous equation $p(D)y = 0$ and that the complete solution of this equation is a general linear combination of $y_1, \cdots, y_n$.

If we put $v_k = D^{k-1}y$ for $k = 1, \cdots, n$, the equation $p(D)y = 0$ is equivalent to the system

$$\begin{cases} v_j' = v_{j+1} & (j = 1, \cdots, n-1), \\ \\ v_n' = - \displaystyle\sum_{k=0}^{n-1} a_{n-k}(x)v_{k+1}, \end{cases}$$

where $v_1 = y$.

Now in a manner similar to that which may be used to prove the existence theorem on pages 17 and 18 for a single equation of first order, it is possible to prove the following theorem, which we state without proof.

Theorem. Suppose functions $F_1, \cdots, F_n$ of $x, v_1, \cdots, v_n$ are continuous and that there exist constants $A_1, \cdots, A_n$ such that

$$|F_j(x, w_1, \cdots, w_n) - F_j(x, u_1, \cdots, u_n)| \leq \sum_{k=1}^{n} A_k |w_k - u_k|$$

$$(j = 1, \cdots, n),$$

for all $x, w_1, \cdots, w_n, u_1, \cdots, u_n$ such that

$$|x - a| \leq b, \quad |w_k - c_k| \leq b_k, \quad |u_k - c_k| \leq b_k.$$

Then there exist unique functions $y_1(x)$, $\cdots$, $y_n(x)$ defined on an interval $|x - a| \leq b'$, such that

$$y_k'(x) = F_k(x, y_1(x), \cdots, y_n(x)) \qquad (k = 1, \cdots, n)$$

for $|x - a| \leq b'$, and such that $y_k(a) = c_k$ for $k = 1, \cdots, n$.

In the case at hand, $F_j = v_{j+1}$ $(j = 1, \cdots, n - 1)$, and

$$F_n = -\sum_{k=0}^{n-1} a_{n-k}(x) v_{k+1}.$$ Let $c_1, \cdots, c_n$ be arbitrary numbers. Since the functions $a_1, \cdots, a_n$ are continuous, they are bounded, and the hypotheses of the theorem are easily verified. Hence our system has a unique solution $(v_1(x), \cdots, v_n(x))$ such that $v_k(a) = c_k$ $(k = 1, \cdots, n)$. But this means that $p(D)y = 0$ has a unique solution $g(x)$ such that

$$g(a) = c_1, \quad g'(a) = c_2, \quad \cdots, \quad g^{(n-1)}(a) = c_n.$$

Note that the solution depends on the specified numbers $c_1, \cdots, c_n$. In particular, if all $c_k = 0$, then $g(x)$ must be the zero function, since the zero function satisfies $p(D)y = 0$.

Let us consider n choices for the vector $(c_1, \cdots, c_n)$, allowing it to be in turn $(1, 0, \cdots, 0)$, $(0, 1, 0, \cdots, 0)$, $\cdots$, $(0, 0, \cdots, 0, 1)$. Correspondingly, there are n solutions $g_1(x), \cdots, g_n(x)$. Denote the wronskian of these functions by $W(x)$. It is clear that

$$W(0) = \begin{vmatrix} 1 & 0 & 0 & \cdots & 0 & 0 \\ 0 & 1 & 0 & \cdots & 0 & 0 \\ \multicolumn{6}{c}{\cdots\cdots\cdots\cdots\cdots} \\ 0 & 0 & 0 & \cdots & 0 & 1 \end{vmatrix} = 1.$$

It follows from the main result of this section that $g_1, \cdots, g_n$ are linearly independent.

It remains to show that any solution $y(x)$ of $p(D)y = 0$ is a linear combination of $g_1, \cdots, g_n$. Define

$$c_1 = y(a), \quad c_2 = y'(a), \quad \cdots, \quad c_n = y^{(n-1)}(a),$$

and define $z(x) = y(x) - \sum_{k=1}^{n} c_k g_k(x)$. By the linearity of $p(D)$,

$p(D)z = 0$. Also,

$$z(a) = y(a) - \sum_{k=1}^{n} c_k g_k(a) = y(a) - c_1 = 0,$$

and similarly, $z'(a) = \cdots = z^{(n-1)}(a) = 0$. These properties of $z(x)$ characterize the zero function, as noted above, so that

$$y(x) = \sum_{k=1}^{n} c_k g_k(x).$$

The proof is complete.

EXERCISES

1. Prove that the functions 1, x, x^2 are linearly independent over the reals. Generalize to 1, x, x^2, $\cdots$, x^n.

2. Prove that the functions $e^{\alpha x} \cos \beta x$, $e^{\alpha x} \sin \beta x$, $e^{-\alpha x} \cos \beta x$, $e^{-\alpha x} \sin \beta x$ are linearly independent if α, $\beta \neq 0$.

3. Prove that a system of functions including the zero function is linearly dependent.

4. Given that y_1, $\cdots$, y_n are linearly independent (over A). Prove that they are all distinct; prove also that y_1, $\cdots$, y_k are linearly independent for $k = 1, 2, \cdots, n$.

5. Prove that the functions e^{mx}, xe^{mx}, $\cdots$, $x^{n-1}e^{mx}$ are linearly independent, where m is a constant. (HINT: Begin by using the definition of linear independence.)

6. Let y_1, $\cdots$, y_n be linearly independent functions over A. Then two linear combinations with constant coefficients $\sum_{k=1}^{n} c_k y_k$ and $\sum_{k=1}^{n} c_k' y_k$ are equal for every x in A if and only if $c_k = c_k'$ for $k = 1, \cdots, n$.

7. Let y_1, y_2 be solutions of the second-order homogeneous equation $y'' + a(x)y' + b(x)y = 0$, and let $W(x)$ be the wronskian of y_1, y_2. Prove that $W(x)$ satisfies the equation $W' + a(x)W = 0$.

8. Continuing exercise 6, show that $W(x) = W_0 e^{-\int_{x_0}^{x} a(t)\, dt}$, and that either $W(x) = 0$ for all values of x or $W(x) \neq 0$ for all values of x.

★9. Using the rule (see Appendix 2) for differentiating a determinant, generalize exercise 7 to the case of a homogeneous equation of order n.

★10. In applying the theorem on pages 120 and 121, it was asserted that the hypotheses follow from the continuity of $a_k(x)$ ($k = 1, \cdots, n$). Prove this assertion in detail.

★11. Prove that a homogeneous linear equation of order n cannot possess $n + 1$ linearly independent solutions. (HINT: Show that if n solutions are linearly independent, then any solution is a linear combination of these. Use the method of this section, page 121.)

5

Special Techniques for
Linear Equations

5–1. PRELIMINARIES

Chapter 4 has shown that the linear equation

(5–1) $p(D)y = [D^n + a_1(x)D^{n-1} + \cdots$
$$+ a_{n-1}(x)D + a_n(x)I\,]y = f(x)$$

has as complete solution the sum $y = y_0 + y_f$ of the complete solution y_0 of the associated homogeneous equation

(5–2) $p(D)y = 0$

and a particular solution y_f of (5–1). Moreover, the complete solution y_0 of (5–2) is a linear combination given by

(5–3) $y_0 = c_1 y_1 + c_2 y_2 + \cdots + c_n y_n$

of n linearly independent solutions of (5–2), where $c_1, \cdots, c_n$ are constants. (See pages 109 and 120 to 122.)

When the coefficients $a_1, \cdots, a_n$ in (5–1) are constants, determination of $y_1, \cdots, y_n$ amounts to finding the distinct characteristic roots of $p(D)$ and their multiplicities, as was shown in (4–47). This problem is algebraic and is adequately treated in books on the theory of equations. No formula for $y_1, \cdots, y_n$ is available in the general case.

In Section 5–2 determination of y_f for certain classes of functions $f(x)$ is considered, but only for the case in which the a_k are constants. Section 5–3 gives a more widely applicable method for finding y_f. Frequently usable techniques depending on the theory of operators are then discussed, followed by a method, occasionally applicable, for the determination of y_f. Finally, systems of linear equations are discussed briefly.

5–2. METHOD OF UNDETERMINED COEFFICIENTS

Assume the coefficients a_k in (5–1) to be constants. It is desired to find a particular solution, if possible, without performing the integrations of Section 4–7.

If in (5–1) $f(x)$ is a polynomial, it is natural to look for a polynomial solution, and notably one of the same degree, since the derivatives of polynomials are polynomials of lower degree. If $f(x) = Ce^{ax}$, it is natural to try $y_f = Be^{ax}$, since the derivatives of e^{ax} are simple multiples of e^{ax}. If $f(x) = C \cos ax$ or $C \sin ax$, we might try $y_f = A \cos ax + B \sin ax$, since the derivatives of cosine and sine are multiples of cosine and sine. [Or we might, as in Example 4–12, convert $f(x)$ to exponentials, and hence reduce the problem to the previous type.] The polynomial case was illustrated in Example 4–7, method 2.

Example 5–1. Find a particular solution of the equation

$$(D^3 + I)y = e^{3x}.$$

Solution: Let $y_f = Ae^{3x}$; then $(D^3 + I)y_f = 28Ae^{3x}$. We choose $A = 1/28$.

Example 5–2. Find a particular solution of

$$(D^2 - D + 3I)y = \sin 2x.$$

Solution: Try $y_f = A \sin 2x + B \cos 2x$. Then

$$(D^2 - D + 3I)y_f = (-4A + 2B + 3A) \sin 2x \\ + (-4B - 2A + 3B) \cos 2x,$$

and we choose A, B, C to satisfy

$$-A + 2B = 1, \quad -2A - B = 0, \quad \text{or} \quad A = -\frac{1}{5}, \quad B = \frac{2}{5}.$$

Therefore

$$y_f = \frac{1}{5}(2 \cos 2x - \sin 2x).$$

The equation $Dy = x$ obviously has no first-degree polynomial solution, but it does have the solution $y_f = \frac{1}{2} x^2$. Under some circumstances, then, the methods just illustrated must be modified.

The "cut-and-try" methods of Examples 5–1 and 5–2 may be systematized in case the real-valued function $f(x)$ is a sum of functions which are solutions of homogeneous linear differential equations with constant coefficients. That is, $f(x)$ is assumed to be a linear combination of terms of the types x^n, e^{ax}, $\cos ax$, $\sin ax$, $x^n e^{ax}$, $x^n \cos ax$, and $x^n \sin ax$. For each such function f there exists a linear homogeneous differential equation $q(D)y = 0$ with real constant coefficients such that f is a solution. Now any particular solution y_f of $p(D)y = f(x)$ must also satisfy $q(D)p(D)y = 0$. But we know all solutions of this equation. Among them will be all solutions of $p(D)y = 0$, which can be dropped from consideration because they are obviously not solutions of $p(D)y = f(x)$. We form a linear combination of the remaining functions and determine the coefficients so that y_f satisfies $p(D)y = f(x)$. It is worth noting that if y_f is a solution of $p(D)y = f(x)$ and y_g is a solution of $p(D)y = g(x)$, then $y_f + y_g$ is a solution of $p(D)y = f(x) + g(x)$. (See Section 4–7, exercise 11.)

To see how to obtain the equation $q(D)y = 0$, consider, for example, the case $f(x) = x + xe^x + \sin x$. The first term x satisfies $D^2 z = 0$. From (4–47) we can see that xe^x appears as a solution of an equation with a twofold characteristic root equal to 1, that is, of $(D^2 - 2D + I)z = 0$. Finally, it is clear that $\sin x$ satisfies $(D^2 + I)z = 0$. Since the polynomials m^2, $(m - 1)^2$, $m^2 + 1$ have no factors in common, Example 4–13 indicates that the product $q(m)$ of these polynomials is such that f satisfies $q(D)y = 0$. Hence the desired equation is

$$D^2(D - I)^2(D^2 + I)y = 0.$$

Example 5–3. Find a particular solution of

$$p(D)y = (D^2 + 4D - 5I)y = xe^x + x + \sin x.$$

Solution: Here $p(D) = (D + 5I)(D - I)$ and, as shown above, $q(D) = D^2(D^2 + I)(D - I)^2$, whence

$$q(D)p(D) = D^2(D^2 + I)(D - I)^3(D + 5I),$$

since the factors in $p(D)$ and $q(D)$ commute. From the list of functions 1, x, $\sin x$, $\cos x$, e^x, xe^x, $x^2 e^x$, e^{-5x}, delete e^{-5x} and e^x. Try

$$y_f = A + Bx + C \sin x + E \cos x + (F + Gx)xe^x.$$

The details of the computation may be simplified by trying

$$u = A + Bx \qquad \text{in } p(D)y = x,$$
$$v = C \sin x + E \cos x \quad \text{in } p(D)y = \sin x,$$
$$w = (F + Gx)xe^x \qquad \text{in } p(D)y = xe^x.$$

The details of the computation follow:

$$p(D)u = -5Bx + 4B - 5A = x; \quad A = -\frac{4}{25}, \quad B = -\frac{1}{5};$$

$$p(D)v = (-C - 4E - 5C)\sin x + (-E + 4C - 5E)\cos x = \sin x;$$

$$6C + 4E = -1 \quad \text{and} \quad 4C - 6E = 0;$$

$$C = -\frac{3}{26}, \quad E = -\frac{1}{13};$$

$$p(D)w = e^x(12Gx + 6F + 2G) = xe^x;$$

$$12G = 1 \quad \text{and} \quad 6F + 2G = 0; \quad F = -\frac{1}{36}, \quad G = \frac{1}{12}.$$

Finally, we have

$$y_f = u + v + w = -\frac{4}{25} - \frac{1}{5}x - \frac{3}{26}\sin x - \frac{1}{13}\cos x$$
$$+ \left(-\frac{1}{36} + \frac{x}{12}\right)xe^x.$$

Example 5-4. Find a particular solution y_f of

$$p(D)y = (D^3 - D + 2I)y = e^{3x} + x\sin x.$$

Solution: Here $q(D) = (D - 3I)(D^2 + I)^2$. No solution of the numerical equation $q(m) = 0$ satisfies $p(m) = 0$. Hence the polynomials $q(m)$ and $p(m)$ have no common linear factors, by the factor theorem. Example 4–13 thus applies to yield that the terms in y_f are of two types, those satisfying $p(D)y = 0$ and those satisfying $q(D)y = 0$. Deleting the former, we try

$$y_f = Ae^{3x} + (B + Cx)\sin x + (E + Fx)\cos x.$$

It is found that $A = 1/26$, $B = 0$, $C = F = 1/4$, $E = 1/2$.

The determination of B, C, E, and F is tedious. An alternate method is to replace $x\sin x$ by $(x/2i)(e^{ix} - e^{-ix})$ (see Example 4–12) and try $(P + Qx)e^{ix} + (R + Sx)e^{-ix}$, where P, Q, R, and S may be complex. Unfortunately, this method is no improvement.

Nevertheless, the reader will find it worthwhile to carry out the details of the computation. After trying both methods he will be ready to appreciate the power of the method of Section 5–4.

The examples given show that use of the method of undetermined coefficients does not require prior determination of the characteristic roots of the given equation. Our main concern is whether $p(m) = 0$ and $q(m) = 0$ have any roots in common. Thus, whether we can factor $p(m)$ readily or not, if we know the roots of $q(m) = 0$, we can easily determine whether they are roots of $p(m) = 0$ and, if so, of what multiplicity. Suppose that a is a root of multiplicity k of $q(m) = 0$. If $p(a) \neq 0$, we include in y_f

$$(c_1 + c_2 x + \cdots + c_{k-1} x^{k-1})e^{ax}.$$

If a is an r-fold root, but not an $(r + 1)$-fold root, of $p(m) = 0$, then we include in y_f

$$(c_1 + c_2 x + \cdots + c_{k-1} x^{k-1})x^r e^{ax}.$$

EXERCISES

In each of the exercises 1 to 4 find a homogeneous linear differential equation with constant coefficients satisfied by the given function.

1. $f(x) = x^2 e^x$.
2. $f(x) = x^2 \cos 2x - x^2 \sin 2x$.
3. $f(x) = x^n e^{ax}$, where a is a constant and n is a positive integer.
4. $f(x) = x^2(x^2 + ax + b)$, where a and b are constants.

In each of exercises 5 to 10, find a particular solution.

5. $(D^5 - D^4 + 2D - I)y = x^4 - 2x + 1$.
6. $(D^4 + I)y = \sin x$.
7. $D(D^2 - 3I)y = e^x + 1$.
8. $(D - 2I)^3 y = x^4 e^{2x}$.
9. $(D^2 + I)^3 y = \cos x$.
10. $(D - I)(D - 2I)(D - 3I)y = x - e^{3x}$.

★11. Find the complete solution of $(D^2 + I)(D + I)(D - 2I)y = \cosh x$. [HINT: Recall that $\cosh x = \dfrac{1}{2}(e^x + e^{-x})$.]

★12. Find the complete solution of $y''' - y = x^n$.

★13. Show that $(D - aI)^n p_1(D)y = x^r e^{ax}$, where $m - a$ is not a factor of $p_1(m)$, has a solution of the form $\displaystyle\sum_{j=n}^{r+n} C_j x^j e^{ax}$.

5–3. METHOD OF VARIATION OF PARAMETERS

In many cases where the methods previously discussed are not effective, and in some cases where the coefficients of the equation

$$(5–1) \qquad\qquad p(D)y = f(x)$$

are not constant, a procedure called the *method of variation of parameters* can be successfully used. Prior to application of this method, it is necessary to know the complete solution (5–3) of the associated homogeneous equation (5–2). Suppose, therefore, that n linearly independent solutions $y_1(x), \cdots, y_n(x)$ of (5–2) have been found.

We consider a wider class of functions than that described by (5–3), namely

$$(5–4) \qquad y = c_1(x)y_1(x) + c_2(x)y_2(x) + \cdots + c_n(x)y_n(x),$$

in which the coefficients are functions of x. From this class, we shall attempt to extract one function which satisfies (5–1) rather than (5–2). It appears that there will be much latitude in the choice, because there is only one condition to be met, namely, (5–1), while there are n functions to be chosen. Hence, presumably further conditions may be imposed as convenient [provided (5–1) is not violated], so as to narrow the choice. Specifically, we shall impose $n - 1$ such further conditions.

From (5–4), we have

$$(5–5) \qquad\qquad y' = \sum_{j=1}^{n} c_j y_j' + \sum_{j=1}^{n} c_j' y_j.$$

Let us tentatively require that

$$(5–6) \qquad\qquad \sum_{j=1}^{n} c_j' y_j = 0 \qquad\qquad \text{(for every } x\text{).}$$

Successive differentiation of (5–5) coupled with corresponding tentative imposition of conditions like (5–6) yields

$$(5–7) \qquad\qquad y^{(k)} = \sum_{j=1}^{n} c_j y_j^{(k)} \qquad (k = 1, \cdots, n - 1),$$

while the imposed conditions have been chosen as

$$(5–8) \qquad\qquad \sum_{j=1}^{n} c_j' y_j^{(k-1)} = 0 \qquad (k = 1, \cdots, n - 1).$$

[Note that (5-7) includes (5-5), and (5-8) includes (5-6), since $y_j^{(0)}$ means y_j.] Differentiating (5-7) with $k = n - 1$ gives

$$(5\text{-}9) \qquad y^{(n)} = \sum_{j=1}^{n} c_j y_j^{(n)} + \sum_{j=1}^{n} c_j' y_j^{(n-1)}.$$

Now substitute from (5-4), (5-7) and (5-9) into (5-1) to obtain

$$f = p(D)y$$

$$= \sum_{j=1}^{n} c_j y_j^{(n)} + a_1 \sum_{j=1}^{n} c_j y_j^{(n-1)} + \cdots + a_n \sum_{j=1}^{n} c_j y_j + \sum_{j=1}^{n} c_j' y_j^{(n-1)}$$

$$= \sum_{j=1}^{n} c_j \left(y_j^{(n)} + a_1 y_j^{(n-1)} + \cdots + a_n y_j \right) + \sum_{j=1}^{n} c_j' y_j^{(n-1)}$$

$$= \sum_{j=1}^{n} c_j \, p(D) y_j + \sum_{j=1}^{n} c_j' y_j^{(n-1)}.$$

But y_j is a solution of (5-2) for $j = 1, \cdots, n$. Hence we obtain

$$(5\text{-}10) \qquad \sum_{j=1}^{n} c_j' y_j^{(n-1)} = f.$$

Equations (5-8) together with (5-10) constitute a system of equations for the c_j. If it happens that this system can be solved, our imposition of conditions (5-7) is vindicated.

First, note that the system (5-8), (5-10) is an algebraic linear system for $c_1', \cdots, c_n'$. The determinant of this system is the wronskian $W(x)$ of the solutions $y_1, \cdots, y_n$. While it is not true in general that the linear independence of a system of functions $y_1, \cdots, y_n$ implies that their wronskian is not zero (see Example 4-16), this implication is true if the y_j satisfy a homogeneous linear equation (5-2) with the $a_k(x)$ continuous. (See page 132.) Therefore, $c_1', \cdots, c_n'$ may be (uniquely) found from (5-8), (5-10). These functions are moreover continuous. Therefore integration yields a desired system of functions $c_1, \cdots, c_n$ which may serve as coefficients in (5-4) to yield a desired particular solution y_f of (5-1).

Example 5-5. Find a particular solution of

$$(D - I)(D^2 + I)y = (D^3 - D^2 + D - I)y = 2x - 3.$$

Solution: The associated homogeneous equation has complete solution

$$y_0 = C_1 e^x + C_2 \sin x + C_3 \cos x,$$

where C_1, C_2, C_3 are constants. We shall find functions $c_1(x)$, $c_2(x)$, $c_3(x)$ satisfying

$$\begin{cases} c_1' e^x + c_2' \sin x + c_3' \cos x = 0, \\ c_1' e^x + c_2' \cos x - c_3' \sin x = 0, \\ c_1' e^x - c_2' \sin x - c_3' \cos x = 2x - 3. \end{cases}$$

Solution of this system yields

$$\begin{cases} c_1' = \dfrac{1}{2} e^{-x}(2x - 3), \\[2mm] c_2' = -\dfrac{1}{2}(2x - 3)(\sin x + \cos x), \\[2mm] c_3' = -\dfrac{1}{2}(2x - 3)(\cos x - \sin x). \end{cases}$$

The functions c_1, c_2, c_3 are found by integration. In this instance it is simpler first to find $c_2 + c_3 = -\int (2x - 3) \cos x \, dx$ and $c_2 - c_3 = -\int (2x - 3) \sin x \, dx$. The results are given by

$$c_1 = e^{-x}\left(-x + \frac{1}{2}\right),$$

$$c_2 + c_3 = -(2x - 3)\sin x - 2\cos x,$$
$$c_2 - c_3 = (2x - 3)\cos x - 2\sin x,$$

$$c_2 = \left(-x + \frac{1}{2}\right)\sin x + \left(x - \frac{5}{2}\right)\cos x,$$

$$c_3 = \left(-x + \frac{5}{2}\right)\sin x + \left(-x + \frac{1}{2}\right)\cos x.$$

(Note that particular rather than general integrals are used, since only one solution of the given equation is desired.) The desired particular solution is given by

$$y_f = c_1 e^x + c_2 \sin x + c_3 \cos x$$

$$= \left(-x + \frac{1}{2}\right) + \left(-x + \frac{1}{2}\right)\sin^2 x + \left(x - \frac{5}{2}\right)\sin x \cos x$$

$$+ \left(-x + \frac{1}{2}\right)\cos^2 x + \left(-x + \frac{5}{2}\right)\sin x \cos x$$

$$= -2x + 1.$$

Needless to say, this method is far more complicated in this example than the method of Section 5–2.

Example 5–6. Find a particular solution of

$$(D^2 + I)y = \tan x.$$

Solution: Here the method of Section 5–2 fails. We have

$$y_0 = C_1 \sin x + C_2 \cos x,$$

and hence seek $c_1(x)$ and $c_2(x)$ satisfying

$$\begin{cases} c_1' \sin x + c_2' \cos x = 0, \\ c_1' \cos x - c_2' \sin x = \tan x. \end{cases}$$

Solution yields $c_1' = \sin x$ and $c_2' = -\tan x \sin x$, whence it follows that $c_1 = -\cos x$ and $c_2 = \sin x - \ln |\sec x + \tan x|$. Therefore

$$y_f = -\cos x \ln |\sec x + \tan x|.$$

Example 5–7. Find the complete solution of

$$p(D)y = [x(x + 1)D^2 + (2 - x^2)D - (2 + x)I]y = (x + 1)^2,$$

given that e^x and $1/x$ satisfy $p(D)y = 0$.

Solution: First, divide the given equation by $x(x + 1)$ to bring it into the form (5–1). To ensure continuity of the resulting coefficients, restrict x to an interval lying between $x = -1$ and $x = 0$, or to the right of $x = 0$, or to the left of $x = -1$.

The given solutions of $p(D)y = 0$ are linearly independent; indeed their wronskian is $e^x(-1/x^2 - 1/x) \neq 0$. Therefore, we attempt to find $c_1(x)$ and $c_2(x)$ satisfying

$$\begin{cases} c_1' e^x + c_2' \dfrac{1}{x} = 0, \\ c_1' e^x - c_2' \dfrac{1}{x^2} = \dfrac{x + 1}{x}. \end{cases}$$

The result is $c_1' = e^{-x}$, $c_2' = -x$, so that $c_1 = -e^{-x}$, $c_2 = -x^2/2$. Therefore

$$y_f = c_1 e^x + c_2 \frac{1}{x} = -1 - \frac{x}{2}.$$

Finally,

$$y = y_0 + y_f = C_1 e^x + C_2 \frac{1}{x} - \frac{x + 2}{2}.$$

★More on Linear Independence. Section 5–3 has used the fact that the non-zero character of the wronskian of solutions $y_1, \cdots, y_n$ of a homogeneous equation $p(D)y = 0$ (where the coefficients are continuous) is implied by their linear independence. This differs from what may happen in general, as shown in Section 4–8. (See Example 4–16.) A further and related difference lies in the fact that in general a wronskian may be equal to zero for some values of x and not others. But this is not the case when the n functions satisfy $p(D)y = 0$. (See Section 4–8, exercises 6 to 9.)

Suppose now that $y_1, \cdots, y_n$ satisfy $p(D)y = 0$, and suppose that their wronskian $W(x) = 0$ for every x. Let x_0 be a particular value of x, and consider the system

$$(5\text{--}11) \qquad \sum_{j=1}^{n} c_j y_j^{(k)}(x_0) = 0 \qquad (k = 0, \cdots, n-1).$$

There exists a non-trivial solution $c_1, \cdots, c_n$, since the determinant of the system is $W(x_0) = 0$. Define

$$y(x) = \sum_{k=1}^{n} c_k y_k(x),$$

using as coefficients the values $c_1, \cdots, c_n$ just obtained, which are not all zero. But

$$p(D)y = \sum_{k=1}^{n} c_k p(D)y_k = 0,$$

since each y_k is a solution by hypothesis. Moreover, it is clear that $y(x_0), y'(x_0), \cdots, y^{(n-1)}(x_0)$ are all zero by (5–11). By the remark following the existence theorem on page 121, $y(x) = 0$ for all values of x. But this means that the functions $y_1, \cdots, y_n$ are linearly dependent.

Another way of stating the result just proved is as follows: If solutions $y_1, \cdots, y_n$ of $p(D)y = 0$ are linearly independent, then their wronskian is not zero (indeed, for any value of x). Hence we have proved the following criterion.

Theorem. Let W be the wronskian of functions $y_1, \cdots, y_n$ satisfying a homogeneous linear equation $p(D)y = 0$, in which the coefficients are continuous over an interval A. Then $y_1, \cdots, y_n$ are linearly independent over A if and only if $W(x) \neq 0$ (for some value of x, or equivalently for all values of x in A); they are linearly dependent if and only if $W = 0$.

EXERCISES

Using the method of variation of parameters, find the complete solution in each of exercises 1 to 4.

1. $y'' - y = 4e^{-x}$.

2. $y'' + y = \sec x$.

3. $y'' + y = \csc^2 x$.

4. $y'' - 4y' + 4y = \dfrac{e^{2x}}{x}$.

5. Find a formula involving definite integrals for a particular solution of $y''' - y'' = f(x)$, using variation of parameters.

6. Show that the method of variation of parameters leads to the formula (4-2) for the solution of a first-order linear equation (4-1).

7. Find the complete solution of $x^2y'' + xy' - y = x^2$, given that x and $1/x$ satisfy the associated homogeneous equation.

8. Find the complete solution of $x^2y'' - xy' + y = x$, given that x and $x \ln x$ satisfy the associated homogeneous equation.

★9. Using the criterion for linear dependence on page 132, give a proof of the result in exercise 11 of Section 4–8 in the case where the coefficients have continuous derivatives.

★10. Prove that two functions whose wronskian is not zero at any point of an interval A satisfy throughout A a homogeneous equation of order 2. Find such an equation for $\sec x$, $\tan x$.

5–4. METHODS BASED ON THE "EXPONENTIAL SHIFT"

In solving an equation (5–1) with constant coefficients it is sometimes useful first to apply a result concerning $p(D)$, which we now develop.

First note that, for any constants a and r,

$$(D - rI)(e^{ax}z(x)) = e^{ax}(D + aI - rI)z(x).$$

If we denote the operator $D + aI$ by G, we have

$$(5\text{–}12) \qquad (D - rI)(e^{ax}z(x)) = e^{ax}(G - rI)z(x).$$

It follows from (5–12) that, for any constants a, r, s,

$$(D - sI)(D - rI)(e^{ax}z) = e^{ax}(G - sI)(G - rI)z.$$

By induction, if $m_1, \cdots, m_n$ are the characteristic roots of $p(D)$, then, in view of the theorem in Section 4–6,

$$(5\text{–}13) \qquad p(D)(e^{ax}z) = e^{ax}p(G)z = e^{ax}p(D + aI)z.$$

Replacing a by $-b$ and $e^{ax}z$ by z, and transposing the exponential factor, we obtain, as equivalent to (5–13),

$$(5\text{–}14) \qquad e^{bx}p(D)z = p(D - bI)(e^{bx}z).$$

Equation (5–13) may be useful in solving equations of the form

$$(5\text{–}15) \qquad p(D)y = e^{ax}f(x).$$

We show that y is a solution of (5–15) if and only if $z = e^{-ax}y$ is a solution of

$$(5\text{–}16) \qquad p(D + aI)z = f(x).$$

If y satisfies (5–15) and $z = e^{-ax}y$, then

$$e^{ax}f(x) = p(D)y = p(D)(e^{ax}z) = e^{ax}p(G)z,$$

so that $f(x) = p(G)z$. Conversely, if z is a solution of (5–16), and $y = e^{ax}z$, then, by (5–13),

$$p(D)y = p(D)(e^{ax}z) = e^{ax}p(D + aI)z = e^{ax}f(x).$$

Thus the problem of solving (5–15) is equivalent to that of solving (5–16). Moreover, to find a particular solution of (5–15) it suffices to find a particular solution of (5–16) and multiply it by e^{ax}. It is frequently easier to find a particular solution of (5–16), and it may even be easier to find the characteristic roots of $p(G) = q(D)$ than those of $p(D)$.

Example 5–8. Find a particular solution of the equation

$$(D^2 - 5D - 3I)y = x^2e^{4x}.$$

Solution: A particular solution results by multiplying by e^{4x} any solution of

$$p(G)z = [(D + 4I)^2 - 5(D + 4I) - 3I]z = (D^2 + 3D - 7I)z = x^2.$$

By the method of undetermined coefficients (Section 5–2), we easily find such a solution to be $z = -\dfrac{1}{7}x^2 - \dfrac{6}{49}x - \dfrac{32}{343}$. Hence a particular solution of the given equation is $y = -e^{4x}\dfrac{49x^2 + 42x + 32}{343}$.

Example 5–9. Find a particular solution of

$$p(D)y = (D + 3I)^2(D - 2I)y = e^{-3x} \cos x.$$

Solution: Method 1. It suffices to solve

$$p(G)z = [(D - 3I) + 3I]^2[(D - 3I) - 2I]z$$
$$= D^2(D - 5I)z = \cos x.$$

A particular solution of this equation is $z = (1/26)(5 \cos x - \sin x)$, obtained by the method of undetermined coefficients, and therefore a particular solution of the given equation is

$$y = \frac{e^{-3x}}{26}(5 \cos x - \sin x).$$

It is worth noting in this case that the equation $D^2(D - 5I)z = \cos x$ may be solved more simply by replacing it by

$$(D - 5I)z = (D^{-1})^2 \cos x = -\cos x + c_1 x + c_2.$$

A trial solution as a linear combination of $\cos x$, x, and 1 need not contain x and 1, since these clearly satisfy the associated homogeneous equation. (See Section 5–2.) Thus it suffices to solve $(D - 5I)z = -\cos x$; this represents a distinct simplification.

Method 2. By using complex numbers we may obtain a particular solution of the given equation in a different way, as follows. Write (as was done in Example 4–12)

$$e^{-3x} \cos x = \frac{1}{2} e^{-3x}(e^{ix} + e^{-ix}),$$

so that the given equation becomes

$$(D + 3I)^2(D - 2I)y = \frac{1}{2}\left[e^{(-3+i)x} + e^{(-3-i)x} \right].$$

To find a solution, it suffices to solve separately each of the following equations and add the results (see Section 4–7, exercise 11):

$$(D + 3I)^2(D - 2I)y = \frac{1}{2} e^{(-3+i)x}$$

and

$$(D + 3I)^2(D - 2I)y = \frac{1}{2} e^{(-3-i)x}.$$

These equations are equivalent, by the respective substitutions $y = e^{(-3+i)x}z$ and $y = e^{(-3-i)x}z$, to

$$(D + iI)^2[D - (5 - i)I]z = [D^3 + \cdots + (5 - i)I]z = \frac{1}{2},$$

and

$$(D - iI)^2[D - (5 + i)I]z = [D^3 + \cdots + (5 + i)I]z = \frac{1}{2}.$$

The first of these has the solution $z_1 = \dfrac{1}{2(5 - i)}$, and the second

has the solution $z_2 = \dfrac{1}{2(5 + i)}$. Hence the given equation has the
solution

$$
\begin{aligned}
y &= e^{(-3+i)x}z_1 + e^{(-3-i)x}z_2 \\
&= \frac{e^{-3x}}{2}\left(\frac{e^{ix}}{5 - i} + \frac{e^{-ix}}{5 + i}\right) \\
&= \frac{e^{-3x}}{2}\cdot\frac{1}{26}\left[5(e^{ix} + e^{-ix}) + i(e^{ix} - e^{-ix})\right] \\
&= \frac{e^{-3x}}{26}(5\cos x - \sin x).
\end{aligned}
$$

Example 5–10. Find a particular solution of

$$p(D)y = (D^2 + D - 3I)y = xe^{2x}\sin x.$$

Solution: Method 1. Let $y = e^{2x}z$, and find a solution of

$$[(D + 2I)^2 + (D + 2I) - 3I]z = (D^2 + 5D + 3I)z = x\sin x.$$

According to Section 5–2 we try

$$z = (A + Bx)\cos x + (C + Ex)\sin x.$$

Then we have

$$
\begin{aligned}
Dz &= (C + Ex + B)\cos x + (E - A - Bx)\sin x, \\
D^2z &= (2E - A - Bx)\cos x + (-2B - C - Ex)\sin x, \\
(D^2 &+ 5D + 3I)z \\
&= (2A + 5B + 5C + 2E)\cos x + (2B + 5E)x\cos x \\
&\quad + (-5A - 2B + 2C + 5E)\sin x + (-5B + 2E)x\sin x.
\end{aligned}
$$

We have therefore to solve the system of equations:

$$
\left\{
\begin{aligned}
2A + 5B + 5C + 2E &= 0, \\
2B \quad\quad\quad + 5E &= 0, \\
-5A - 2B + 2C + 5E &= 0, \\
-5B \quad\quad + 2E &= 1.
\end{aligned}
\right.
$$

The system has a unique solution given by

$$A = \frac{142}{841}, \quad B = -\frac{5}{29}, \quad C = \frac{65}{841}, \quad E = \frac{2}{29}.$$

Our particular solution is therefore

$$z = \frac{1}{841}\,[(142 - 145x)\cos x + (65 + 58x)\sin x].$$

Method 2. First we write

$$e^{2x}\sin x = \frac{e^{2x}(e^{ix} - e^{-ix})}{2i} = \frac{e^{(2+i)x} - e^{(2-i)x}}{2i}.$$

As in Example 5–9, we may solve separately

$$p(D)y = \frac{x}{2i}\,e^{(2+i)x} \quad \text{and} \quad p(D)y = -\frac{x}{2i}\,e^{(2-i)x},$$

and add the results. In the first of these equations, let $y = e^{(2+i)x}z$ and solve

$$[(D + (2 + i)I)^2 + (D + (2 + i)I) - 3I]z$$
$$= [D^2 + (5 + 2i)D + (2 + 5i)I]z = \frac{x}{2i}.$$

Try $z = Ax + B$. Then we have
$$[D^2 + (5 + 2i)D + (2 + 5i)I]z$$
$$= A(5 + 2i) + (2 + 5i)(Ax + B) = \frac{x}{2i}.$$

Choosing $A = -\dfrac{5 + 2i}{58}$ and $B = \dfrac{142 - 65i}{2 \cdot 841}$ yields the solution

$$z_1 = -\frac{5 + 2i}{58}\,x + \frac{142 - 65i}{2 \cdot 841}.$$

Secondly, we find a particular solution of

$$p(D)y = -\frac{x}{2i}\,e^{(2-i)x}$$

by letting $y = e^{(2-i)x}z$ and solving

$$[(D + (2 - i)I)^2 + (D + (2 - i)I) - 3I]z$$
$$= [D^2 + (5 - 2i)D + (2 - 5i)I]z = -\frac{x}{2i}.$$

It is easily verified that $z_2 = -\dfrac{5 - 2i}{58}\,x + \dfrac{142 + 65i}{2 \cdot 841}$ is a solution.

In fact, this second-part solution can always be obtained in such cases from the first-part solution by replacing each complex coefficient by its conjugate (see the discussion which follows). Therefore a solution of the given equation is

$$y = e^{(2+i)x}z_1 + e^{(2-i)x}z_2.$$

Since the two terms in y are conjugates of each other, y is twice the real part of

$$e^{(2+i)x}z = e^{2x} (\cos x + i \sin x) \left(- \frac{5 + 2i}{58} x + \frac{142 - 65i}{2 \cdot 841} \right),$$

that is,

$$y = \frac{e^{2x}}{841} [(142 - 145x) \cos x + (65 + 58x) \sin x].$$

★A Simplification Using Complex Conjugates. In the solution of Example 5–10 by complex exponents a short cut was made possible through use of complex conjugates. The validity of this procedure stems from the following theorem.

Theorem. Let $p(m)$ be a polynomial with (constant) complex coefficients. Denote by $p^*(m)$ the polynomial obtained from $p(m)$ by replacing each coefficient by its conjugate. For a function $z(x) = u(x) + iv(x)$, denote by z^* the conjugate $u - iv$ of z. Then

$$(p(D)z)^* = p^*(D)z^*.$$

To prove the theorem, note that $p(m)$ may be written $q(m) + ir(m)$, where $q(m)$ and $r(m)$ are real. Then $p(D) = q(D) + ir(D)$, and $p^*(D) = q(D) - ir(D)$. It follows that

$$
\begin{aligned}
(p(D)z)^* &= [(q(D) + ir(D))(u + iv)]^* \\
&= [q(D)u - r(D)v + i(q(D)v + r(D)u)]^* \\
&= q(D)u - r(D)v - i(q(D)v + r(D)u) \\
&= (q(D) - ir(D))(u - iv) \\
&= p^*(D)z^*.
\end{aligned}
$$

It follows from this theorem that if z satisfies $p(D)z = f$, then z^* satisfies $p^*(D)z = f^*$. That is, a solution z of a given equation leads to a solution z^* of the "conjugate" equation.

A case of special interest is that in which $p(m)$ is a real **polynomial**. Then $p^*(m) = p(m)$, and we have

$$(p(D)z)^* = p(D)z^*.$$

If we wish to solve $p(D)u = f$, we may solve instead

$$p(D)(u + iv) = f + ig.$$

It follows that

$$p(D)(u - iv) = f - ig,$$

whence, by addition,

$$p(D)(2u) = 2f,$$

and $p(D)u = f$. For example, we may solve $p(D)u = \cos x$ by solving $p(D)z = \cos x + i \sin x = e^{ix}$ and taking u to be the real part of z.

EXERCISES

In exercises 1 to 8, find the complete solution, using the method of this section to determine a particular solution.

1. $(D + I)^2 y = e^{3x} \sin 3x$.
2. $(D - 2I)^3 y = 2xe^{3x}$.
3. $D^2(D - I)^2 y = e^x$.
4. $(D - I)^2 y = e^x \dfrac{\ln x}{x}$.
5. $(D^3 - D^2 + D - I)y = xe^x \sin x$.
6. $(D + kI)^3 y = e^{-kx} f'''(x)$.
7. $(D^2 - 4D + 5I)y = e^{2x} \sec^2 x$.
8. $(D^3 - 3D - 2I)y = 2 + x + xe^{-x} + x^2 e^{2x}$.

★**9.** Solve $(D^2 + I)y = \cos x$ by solving $(D^2 + I)y = e^{ix}$ and taking the real part. (Use the method of this section.)

★**10.** Devise a method similar to that in exercise 9 for the equation $(D^2 + I)y = \sin x$, and solve.

★**11.** Carry out in detail the induction needed to prove (5–13).

5–5. METHODS BASED ON SPECIAL PROPERTIES OF THE OPERATOR D

Let us continue consideration of an equation (5–1) with constant coefficients. Again, we assume the characteristic roots are known and that only a particular solution is desired. That is, we seek a function y_f such that $y_f = (p(D))^{-1} f$.

The general method of Section 4–7 was based on replacement of $(p(D))^{-1}$ by a product of simpler operators. It is proposed now to attempt to replace $(p(D))^{-1}$ by a sum of two or more simpler operators. Suppose, for example, that A and B are two operators such that, for every pair of functions (f, g) for which $g = (A + B)f$, it is true that $g = (p(D))^{-1}f$ [that is, that $f = p(D)g$]. Then, if functions g_1 and g_2 can be found such that $g_1 = Af$ and $g_2 = Bf$, it follows from the definition of sum that $g_1 + g_2 = (A + B)f$. Hence, by our hypothesis, $g_1 + g_2 = (p(D))^{-1}f$, and $g_1 + g_2$ is a solution of (5–1). A similar argument applies to finite sums generally.

In order to express $(p(D))^{-1}$ as a sum, we study first the numerical rational form $(p(m))^{-1} = 1/p(m)$, where

$$p(m) = (m - m_1)^{r_1} (m - m_2)^{r_2} \cdots (m - m_k)^{r_k},$$

in which $m_1, \cdots, m_k$ are the distinct characteristic roots and $r_1, \cdots, r_k$ their respective multiplicities. It is shown in algebra that there exist numbers a_{ji} $(i = 1, \cdots, r_j; j = 1, \cdots, k)$ such that the "decomposition into partial fractions"

(5–17)
$$\frac{1}{p(m)} = \sum_{j=1}^{k} \sum_{i=1}^{r_j} \frac{a_{ji}}{(m - m_j)^i}$$

is valid. For example,

$$\frac{1}{(m - 1)^2(m - 2)^3} = \frac{a_{11}}{m - 1} + \frac{a_{12}}{(m - 1)^2} + \frac{a_{21}}{m - 2}$$
$$+ \frac{a_{22}}{(m - 2)^2} + \frac{a_{23}}{(m - 2)^3}.$$

The numerators in (5–17) need not be real, since the roots m_j may be complex; if $k \neq 1$, it may be proved that each numerator is not zero.

While it has been indicated that the algebra of rational forms cannot in general be carried over into rational operator forms, the operator counterpart of (5–17) is nevertheless true:

(5–18)
$$(p(D))^{-1} = \sum_{j=1}^{k} \sum_{i=1}^{r_j} a_{ji}(D - m_jI)^{-i},$$

where the coefficients a_{ji} are obtained from (5–17). [For a discussion of (5–18), see pages 144 and 145.]

In practice, it is not necessary to know the general validity of (5–18). All that is needed for any special equation (5–1) is a verification that every pair of functions belonging to the right side of (5–18) also belongs to the left, since, as was indicated above, a particular solution of (5–1) may then be obtained.

Example 5–11. Find a particular solution of $(D^2 - I)y = e^x$.

Solution: By (5–17) we expect the "partial fractions decomposition"

$$\frac{1}{m^2 - 1} = \frac{a}{m - 1} + \frac{b}{m + 1}.$$

Rewriting the right side as $\dfrac{a(m + 1) + b(m - 1)}{m^2 - 1}$ and equating to the left, we have

$$\begin{cases} a + b = 0 \\ a - b = 1, \end{cases}$$

whence $a = 1/2$, $b = -1/2$. From (5–18), we expect that

$$(D^2 - I)^{-1} = \frac{1}{2}(D - I)^{-1} - \frac{1}{2}(D + I)^{-1}.$$

Let us verify only that if

$$g = \left[\frac{1}{2}(D - I)^{-1} - \frac{1}{2}(D + I)^{-1} \right] f,$$

then $g = (D^2 - I)^{-1}f$, that is, $f = (D^2 - I)g$. We have[1]

$$(D^2 - I)g = (D^2 - I)\left[\frac{1}{2}(D - I)^{-1} - \frac{1}{2}(D + I)^{-1} \right] f$$

$$= (D^2 - I)\left[\frac{1}{2}(D - I)^{-1}f - \frac{1}{2}(D + I)^{-1}f \right]$$

$$= \frac{1}{2}(D^2 - I)[(D - I)^{-1}f] - \frac{1}{2}(D^2 - I)[(D + I)^{-1}f]$$

$$= \frac{1}{2}(D + I)(D - I)(D - I)^{-1}f$$

$$\qquad - \frac{1}{2}(D - I)(D + I)(D + I)^{-1}f$$

$$= \frac{1}{2}(D + I)f - \frac{1}{2}(D - I)f = f.$$

[1]Note the use, in the next to last step of the argument, of part i of the theorem of Section 4–5.

To complete the solution, we find particular functions g_1 and g_2 such that

$$g_1 = \frac{1}{2}(D - I)^{-1}e^x \quad \text{and} \quad g_2 = -\frac{1}{2}(D + I)^{-1}e^x,$$

and add the results. That is, we solve

$$(D - I)g_1 = \frac{1}{2}e^x \quad \text{and} \quad (D + I)g_2 = -\frac{1}{2}e^x.$$

Suitable solutions are $g_1 = \frac{1}{2}xe^x$ and $g_2 = -\frac{1}{4}e^x$. It follows that $\frac{1}{2}xe^x - \frac{1}{4}e^x$ is a desired particular solution. (A simpler particular solution here is $\frac{1}{2}xe^x$, since the other term satisfies the associated homogeneous equation.)

Example 5–12. Find a particular solution of $(D - I)^2(D + I)y = 1$.

Solution: Equation (5–17) suggests

$$\frac{1}{(m - 1)^2(m + 1)} = \frac{a}{m - 1} + \frac{b}{(m - 1)^2} + \frac{c}{m + 1},$$

whence we have the identity

$$1 = a(m^2 - 1) + b(m + 1) + c(m - 1)^2.$$

There result $a = -1/4$, $b = 1/2$, $c = 1/4$. Hence we replace $[(D - I)^2(D + I)]^{-1}$ by

$$-\frac{1}{4}(D - I)^{-1} + \frac{1}{2}(D - I)^{-2} + \frac{1}{4}(D + I)^{-1}.$$

It is required to find g_1, g_2, g_3 such that

$$(D - I)g_1 = -\frac{1}{4}, \quad (D - I)^2g_2 = \frac{1}{2}, \quad (D + I)g_3 = \frac{1}{4}.$$

Suitable functions are $g_1 = 1/4, g_2 = 1/2, g_3 = 1/4$. It follows that a desired particular solution is $(1/4) + (1/2) + (1/4) = 1$. A check in the given equation actually validates the procedure for this problem.

When $f(x)$ in (5–1) is a polynomial, a different type of replacement for $(p(D))^{-1}$ is possible. We shall only illustrate the method here, reserving a discussion of its validity for the starred subsection that follows.

Example 5-13. Find a particular solution of $p(D)y = (D - 3I)y = 4x - 9$.

Solution: The reciprocal of the numerical polynomial $p(m) = (m - 3)$ may be written

$$\frac{1}{m - 3} = -\frac{1}{3} \cdot \frac{1}{1 - m/3} = -\frac{1}{3}\left(1 + \frac{m}{3} + \frac{1}{9} \cdot \frac{m^2}{1 - m/3}\right).$$

Here the expression on the right is obtained through division carried out to yield a remainder of degree one higher than the degree of $f(x) = 4x - 9$. Now the operator $(D - 3I)^{-1}$ may be replaced by

$$A = -\frac{1}{3}\left[I + \frac{1}{3}D - \frac{1}{9}(D - 3I)^{-1}D^2\right],$$

in the sense that a particular solution of $y = Af$ is also one of $y = (p(D))^{-1}f$, as may be shown.
    We have

$$A(4x - 9) = -\frac{1}{3}\left(I + \frac{1}{3}D\right)(4x - 9) + \frac{1}{27}(D - 3I)^{-1}D^2(4x - 9)$$

$$= -\frac{1}{3}\left(I + \frac{1}{3}D\right)(4x - 9) + \frac{1}{27}(D - 3I)^{-1}0.$$

But 0 is a particular function in $(D - 3I)^{-1}0$, since $(D - 3I)0 = 0$. Hence a desired particular solution of the given equation is

$$y_f = -\frac{1}{3}\left(I + \frac{1}{3}D\right)(4x - 9)$$

$$= -\frac{4}{3}x + \frac{23}{9}.$$

The method may be justified for this problem by a check by substitution.
    Note that the operator A may even be replaced by the operator

$$B = -\frac{1}{3}\left(I + \frac{1}{3}D\right),$$

in view of the fact that the last term in A has no effect on the solution. It is a curious fact that a particular solution, normally obtained by integration, may be found by differentiation when $f(x)$ is a polynomial.

Example 5-14. Find a particular solution of

$$D^2(D^6 - 3D^4 - I)y = f(x) = x^7 + 3x^5 - 2x^3 + 1.$$

Solution: Let $D^2y = z$, and solve

$$p(D)z = (D^6 - 3D^4 - I)z = x^7 + 3x^5 - 2x^3 + 1.$$

We have

$$\frac{1}{p(m)} = -\frac{1}{1 + (3m^4 - m^6)}$$

$$= -\left[1 - 3m^4 + m^6 + \frac{r(m)}{1 + (3m^4 - m^6)}\right],$$

where $r(m)$ is a polynomial containing a factor m^8. The operator $(p(D))^{-1}$ is replaced by

$$B = -(I - 3D^4 + D^6),$$

since a term containing D^8 will have no effect on the solution. A particular solution is

$$z_f = Bf(x) = -f(x) + 3(7 \cdot 6 \cdot 5 \cdot 4x^3 + 3 \cdot 5 \cdot 4 \cdot 3 \cdot 2x)$$
$$- 7 \cdot 6 \cdot 5 \cdot 4 \cdot 3 \cdot 2x$$
$$= -x^7 - 3x^5 + (3 \cdot 4 \cdot 5 \cdot 6 \cdot 7 + 2)x^3 - 33 \cdot 5 \cdot 4 \cdot 3 \cdot 2x - 1.$$

It follows that a desired particular solution of the given equation is

$$y_f = D^{-2}z_f = -\frac{x^9}{8 \cdot 9} - \frac{x^7}{14} + \frac{1261x^5}{10} - 660x^3 - \frac{x^2}{2}.$$

*Validity of Certain Replacement Techniques. It has been asserted that equation (5–18) is true, so that the right side may replace the left in the process of solving equations of the form (5–1) with constant coefficients. In the text and examples we did not require the identity of the two sides of (5–18), and, in fact, in special cases replacement of one side by the other could be justified, for particular solutions, by checking the solution found.

It is notationally complicated to present a general proof of (5–18). However, the method can be understood from the treatment of a special case, which we now give.

Consider $p(m) = (m - m_1)(m - m_2)^2$, so that $r_1 = 1$, $r_2 = 2$. The partial fractions decomposition is

$$\frac{1}{(m - m_1)(m - m_2)^2} = \frac{a_{11}}{m - m_1} + \frac{a_{21}}{m - m_2} + \frac{a_{22}}{(m - m_2)^2},$$

where

$$(5\text{-}19) \quad a_{11} = \frac{1}{(m_2 - m_1)^2}, \quad a_{21} = -\frac{1}{(m_2 - m_1)^2}, \quad a_{22} = \frac{1}{m_2 - m_1}.$$

It is to be shown that

$$(5\text{-}20) \quad (D - m_1 I)^{-1} (D - m_2 I)^{-2}$$
$$= a_{11}(D - m_1 I)^{-1} + a_{21}(D - m_2 I)^{-1} + a_{22}(D - m_2 I)^{-2}.$$

A pair (g, f) belongs to the left side of (5-20) when

$$(D - m_1 I) (D - m_2 I)^2 f = g,$$

that is, when there exist functions h and k such that

$$(5\text{-}21) \quad g = (D - m_1 I)h, \quad h = (D - m_2 I)k, \quad k = (D - m_2 I)f.$$

On the other hand, (g, f) belongs to the right side of (5-20) when there exist functions f_{11}, f_{21}, f_{22} such that

$$(5\text{-}22) \quad \begin{cases} f = f_{11} + f_{21} + f_{22}, \\ (D - m_1 I)f_{11} = a_{11}\, g, \\ (D - m_2 I)f_{21} = a_{21}\, g, \\ (D - m_2 I)^2 f_{22} = a_{22}\, g. \end{cases}$$

Assuming (5-21), define

$$(5\text{-}23) \quad \begin{cases} f_{11} = a_{11} h, \\ f_{21} = a_{21}(D - m_1 I)k = a_{21}[(D - m_2 I)k + (m_2 - m_1)k] \\ \qquad = a_{21}[h + (m_2 - m_1)k], \\ f_{22} = a_{22}(D - m_1 I)f = a_{22}[(D - m_2 I)f + (m_2 - m_1)f] \\ \qquad = a_{22}[k + (m_2 - m_1)f]. \end{cases}$$

From (5-23) and (5-19) one easily verifies that $f_{11} + f_{21} + f_{22} = f$. The other three equations in (5-22) follow directly from those in (5-21), in view of (5-23).

Conversely, assuming (5-22), we may define

$$h = \frac{f_{11}}{a_{11}}, \quad k = (m_1 - m_2)\, f_{11} + (D - m_2 I)\, f_{22}.$$

A simple calculation shows that (5-21) holds. This completes the proof of (5-20).

In Examples 5-13 and 5-14 we were interested in a simple replacement for the inverse of an operator based on a numerical polynomial having a non-zero constant term. Such a polynomial may be written, apart from a constant factor, as $1 - q(m)$, in which $q(m)$ has zero constant term. It is clear that, for $k = 0, 1, 2, \cdots$,

$$\frac{1}{1 - q(m)} = 1 + q(m) + (q(m))^2 + \cdots + (q(m))^k + \frac{(q(m))^{k+1}}{1 - q(m)}.$$

It may be shown correspondingly that $(I - q(D))^{-1}$ may always be replaced by

(5–24) $I + q(D) + (q(D))^2 + \cdots + (q(D))^k$
$$+ (I - (q(D))^{-1})(q(D))^{k+1},$$

in the sense that every pair of functions in (5–24) is also in $(I - q(D))^{-1}$.

Of course, (5–24) is of little value in solving a differential equation (5–1) unless $f(x)$ is a polynomial; its greatest value then lies in the possibility of choosing k so that $(q(D))^{k+1}$ contains as a factor a power of D greater than the degree of $f(x)$, as was seen in the examples.

We now show that if (f, g) is in (5–24), then (f, g) is in $(I - q(D))^{-1}$. For simplicity, denote $q(D)$ by A and assume that there exist functions $g_0, \cdots, g_{k+1}, h$ such that $g = g_0 + \cdots + g_{k+1}$, and

$$g_0 = If, \quad g_1 = Af, \quad \cdots, \quad g_k = A^k f,$$
$$h = A^{k+1}f, \quad g_{k+1} = (I - A)^{-1}h.$$

It follows that

$$g = (I + A + \cdots + A^k)f + g_{k+1} \quad \text{and} \quad h = (I - A)g_{k+1},$$

whence

$$(I - A)g = (I - A^{k+1})f + (I - A)g_{k+1} = f - h + h = f.$$

The converse of this result is not true.

EXERCISES

In each of exercises 1 to 4, find a particular solution, using the method of partial fractions decomposition.

    1. $(D^3 - 4D)y = x^2 - x$.
    2. $D^2(D + 4I)y = e^{-4x}$.
    3. $(D^2 - 3D + 2I)y = xe^x$.
    4. $(D^4 + D^2)y = \sin x$.

In each of exercises 5 to 8, find a particular solution, using a suitable replacement for $(p(D))^{-1}$.

    5. $(D^6 + D^4 - I)y = 4x^5 - 6x^2 + 2.$
    6. $(D^8 + I)y = x^{15}.$
    7. $(D^2 + 2D - 2I)y = 3 + 4x + x^2.$
    8. $(D^2 + 3I)y = x^4 - x^6.$

In each of exercises 9 to 12, find the complete solution by either method of this section. Use exponential shifts where practicable.

    9. $(D^2 + 5D + 6I)y = x^2.$
    10. $((D + I)^8 - I)y = e^{-x}x^9.$
    11. $(D^2 - 6D + 8I)y = x^2 e^x.$
    12. $(D^2 - I)^3 y = e^{2x} \cos 3x.$

★13. Verify in detail the steps in the starred subsection on page 145, showing that (5–21) leads to (5–22) and vice versa.

★14. As in the starred subsection on pages 144 and 145, carry out a proof of (5–18) for the case $k = 3$, $r_1 = r_2 = r_3 = 1$.

5-6. SPECIAL METHODS FOR EQUATIONS WITH NON-CONSTANT COEFFICIENTS

In the theory of algebraic polynomial equations $f(x) = 0$, when by some means a root r has been found, the problem of finding all the roots is equivalent to that of solving an equation of degree one less than that of the original. An analogous procedure is available for differential equations (5–1), in which the coefficients need not be constants. The method is applicable even when the leading coefficient is not 1.

Let

$$p(D) = a_0(x)D^n + a_1(x)D^{n-1} + \cdots + a_{n-1}(x)D + a_n(x)I,$$

and assume $y_1(x)$ to be a solution (not the zero solution) of the homogeneous equation associated with

$$(5\text{–}25) \qquad\qquad p(D)y = f.$$

Let $y = y_1z$, where z is to be determined in such a way that y is a solution of (5–25). Then

$$a_0 D^n(y_1z) + a_1 D^{n-1}(y_1z) + \cdots + a_{n-1}D(y_1z) + a_n y_1 z = f,$$

or

$$(5\text{–}26) \qquad\qquad q(D)(Dz) + z(p(D)y_1) = f,$$

where the second term is the result of grouping together all terms in z. Since $p(D)y_1 = 0$, (5–26) may be written

$$q(D)(Dz) = f.$$

It is seen that $q(D)$ is a polynomial of degree $n - 1$. The substitution $Dz = w$ yields $q(D)w = f$. The complete solution of this equation is expected to take the form

$$w = c_1w_1 + \cdots + c_{n-1}w_{n-1} + w_f,$$

where $w_1, \cdots, w_{n-1}$ are linearly independent. Therefore

$$(5\text{--}27) \quad z = c_1\int w_1\,dx + \cdots + c_{n-1}\int w_{n-1}\,dx + \int w_f\,dx + c_n,$$

and finally, the complete solution of (5–25) is given by

$$y = y_1 z = c_1 y_1\int w_1\,dx + \cdots + c_{n-1} y_1\int w_{n-1}\,dx + c_n y_1 + y_1\int w_f\,dx.$$

It is easy to prove that the functions $y_1\int w_1\,dx, \cdots, y_1\int w_{n-1}\,dx, y_1$ are linearly independent.

The method just presented is useful primarily in the case of equations of second order, since the equation for w, being of first order, can always be solved. For a non-homogeneous equation, one may first solve the associated homogeneous equation and then use the method of variation of parameters, if this proves desirable.

Example 5–15. Find the complete solution of

$$[(x - 1)D^2 - xD + I]y = 0.$$

Solution: It is easy to verify that e^x is a solution. Hence let $y = e^x z$. The equation becomes

$$(x - 1)(ze^x + 2e^x Dz + e^x D^2 z) - x(ze^x + e^x Dz) + ze^x = 0,$$

or

$$[(x - 1)D + (x - 2)I]Dz = 0.$$

Let $w = Dz$ and obtain

$$(x - 1)w' + (x - 2)w = 0.$$

A solution is found to be $w = c_1(x - 1)e^{-x}$, so that $z = -c_1 xe^{-x} + c_2$, and therefore $y = e^x z = -c_1 x + c_2 e^x$ is the complete solution of the given equation.

Example 5-16. Discuss the solution of the equation

$$[(2x^2 + 3)D^2 - xD - 2I]y = f(x).$$

Solution: It is reasonable to guess that the associated homogeneous equation has a solution of the form $y_1 = ax^2 + bx + c$. Since

$$[(2x^2 + 3)D^2 - xD - 2I](ax^2 + bx + c)$$
$$= 2a(2x^2 + 3) - x(2ax + b) - 2(ax^2 + bx + c)$$
$$= (4a - 2a - 2a)x^2 + (-b - 2b)x + (6a - 2c),$$

we obtain a solution by taking $b = 0$ and $6a = 2c$. That is, for every choice of a, $ax^2 + 3a$ is a solution. Clearly, no two of these solutions are linearly independent. Let us choose $a = 1$ and let $y = (x^2 + 3)z$. Then we have

$$[(2x^2 + 3)D^2 - xD - 2I]\,[(x^2 + 3)z]$$
$$= (2x^2 + 3)[(x^2 + 3)D^2z + 4xDz + 2z]$$
$$\quad - x[(x^2 + 3)Dz + 2xz] - 2(x^2 + 3)z$$
$$= (2x^2 + 3)\,(x^2 + 3)D^2z + (8x^3 + 12x$$
$$\quad - x^3 - 3x)Dz = f(x).$$

In this way the problem of solving the given equation is reduced to that of solving successively the equations

$$(2x^2 + 3)\,(x^2 + 3)w' + x(7x^2 + 9)w = f(x) \quad \text{and} \quad z' = w.$$

Let $g(x) = f(x)/[(2x^3 + 3)\,(x^2 + 3)]$. The chief task now is to find

$$w_0(x) = \int \frac{x(7x^2 + 9)}{(2x^2 + 3)(x^2 + 3)}\, dx \quad \text{and} \quad \int e^{w_0(x)}g(x)\, dx.$$

While $w_0(x)$ can be readily found, it is doubtful that the second integral can be found in terms of elementary functions, except perhaps for a few specially chosen functions f.

EXERCISES

In each of exercises 1 to 8, find the complete solution.

1. $6x^2y'' - 5xy' + 4y = 0$ (given that $\sqrt{x}$ is a solution).
2. $x^2y'' + 3xy' + y = 0$ (given that $1/x$ is a solution).
3. $x(x + 1)y'' + (2 - x^2)y' - (2 + x)y = 0$ (given that e^x is a solution).
4. $x^2y'' + x^2y' - xy = 0$ (given that a polynomial solution exists).

5. $x^2y'' - 3xy' + 4y = 0$ (given that a polynomial solution exists).

6. $y'' + xy' + (3x - 9)y = 0$ (given that e^{mx} is a solution, for some constant m).

7. $x^2y'' - 3xy' + 4y = 6$ (see exercise 5).

8. $x^2y'' + x^2y' - xy = 2x$ (see exercise 4).

9. Prove that $y'' + p(x)y' + q(x)y = 0$ has a solution e^{mx} with m a constant if and only if $q = -m^2 - mp$.

10. Let $p(x) = \ln x$, $m = 4$ in exercise 9 and find the complete solution, assuming $q = -m^2 - mp$.

11. Show that, after division by $x(x - 1)$, the equation $x(x - 1)y'' + (1 + 2x - x^2)y' - (1 + x)y = 0$ meets the requirement of exercise 9. Then find the complete solution.

12. Prove that, if p and q meet the requirement in exercise 9, then $qp'^2 = -q'^2 + pp'q'$.

13. In the treatment in the text, if $n = 2$, prove that if y_1 and w_1 do not vanish, then the wronskian of the functions $y_1 \int w_1 \, dx$, y_1 is not zero.

★14. Generalize exercise 13 by proving that, if W is the wronskian of $w_1, \cdots, w_{n-1}$, and if Y is the wronskian of $y_1 \int w_1 \, dx, \cdots$, $y_1 \int w_{n-1} \, dx$, y_1, then $Y = (-1)^{n+1} y_1^n W$.

★15. Prove directly from the definition of linear independence that, if $w_1, \cdots, w_{n-1}$ are linearly independent, then $y_1 \int w_1 \, dx, \cdots$, $y_1 \int w_{n-1} \, dx$, y_1 are also linearly independent, where these functions are those of the text.

5-7. SYSTEMS OF LINEAR EQUATIONS

Let polynomials $p_{ij}(m)$ $(i, j = 1, \cdots, n)$, each having constant coefficients, be given, and consider a system of the form

$$(5\text{-}28) \qquad \sum_{j=1}^{n} p_{ij}(D)y_j = f_i(x) \qquad (i = 1, \cdots, n).$$

We shall see that under suitable conditions it is possible to eliminate $n - 1$ of the unknown functions $y_1, \cdots, y_n$ and solve for the remaining one by the methods already available for linear equations.

Consider the algebraic system

$$(5\text{-}29) \qquad \sum_{j=1}^{n} p_{ij}(m)u_j = v_i \qquad (i = 1, \cdots, n).$$

Let $P_{ij}(m)$ be the cofactor (signed minor) of p_{ij} in the square array (p_{ij}) and consider

$$\sum_{i=1}^{n} P_{ik} v_i = \sum_{i=1}^{n} P_{ik} \left(\sum_{j=1}^{n} p_{ij} u_j \right)$$

$$= \sum_{i=1}^{n} \sum_{j=1}^{n} P_{ik} \, p_{ij} \, u_j$$

$$= \sum_{j=1}^{n} \sum_{i=1}^{n} P_{ik} \, p_{ij} \, u_j,$$

for some particular $k = 0, 1, \cdots, n$. It is an elementary result in the theory of determinants that

$$\sum_{i=1}^{n} P_{ik} \, p_{ij} = 0 \qquad \text{for } j \neq k,$$

and

$$\sum_{i=1}^{n} P_{ik} \, p_{ij} = \Delta(m) \quad \text{for } j = k,$$

where $\Delta(m)$ is the determinant of the square array (p_{ij}). Thus we have, as a consequence of (5–29),

$$(5\text{–}30) \qquad \Delta(m) u_k = \sum_{i=1}^{n} P_{ik}(m) v_i \qquad (k = 1, \cdots, n).$$

When $\Delta(m) \neq 0$, (5–30) may be solved for u_k ($k = 1, \cdots, n$), and there result the usual Cramer formulas for the solution, since the right side of (5–30) is the expansion of the appropriate determinant. The solutions are rational forms in m.

Now assume in (5–28) the functions $f_i(x)$ to have continuous derivatives of as high order as needed. Let $P_{ik}(D)$ and $\Delta(D)$ be the polynomials in D corresponding to $P_{ik}(m)$ and $\Delta(m)$, respectively. It follows that operation on (5–28) by the $P_{ik}(D)$ and summation are possible and yield

$$(5\text{–}31) \qquad \Delta(D) y_k = \sum_{i=1}^{n} P_{ik}(D) f_i \qquad (k = 1, \cdots, n).$$

If $\Delta(m)$ is not the zero polynomial, then the kth equation in (5–31) is of the form (5–1) and may be solved for y_k. Since (5–31) was deduced from (5–28), every solution of (5–28) must be a solution of

(5–31); the converse is not generally true. (See the example below.) It is then necessary to substitute in (5–28) the functions y_k found and discard those which fail to satisfy (5–28).

A determinantal notation for each equation in (5–31) is permissible, provided such determinants are properly understood. Thus, if $n = 3$, we may write

$$
\begin{vmatrix}
p_{11}(D) & p_{12}(D) & p_{13}(D) \\
p_{21}(D) & p_{22}(D) & p_{23}(D) \\
p_{31}(D) & p_{32}(D) & p_{33}(D)
\end{vmatrix} y_2 =
\begin{vmatrix}
p_{11}(D) & f_1 & p_{13}(D) \\
p_{21}(D) & f_2 & p_{23}(D) \\
p_{31}(D) & f_3 & p_{33}(D)
\end{vmatrix}.
$$

Here the determinant on the left is $\Delta(D)$ and may be "expanded" by the usual rules, since polynomials in D commute. On the right, the "expansion" is carried out by minors as usual, employing the second column, and placing the "factors" f_1, f_2, f_3 on the right in the terms of the "expansion."

Example 5–17. Find the complete solution of the system

$$
\begin{cases}
y'' - z'' + w = 0, \\
z'' - w'' + y = 1, \\
w'' - y'' - y = x.
\end{cases}
$$

Solution: Write the system in the form

$$
\begin{cases}
D^2 y - D^2 z + I w = 0, \\
I y + D^2 z - D^2 w = 1, \\
-(D^2 + I)y + D^2 w = x.
\end{cases}
$$

Then

$$
\Delta(D) =
\begin{vmatrix}
D^2 & -D^2 & I \\
I & D^2 & -D^2 \\
-(D^2 + I) & 0 & D^2
\end{vmatrix} = D^4 + D^2 = D^2(D^2 + I).
$$

It follows that

$$
\Delta(D)y =
\begin{vmatrix}
0 & -D^2 & I \\
1 & D^2 & -D^2 \\
x & 0 & D^2
\end{vmatrix} = D^4 1 + (D^4 - D^2)x = 0,
$$

$$\Delta(D)z = \begin{vmatrix} D^2 & 0 & I \\ I & 1 & -D^2 \\ -(D^2 + I) & x & D^2 \end{vmatrix}$$

$$= (2D^4 + I)1 + (D^4 + I)x = 1 + x,$$

$$\Delta(D)w = \begin{vmatrix} D^2 & -D^2 & 0 \\ I & D^2 & 1 \\ -(D^2 + I) & 0 & x \end{vmatrix}$$

$$= (D^4 + D^2)1 + (D^4 + D^2)x = 0.$$

The given system thus implies the system

$$\begin{cases} D^2(D^2 + I)y = 0, \\ D^2(D^2 + I)z = 1 + x, \\ D^2(D^2 + I)w = 0. \end{cases}$$

Using familiar methods of solution, we obtain

$$\begin{cases} y = a + bx + c \sin x + d \cos x, \\ z = g + hx + k \sin x + l \cos x + \dfrac{x^2}{2} + \dfrac{x^3}{6}, \\ w = m + nx + p \sin x + q \cos x, \end{cases}$$

in which the constants $a, \cdots, q$ are still subject to restriction. Substitution into the given system gives

$$(m - 1) + (n - 1)x + (-c + k + p) \sin x$$
$$+ (-d + l + q) \cos x = 0,$$
$$(1 + a) + (1 + b)x + (-k + p + c) \sin x$$
$$+ (-l + q + d) \cos x = 1,$$
$$- a - bx - p \sin x - q \cos x = x.$$

Since $1, x, \sin x, \cos x$ are linearly independent, we may equate coefficients to obtain $a = p = q = 0, b = -1, k = c, l = d, m = n = 1$. The desired complete solution is therefore given by

$$\begin{cases} y = -x + c \sin x + d \cos x, \\ z = g + hx + c \sin x + d \cos x + \dfrac{x^2}{2} + \dfrac{x^3}{6}, \\ w = 1 + x, \end{cases}$$

in which the constants c, d, g, h are arbitrary.

EXERCISES

In each of exercises 1 to 8, find the complete solution of the system.

1. $\begin{cases} (D + I)y + D^2z = x, \\ \qquad\quad y + Dz \;= e^x. \end{cases}$

2. $\begin{cases} Dy - (D^2 + D + I)z = e^{x^2}, \\ \;\; y - (D + I)z \qquad\quad = \ln \tan x. \end{cases}$

3. $\begin{cases} D^3(y - z) \qquad\qquad\qquad = e^{2x}, \\ (D^2 - I)y + (D + 2I)z = \cos x. \end{cases}$

4. $\begin{cases} \;\; y + z \quad\;\; = 1, \\ D^4y + D^5z = 0. \end{cases}$

5. $\begin{cases} (D + I)y - (2D + 2I)z = 0, \\ \qquad\; Dy + (2D - I)z \;\; = e^x. \end{cases}$

6. $\begin{cases} D^2y + (D^2 + D - I)z \qquad\qquad = 0, \\ (2D - I)y + (3D - 2I)z \qquad\qquad = 0, \\ (D + 3I)y + (2D - I)z + 3w = 0. \end{cases}$

7. $\begin{cases} (2D - I)y \qquad\qquad\quad = 0, \\ (3D + I)y + Dz \qquad\; = 1, \\ \qquad\qquad\;\, 4Dz - w = x. \end{cases}$

8. $\begin{cases} \;\, y + \quad z + \quad w = 0, \\ Dy + D^2z + D^3w = 0, \\ D^2y + D^4z + D^6w = 0. \end{cases}$

In each of exercises 9 to 12, express as best you can the complete solution.

★9. $\begin{cases} (D - I)y + \qquad\qquad z = 1 + x, \\ (D^2 - I)y + (D + I)z = 2 + x. \end{cases}$

★10. $\begin{cases} (D - I)y + \qquad\qquad z = 1 + x, \\ (D^2 - I)y + (D + I)z = 1. \end{cases}$

★11.
$$
\begin{cases}
Dy && + \, Dw = 1, \\
y + D^2z && = 0, \\
(D - I)y - D^2z + Dw = 1.
\end{cases}
$$

★12.
$$
\begin{cases}
Dy_j - \quad\quad\quad y_{j+1} = 0 \quad\quad\quad (j = 1, \cdots, n - 1), \\
Dy_n + \sum_{k=0}^{n-1} a_{n-k} y_{k+1} = 0,
\end{cases}
$$

where $a_1, \cdots, a_n$ are constants.

5-8. THE LAPLACE TRANSFORM

An operator which has considerable importance in applied mathematics, and in particular in the solution of differential equations, is known as the *Laplace transform* L, defined as follows. A pair (f, g) of real-valued functions is in L in case 1) the domain of f consists of all non-negative real numbers; 2) the domain of g consists of all real numbers x for which the improper integral $\int_0^\infty e^{-xt} f(t) \, dt$ exists; and 3) for every x in the domain of g,

$$
(5\text{--}32) \qquad\qquad g(x) = \int_0^\infty e^{-xt} f(t) \, dt.
$$

If f, g are complex-valued, so that $f = f_1 + if_2$, $g = g_1 + ig_2$, then (f, g) is in L in case (f_1, g_1) and (f_2, g_2) are in L.

It follows that, in all cases,

$$
(Lf)(x) = \int_0^\infty e^{-xt} f(t) \, dt,
$$

wherein the notation $(Lf)(x)$ means the function Lf evaluated at x. Thus L is real, linear, and single-valued, as is easily seen. We shall be concerned here only with the case in which f is continuous, and of *exponential order*, that is, f is such that $|f(t)| < Me^{at}$ when $t > c$, for some choice of real constants M, a, c. In this case, the domain of Lf includes all $x > c'$ for some c', since the integral in (5–32) may be proved to exist.

While L^{-1} is not single-valued, it does possess a property approaching single-valuedness, namely, if (g, f_1), (g, f_2) are in L^{-1} and if f_1, f_2 are continuous, then $f_1 = f_2$. We shall designate by

$L^{-1}g$ the unique continuous f such that $g = Lf$, provided it exists. In the table at the back of this book, the transforms Lf of many of the simpler functions are given. Inverse use of this table serves to produce functions $L^{-1}g$ for given functions g. The usefulness of the operators L and L^{-1} for our purpose stems from the following theorem, whose proof is sketched in the starred subsection on pages 159 and 160.

Theorem. Let $p(m)$ be a polynomial of degree n with constant coefficients $1 \ (=a_0), a_1, \cdots, a_n$. Let $y(x)$ and its first n derivatives be continuous for $x \geq 0$ and of exponential order. Finally, let $c_1 = y(0), \cdots, c_n = y^{(n-1)}(0)$. Then

$$(5\text{-}33) \qquad [(Lp(D))y](x) = p(x) \cdot [(Ly)(x)] - \sum_{k=1}^{n} c_k q_k(x),$$

where the $q_k(x)$ are polynomials given by

$$q_1 = x^{n-1} + a_1 x^{n-2} + \cdots + a_{n-1},$$
$$q_2 = x^{n-2} + a_1 x^{n-3} + \cdots + a_{n-2},$$
$$\cdots \cdots \cdots \cdots \cdots \cdots \cdots \cdots$$
$$q_{n-1} = x + a_1,$$
$$q_n = 1.$$

To use the theorem in solving (5-1), where f is in the domain of L, we apply L to both sides of (5-1) and obtain

$$(5\text{-}34) \qquad\qquad (Lp(D))y = Lf.$$

Substituting into (5-33) from (5-34), we have

$$p(x) \cdot [(Ly)(x)] = \sum_{k=1}^{n} c_k q_k(x) + (Lf)(x),$$

whence

$$(5\text{-}35) \qquad\qquad (Ly)(x) = \frac{\sum_{k=1}^{n} c_k q_k(x)}{p(x)} + \frac{(Lf)(x)}{p(x)}.$$

The function Ly is thus given by (5-35); it follows that y will be found as $L^{-1}(Ly)$, since y is to be continuous. Since L^{-1} is linear, it is clear from (5-35) that the usual form of y will emerge, namely, $\sum c_k y_k + y_f$.

Note. In using (5-35), if only a particular solution is desired, one applies L^{-1} only to the second term on the right side. If the complete solution is desired, and if Lf is a polynomial, the two terms on the right side are combined, and a partial fractions decomposition may be found. This leads to a sum, whence L^{-1} is applied to each term. If a solution is desired which meets initial conditions $y(0) = c_1, \cdots, y^{(n-1)}(0) = c_n$, with $c_1, \cdots, c_n$ given, this latter technique gives the desired solution.

In order to apply the present method, it is clear that the function f, so as to be in the domain of L, must have as its domain the set of all non-negative real numbers. In practice, the right side of (5–1) may be initially a function with a larger domain, for example, the set of all real numbers; in this case, the function is first replaced by its restriction to the requisite domain. In turn, the domain of any solution y which emerges will consist of all non-negative real numbers. In many cases, the solution may exist with a larger domain. Where the form of y suggests a larger domain, substitution in the equation will determine the maximal domain.

Example 5–18. Find a particular solution of $(D^2 - I)y = e^x$.

Solution: Here $p(x) = x^2 - 1$, $f(x) = e^x$ $(x \geq 0)$. Then from the table of Laplace transforms, we have $(Lf)(x) = 1/(x - 1)$, so that

$$g(x) = \frac{(Lf)(x)}{p(x)} = \frac{1}{(x - 1)^2(x + 1)}$$

$$= -\frac{1}{4} \cdot \frac{1}{x - 1} + \frac{1}{2} \cdot \frac{1}{(x - 1)^2} + \frac{1}{4} \cdot \frac{1}{x + 1}.$$

It follows, by inverse use of the table, that

$$y_f(x) = (L^{-1}g)(x) = -\frac{1}{4}e^x + \frac{1}{2}xe^x - \frac{1}{4}e^{-x} \qquad (x \geq 0).$$

Of course, only the term xe^x need be retained, since the others satisfy the associated homogeneous equation. That the function xe^x with the set of all real numbers as domain is a solution is easily verified by direct substitution in the given equation.

Example 5–19. Find the complete solution of $(D^2 - 3D + 2I)y = e^x \cos x$.

Solution: We have $p(x) = x^2 - 3x + 2$, $f(x) = e^x \cos x$ $(x \geq 0)$.

$$g(x) = \frac{(Lf)(x)}{p(x)} = \frac{x - 1}{[(x - 1)^2 + 1](x - 1)(x - 2)}$$

$$= \frac{1}{[(x - 1)^2 + 1](x - 2)}.$$

Decomposition takes the form

$$g(x) = \frac{Ax + B}{(x - 1)^2 + 1} + \frac{C}{x - 2},$$

and it follows that

$$1 = (Ax + B)(x - 2) + C[(x - 1)^2 + 1].$$

There result $A = -1/2$, $B = 0$, $C = 1/2$, so that

$$g(x) = -\frac{1}{2} \cdot \frac{x}{(x - 1)^2 + 1} + \frac{1}{2} \cdot \frac{1}{x - 2}$$

$$= -\frac{1}{2} \cdot \frac{x - 1}{(x - 1)^2 + 1} - \frac{1}{2} \cdot \frac{1}{(x - 1)^2 + 1} + \frac{1}{2} \cdot \frac{1}{x - 2}.$$

Therefore

$$y_f(x) = (L^{-1}g)(x) = -\frac{1}{2} e^x \cos x - \frac{1}{2} e^x \sin x + \frac{1}{2} e^{2x} \quad (x \geq 0).$$

The complete solution is given by

$$y = C_1 e^{2x} + C_2 e^x - \frac{1}{2} e^x (\cos x + \sin x),$$

in which the restriction $x \geq 0$ is omitted as justified by substitution in the given equation.

Example 5–20. Solve $y'' + y = e^x$ $(x \geq 0)$, given that $y'(0) = y(0) = 1$.

Solution: We have $p(x) = x^2 + 1$, $f(x) = e^x$ $(x \geq 0)$, $c_1 = c_2 = 1$, $q_1(x) = x$, $q_2(x) = 1$. Thus (5–35) becomes

$$(Ly)(x) = \frac{x + 1}{x^2 + 1} + \frac{1}{(x - 1)(x^2 + 1)} = \frac{1}{2} \cdot \frac{x + 1}{x^2 + 1} + \frac{1}{2} \cdot \frac{1}{x - 1}.$$

Hence

$$y(x) = \frac{1}{2} (\cos x + \sin x) + \frac{1}{2} e^x \qquad (x \geq 0).$$

Example 5-21. Solve $y' - y = x$ subject to the condition $y(1) = 2e - 2$.

Solution: Let $x = t + 1$ and designate $y(x) = y(t + 1)$ by $z(t)$. Then we have

$$\frac{dz}{dt} = \frac{dy}{dx} \cdot \frac{dx}{dt} = \frac{dy}{dx} .$$

The equation becomes $(D - I)z = t + 1$, subject to $z(0) = 2e - 2$. It follows that

$$(Lz)(t) = \frac{2e - 2}{t - 1} + \frac{1}{t - 1}\left(\frac{1}{t^2} + \frac{1}{t} \right),$$

whence

$$z(t) = 2(e - 1)e^t + e^t - t - 1 - (1 - e^t)$$
$$= 2e \cdot e^t - t - 2,$$
$$y(x) = 2e^x - x - 1.$$

*More on the Laplace Transform. It has been observed that continuous functions of exponential order are in the domain of L. This may be proved by investigating the existence of the improper integral in (5–32) in the following way. Suppose $|f(t)| < Me^{at}$ when $t > c$. Then

$$| e^{-xt}f(t) | < Me^{(a-x)t}.$$

For $x > a$, $\int_0^\infty Me^{(a-x)t}\, dt$ exists, since

$$\lim_{b \to \infty} \frac{Me^{(a-x)t}}{a - x}\bigg|_{t=0}^{t=b} = \frac{M}{x - a} .$$

It follows from the comparison test for integrals that the desired integral converges (absolutely).

The proof of the theorem of Section 5–8 may be made by induction. Suppose y, y' are of exponential order and continuous. Then, by integration by parts, we have

$$[L(Dy)](x) = \int_0^\infty e^{-xt}y'(t)\, dt = \lim_{b \to \infty} \int_0^b e^{-xt}y'(t)\, dt$$

$$= \lim_{b \to \infty} \left[e^{-xt}y(t)\bigg|_0^b + x\int_0^b e^{-xt}y(t)\, dt \right]$$

$$= -y(0) + x\int_0^\infty e^{-xt}y(t)\, dt,$$

whence

(5–36) $$(LDy)(x) = x \cdot [(Ly)(x)] - y(0).$$

Application of (5–36) to Dy in place of y gives

$$(LD^2y)(x) = x[(LDy)(x)] - y'(0)$$
$$= x^2[(Ly)(x)] - y(0)x - y'(0).$$

Proceeding inductively, we obtain, for $k = 0, \cdots, n$,

(5–37) $$(LD^ky)(x) = x^k[(Ly)(x)] - c_1 x^{k-1} - c_2 x^{k-2} - \cdots - c_k,$$

where $c_j = y^{(j-1)}(0)$ $(j = 1, \cdots, k)$. From (5–37), it follows by multiplication and summation, and use of the linearity of L, that

(5–38) $$[(Lp(D))y](x) = \left(\sum_{k=0}^{n} a_{n-k} x^k\right)[(Ly)(x)] - \sum_{k=1}^{n}\sum_{j=1}^{k} c_j a_{n-k} x^{k-j}.$$

But (5–38) may be written equivalently as (5–33), as the reader may readily show.

Further results concerning Laplace transforms are found in the exercises and in the many treatises on this subject.

EXERCISES

In each of exercises 1 to 4, verify the entry in the table for Lf corresponding to the given function f, by evaluating an appropriate integral.

1. $f(x) = 1.$
2. $f(x) = x.$
3. $f(x) = x^2.$
4. $f(x) = \cos ax.$

In each of exercises 5 to 8, use the methods of the present section to find a particular solution.

5. $(D^2 - 2D + I)y = 2e^x.$
6. $(D^2 + I)y = x \sin x.$
7. $(D^3 + I)y = e^x \sin x.$
8. $(D^4 + 16I)y = x^2 - 4 \cos 3x.$

In each of exercises 9 to 12, use the present method to find the complete solution.

9. $D^2(D - 2I)^2y = 16e^{2x}.$
10. $(D - 3I)^4y = x^2e^{3x}.$
11. $(D^4 - 2D^3 - D + 2I)y = x^2 - 2x^4.$
12. $(D^4 + 4D^3 + 4D^2)y = \cosh 2x.$

In each of exercises 13 to 18, use Laplace transforms to solve the equation, subject to the given initial conditions.

13. $(D^2 + 3D + 2I)y = 4x^2;$ $y(0) = y'(0) = 0.$

14. $(D^2 + 9I)y = 3x - 6;$ $y(0) = \dfrac{1}{3}, y'(0) = \dfrac{4}{3}.$

15. $D(D + 2I)y = 2x;$ $y(0) = 0, y'(0) = -\dfrac{1}{2}.$

16. $D^5 y = 5!;$ $y(0) = y'(0) = y''(0) = 0, y'''(0) = 3!,$
$$y^{iv}(0) = 4!.$$

17. $(2D + I)y = e^x;$ $y(2) = \dfrac{4}{3}e^2.$

18. $(D^2 + I)y = x^2;$ $y\left(\dfrac{\pi}{2}\right) = \dfrac{\pi^2}{4}, y'\left(\dfrac{\pi}{2}\right) = 2\pi.$

★19. Let $g(x) = e^{-ax}f(x).$ Show that
$$(Lg)(x) = (Lf)(x + a).$$

★20. Show that, if $f(x) = \sinh ax - \sin ax,$ then
$$(Lf)(x) = \dfrac{2a^3}{x^4 - a^4}.$$

★21. Prove in detail the inductive argument suggested on page 160 leading to (5–38), and show that (5–38) is equivalent to (5–33).

★22. By successive differentiation of the integral defining the Laplace transform, prove that, if $g(x) = x^n f(x),$ then
$$(Lg)(x) = (-1)^n(D^n Lf)(x) \qquad (n = 1, 2, \cdots).$$

★23. Determine whether the operators L and D commute.

★24. If f, g are given, it may be shown that
$$(Lf) \cdot (Lg) = Lh,$$

where $h(x)$ is the convolution integral given by
$$h(x) = \int_0^x f(x - t)g(t)\, dt.$$

Apply the method of Laplace transforms to

(4–3) $y' + ay = Q(x)$

and show, with the help of the result above, how the solution takes the form (4–9).

MISCELLANEOUS EXERCISES

In each of exercises 1 to 20, find the complete solution. Where initial conditions are given, find also the solution which satisfies them.

1. $y''' - y' = x^3 + e^{-2x}$.

2. $(D - I)^2 y = e^x \cos x$.

3. $x^2 y'' - xy' + 2y = \ln x$ (let $x = e^t$).

4. $y'' + y' = x + e^{-x}$ $[y(0) = y'(0) = 0]$.

5. $(D - I)^n y = x$ $(n = 1, 2, \cdots)$.

6. $y'' + y' - 2y = \ln x + 1$.

7. $(D^{10} + I)y = x^{10}$.

8. $(D - I)(D - 2I)(D - 3I) = e^x + e^{2x} + e^{3x}$.

9. $\begin{cases} (D - I)x - Dy = 0 \\ 3x + (D - 2I)y = 0. \end{cases}$ (The independent variable is t.)

10. $y'' + 3y' - 4y = 12e^{2x}$ $[y(0) = 2, y'(0) = 4]$.

11. $y'' - 2y' + y = \dfrac{e^{2x}}{(e^x + 1)^2}$.

12. $(D + aI)^n y = e^x$ $(a \ne -1; n = 1, 2, \cdots)$.

13. $(D^3 - 2D^2 + I)y = x^5 + 2x^2$.

14. $(D^2 + iI)y = \cosh x$.

15. $y'' + 4y = x - 4$ $\left[y(0) = \dfrac{1}{2}, y'(0) = 0 \right]$.

16. $(D^2 - 4D - 5I)y = x^2 e^{-x}$.

17. $(D^2 - D - I)y = \sinh x$.

18. $(D^6 + I)y = x^7 + 2x^3$.

19. $y'' + y = \cot x$.

20. $\begin{cases} x - y + Dz = 0, \\ Dx - y = 1, \\ (D - I)y + z = 0. \end{cases}$ (The independent variable is t.)

21. Show that

$$p_1(x) y'' + p_2(x)y' - (a^2 p_1(x) + a p_2(x))y = f(x)$$

may be solved by letting $y = e^{ax}v$.

22. Prove that Euler's equation

$$x^2 y'' + axy' + by = f(x),$$

where a, b are constants, may be solved with the help of the transformation $x = e^t$.

6

Applications of
Linear Differential Equations

6–1. PRELIMINARIES

In the natural sciences one frequently wishes to study the effects on, or behavior of, a system or device resulting from the imposition on it of certain external conditions. An admissible imposition of such external conditions may be called a *stimulus* or *input*, while the effects resulting therefrom may be called a *response* or *output*. Operationally, the natural situation under study may then be regarded abstractly as the correspondence between inputs and associated outputs.

Let us designate the set of all stimuli by $\mathcal{S}$ and the set of all responses by $\mathcal{R}$; also, let us designate by A the set of all pairs (f, y) with f in $\mathcal{S}$ and y in $\mathcal{R}$ such that y is a response associated with, or resulting from, the stimulus f. It is reasonable to call A an *operator*, even though here the objects f and y need not be functions as was demanded in Section 4–5. The definitions of domain, range, and single-valuedness given in Section 4–5 all apply here.

Abstractly the operator A may be identified with the physical system under study, for the purposes at hand. Thus a vending machine is a device that accepts as input a coin and produces as output a piece of merchandise or a coin. So far as the observable attributes are concerned, the machine is described fully by the set of pairs (f, y), where f is an admissible coin and y an associated output.

It is sometimes true that the operator is single-valued, but more often this is not the case. Thus any of a number of responses may result from a given input, depending on some additional factor or *side condition*. In the case of the vending machine, for example, the output corresponding to a given input depends on whether or not the machine is out of the merchandise.

In the study of certain mechanical systems, the applied force is the stimulus, and the resulting motions constitute the response. Similarly, in the study of electric networks, the input is one or more applied voltages, and the output consists of resulting currents.

In these and other examples, as we shall see, $\mathcal{S}$ and $\mathcal{R}$ consist of functions and the operator A is of the form $(p(D))^{-1}$. The problem of finding the responses corresponding to a given stimulus is then that of solving the differential equation (4–37), that is, $p(D)y = f$. It is in this way that many applications of the theory already presented in Chapters 4 and 5 are made possible. In the following sections several of these applications will be considered.

In every application the mathematical model used is an idealization of the natural phenomenon. Mathematical results obtained concerning the model are then but approximations to the properties of the real situation; applicability of the results will depend on the closeness with which the model represents the phenomenon for which it was constructed. In what follows, the idealizations involved should always be carefully noted.

6–2. LINEAR UNDAMPED SPRING OSCILLATORS

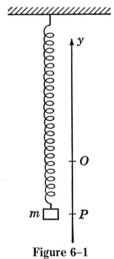

Consider a particle P of mass m attached to the end of a massless spring (Figure 6–1) and subjected to an applied force acting positively upward along the vertical and having component $f(t)$ at time t. Assume the lower end of the spring to be at the origin O when the spring is neither expanded nor compressed, and the y-axis to be directed vertically upward.

It is supposed that the spring tension obeys Hooke's law; thus the spring exerts upon P a force whose magnitude is proportional to the displacement of P from the origin and which acts in a direction opposite to that of the displacement. When P is displaced above O, the spring is compressed and exerts a force of magnitude $k\,|\,y\,|$

Figure 6–1

which is directed downward; when P is displaced below O, the spring is expanded and exerts a force of magnitude $k\,|\,y\,|$ directed upward. Here k is a positive constant whose value depends on the particular spring.

Newton's law of motion asserts that, at any time t,

(6-1) $$\mathbf{F} = m\mathbf{A},$$

where the vector $\mathbf{A}$ is the acceleration for P and the vector $\mathbf{F}$ is the total force acting upon P. Since $\mathbf{F}$ is the sum of the applied force and the tension force, and since these forces both act vertically, it suffices to consider only the vertical component of $\mathbf{F}$, and hence, by (6-1), of $\mathbf{A}$. Thus (6-1) yields

(6-2) $$f(t) - ky = m\frac{d^2y}{dt^2},$$

which may be written[1]

(6-3) $$m\ddot{y} + ky = f(t),$$

or

(6-4) $$(mD^2 + kI)y = f(t).$$

The term $-ky$ in (6-2) represents the vertical component of the tension force, since, as has been indicated, this component must be positive when y is negative and must be negative when y is positive.

Some of the idealizations involved in the derivation of (6-2) may be noted. First, we have assumed the spring to behave *linearly*, that is, that the tension force is given by Hooke's law. This law is only an approximation, reasonably good for certain springs constructed, say, of steel; it is valid even then only for small displacements. For example, a spring expanded nearly to or beyond its elastic limit does not obey Hooke's law, nor does one which is compressed close to its limit of compression. Secondly, we have assumed the spring to be without mass; our idealization in this respect will approximate reality only if the mass m is large when compared to the mass of the spring. Moreover, the total spring force is thus applied to P, while in reality a portion of this force is distributed throughout the spring to produce the motions of its mass particles. Finally, frictional effects, such as would result in energy losses through heating of the spring, are neglected. [The nature of this idealization would be clearer if (6-2) had been derived from the principle of conservation of energy.]

---

[1] Differentiation with respect to time is denoted by dots: $\dot{y} = \dfrac{dy}{dt}$, $\ddot{y} = \dfrac{d^2y}{dt^2}$, etc. The operator D is to be interpreted here as differentiation with respect to t.

In the notation of Section 6–1, $\mathcal{S}$ and $\mathcal{R}$ here are both equal to the set of all real-valued functions of the real variable t. The operator A is $(mD^2 + kI)^{-1}$. Since A is not single-valued, the response $y(t)$ corresponding to a given stimulus $f(t)$ is not unique. However, if one specifies an initial state of the system, that is, if one specifies y and $\dot{y}$ at an initial time, then a unique output corresponding to a given input may be found. Finally, A is linear, reflecting what has been called the linearity of the behavior of the spring.

Evidently (6–4) is a linear differential equation with constant coefficients of second order. The physical system, that is, the operator A, is completely described by the coefficients m and k; hence these are called the *system parameters*. (Units for k and m are such that ky and $m\ddot{y}$ have the units of a force.)

When $f(t)$ is the zero function, (6–4) represents the *non-forced* or *free* (also called *natural*) *oscillations* of the system. Indeed, from Section 4–3 we know that the complete solution of (6–4) with $f(t) = 0$ is given by

$$(6\text{–}5) \qquad\qquad y = C_1 \sin \omega t + C_2 \cos \omega t,$$

where $\omega = \sqrt{\dfrac{k}{m}}\,\cdot$ In order to see better the character of the free oscillations, we may rewrite (6–5) in the form

$$y = \pm\sqrt{C_1^2 + C_2^2}\left(\frac{C_1}{\pm\sqrt{C_1^2 + C_2^2}} \sin \omega t + \frac{C_2}{\pm\sqrt{C_1^2 + C_2^2}} \cos \omega t \right),$$

provided $C_1^2 + C_2^2 \neq 0$. If we define an angle ϕ_0 so that

$$\cos \phi_0 = \frac{C_2}{\pm\sqrt{C_1^2 + C_2^2}}, \quad \sin \phi_0 = \frac{C_1}{\mp\sqrt{C_1^2 + C_2^2}},$$

then we obtain further

$$(6\text{–}6) \qquad\qquad y = a \cos (\omega t + \phi_0),$$

where $a = \sqrt{C_1^2 + C_2^2}$. The zero function occurring in (6–5) for $C_1 = C_2 = 0$ occurs also in (6–6) for $a = 0$; hence every function in the family (6–5) appears in (6–6). The converse of this follows by expanding (6–6) and letting $C_1 = -a \sin \phi_0$, $C_2 = a \cos \phi_0$. Hence (6–5) and (6–6) are equivalent.

The interpretation of (6–6) as a particle motion can be seen from Figure 6–2. A point Q moves about the origin on a circle of radius a as shown. The central or polar angle θ is given by

$$\theta = \omega t + \phi_0,$$

so that $\dfrac{d\theta}{dt} = \omega$. Hence ω is the constant *angular velocity* of Q. If $P(0, y)$ is the projection of Q on the y-axis, then y is given by (6–6). The induced motion of P as the projection of a uniform circular motion is called *simple harmonic*. It follows that the free oscillations

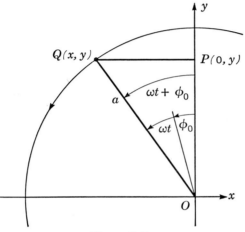

Figure 6–2

of our spring system are simple harmonic. The *period* of the motion is $2\pi/\omega$, and the *frequency* is the reciprocal of the period, namely,

$\dfrac{1}{2\pi}\sqrt{\dfrac{k}{m}}$ cycles per unit time. The angle $-\phi_0$ is called the *phase angle*.

Returning to (6–4), we recall that the complete solution is equal to a particular solution plus the complete solution of the associated homogeneous equation. Hence, every response of the system to the input $f(t)$ is composed of a particular response plus a term representing a free oscillation. Such a particular response, which depends on the function $f(t)$, may be regarded as superimposed upon the free oscillation, which depends only on the system parameters and the initial conditions; the two responses combine to produce the overall or composite output. Any appropriate method of Chapter 4 or 5 may be used to find the complete solution of (6–4) or a particular solution for which initial values $y(t_0)$ and $\dot{y}(t_0)$ are given.

The remarks of Section 6–1 suggest that the physical situation we have just analyzed is to be identified with the operator $A = (mD^2 + kI)^{-1}$, or more simply with the differential equation (6–4). The spring oscillator is called a *realization* of A or of (6–4). There are many other natural phenomena differing widely from this one which are nevertheless described by the same operator. These phenomena are said to be *equivalent*.[2] It suffices to study in detail only one of a class of equivalent phenomena, since all attributes of one are possessed by any other.

Example 6–1. A spring obeys Hooke's law. To expand it 1 inch beyond its natural length requires a force of 2 pounds. A weight of 3 pounds is attached to the lower end P of the vertically mounted spring. The applied force is that of gravity acting on the weight. At time $t = 0$ the spring is expanded 4 inches and the weight is at rest. Find the motion and the frequency of the free oscillation.

Solution: We may use Figure 6–1. Since the tension is $k\,|y|$, we have $2 = k \cdot \dfrac{1}{12}$, whence $k = 24$ (pounds per foot). Since the weight is 3 pounds, $m = \dfrac{3}{g} = \dfrac{3}{32}$ mass units (slugs). Equation (6–4) becomes

$$\left(\frac{3}{32} D^2 + 24I \right) y = -3.$$

We have

$$\omega = \sqrt{\frac{24 \cdot 32}{3}} = 16,$$

and the frequency of the free oscillation is $\dfrac{16}{2\pi} = \dfrac{8}{\pi}$ cycles per second.

The complete solution of the differential equation is

$$y = C_1 \sin 16t + C_2 \cos 16t - \frac{1}{8}.$$

Differentiation yields

$$\dot{y} = 16C_1 \cos 16t - 16C_2 \sin 16t.$$

[2]The term *equivalent* means what is frequently called *analogous*. Thus one speaks of a "mechanical analogy" of an electrical system, etc., referring to different realizations of the same operator.

When $t = 0$, $y = -1/3$ and $\dot{y} = 0$. Thus

$$\left\{ \begin{array}{l} -\dfrac{1}{3} = C_2 - \dfrac{1}{8}, \\[2mm] 0 = 16C_1. \end{array} \right.$$

The values of C_1 and C_2 may be substituted into the formula for y to give the desired solution,

$$y = -\frac{5}{24} \cos 16t - \frac{1}{8}.$$

In this case the composite output is obtained from the free oscillation by a simple translation.

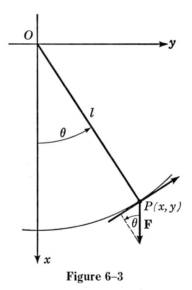

Figure 6-3

Example 6-2. A simple pendulum consisting of a mass m at the end P of a massless rigid rod mounted at the top O is free to move in a plane. Set up a differential equation for the motion. Assuming small displacements, find a spring oscillator approximately equivalent to the pendulum. Find the period.

Solution: In view of the given conditions, P must move in a circle about O as center. We employ polar coordinates as shown in Figure 6-3. The vector equation (6-1) applies; we resolve the vectors in it along OP and along the tangent to the circle. The former component is of no interest since $r = |OP| = l$ is constant.

The vector **F** has magnitude mg, whence its tangential component is $-mg \sin \theta$. The vector $m\mathbf{A}$ has x- and y-components $m\ddot{x}$ and $m\ddot{y} = 0$. Two differentiations of $x = l \cos \theta$, $y = l \sin \theta$ yield

$$\ddot{x} = -l \sin \theta \, \ddot{\theta} - l \cos \theta \, \dot{\theta}^2,$$

$$0 = \ddot{y} = l \cos \theta \, \ddot{\theta} - l \sin \theta \, \dot{\theta}^2.$$

Multiplying these equations respectively by $-\sin \theta$ and $\cos \theta$ and adding, we have

$$-\ddot{x} \sin \theta = l\ddot{\theta}.$$

The tangential component of $m\mathbf{A}$ is therefore

$$-m\ddot{x} \sin \theta = ml\ddot{\theta}.$$

Equating tangential components of **F** and $m\mathbf{A}$, we have $ml\ddot{\theta} = -mg \sin \theta$, or

$$l\ddot{\theta} + g \sin \theta = 0,$$

which is the desired equation.

If the values of θ are so small that $\sin \theta$ may be adequately approximated by θ, we have

$$l\ddot{\theta} + g\theta = 0.$$

A spring oscillator in which the mass, spring constant, and displacement are represented by l, g, and θ, respectively, is clearly (approximately) equivalent to the pendulum. All results concerning the spring oscillator may be applied to the pendulum. For example, the free motion is simple harmonic with period $2\pi \sqrt{\dfrac{l}{g}}$. Note that the pendulum is in fact a forced system, since the gravitational force is external; yet its spring equivalent is unforced.

EXERCISES

Exercises 1 to 4 refer to Example 6–1.

1. Find the central position in the motion of P and show that here the resultant force acting on P is zero.

2. Find the lowest and highest positions of P in its motion and show that at these points the velocity is zero and the magnitude of the resultant force on P is a maximum.

3. Solve the problem with the same conditions except that initially the spring is expanded 1.5 inches.

4. Solve the problem assuming that initially P is given an upward velocity of 40 inches per second.

5. Find the relationship between the mass m and the spring constant k if the natural frequency of a spring oscillator is to be 500 cycles per second.

6. A vibrating tuning fork is equivalent to a non-forced vibrating spring with mass 3 grams and spring constant $k = 480,000$ dynes per centimeter. Find the frequency.

7. The small oscillations of a simple pendulum have a period of 8 seconds. Find the length of the pendulum.

8. A mass m in the shape of a solid homogeneous cube of side a floats in a fluid to a depth of h feet. If the cube is displaced slightly downward, it will oscillate. Show this system to be equivalent to the oscillating spring. (HINT: The force on the lower face considered as a particle is the resultant of a downward force mg and an upward force equal to the area of the base times the pressure at the depth of the force; the pressure at depth d is d times the density of the fluid. Select the origin at the original depth h.)

9. List all idealizations that you can detect in the formulation of exercise 8.

10. In exercise 8, take $a = 15$ feet, assume that the cube weighs 500 pounds, and assume the fluid to be water having density 62.5 pounds per cubic foot. Write the differential equation and find the period of vibration.

11. It may be shown that a particle inside a homogeneous sphere is acted on by a force directed toward the center and having magnitude proportional to its distance from the center. Derive a differential equation of motion of a particle starting at rest at the surface and constrained to move along a diameter.

12. Apply exercise 11 to motion through the earth, determining the system parameters. Use the fact that at the surface the central force has magnitude equal to the weight of the particle at the surface; take the radius of the earth as 4000 miles. Find the speed of the particle when it reaches the center.

6–3. ALTERNATING-CURRENT NETWORKS

A *lumped-constant electric network* consists of a number of elements classed as voltage generators, current generators, resistors, capacitors, inductors, and transformers with indicated connections among them.

We shall consider the elementary circuit of Figure 6–4 in which a voltage generator applying an e.m.f. $E(t)$ at time t, a resistor R, a capacitor C, and an inductor L are connected in *series*. It is assumed that R, L, C are non-negative constants determining fully the operation of the system. It is further assumed that each element performs *linearly*, that is, if q is the charge on the capacitor at time t, then q/C, $R\dot{q}$, $L\ddot{q}$ are the "drops" in e.m.f. "across" the respective elements C, R, L. From elementary physics, we have that $E(t)$ is the sum of these drops in e.m.f., whence

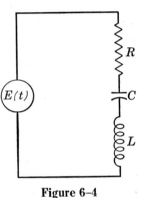

Figure 6–4

$$(6\text{–}7) \qquad\qquad L\ddot{q} + R\dot{q} + \frac{1}{C} q = E(t).$$

Here q is to be interpreted as a response of the system corresponding to the input $E(t)$.

Frequently one is concerned with the *current* $I = \dot{q}$ flowing in the circuit. If $E(t)$ is differentiable, every solution q of (6–7) having a third derivative must satisfy

$$L\dddot{q} + R\ddot{q} + \frac{1}{C}\dot{q} = \dot{E}(t),$$

or

$$(6\text{–}8) \qquad\qquad L\ddot{I} + R\dot{I} + \frac{1}{C} I = \dot{E}(t).$$

Relative to (6–8), the input to the system is $\dot{E}$, while I is an output.

The problems posed by (6–7) and (6–8) are of course equivalent. The *system parameters* in each case are the non-negative numbers L, R, $1/C$; it is assumed that $L \neq 0$, but that R and $1/C$ may be equal to 0. [Here $1/C = 0$ is understood to mean that in Figure 6–4 the capacitor is omitted and replaced by a direct connection, and that the term $(1/C) q$ or $(1/C) I$ is deleted from (6–7) or (6–8).]

A word about the units of the various quantities appearing is in order. Of the various systems in common use, we choose to use the so-called MKS practical units. Thus C is measured in farads, R in ohms, L in henrys, q in coulombs, I in amperes, E in volts, and t in seconds.

In solution of (6–7) or (6–8) we find the characteristic roots m_1, m_2 of $p(D) = \left(LD^2 + RD + \dfrac{1}{C} I \right)$ to be

(6–9)
$$m_1 = -\frac{R}{2L} + \frac{1}{2L}\sqrt{R^2 - \frac{4L}{C}},$$

$$m_2 = -\frac{R}{2L} - \frac{1}{2L}\sqrt{R^2 - \frac{4L}{C}}.$$

The complementary function based on these roots gives the *free* responses of the system.

Case 1. $R \neq 0$, $R^2 - 4L/C \geq 0$. It is clear from (6–9) that m_1 and m_2 are negative real numbers; hence the complementary function

$$C_1 e^{m_1 t} + C_2 e^{m_2 t} \quad \text{or} \quad (C_1 + C_2 t)e^{m_1 t}$$

approaches zero as t increases indefinitely, regardless of C_1 and C_2. Interpretation of this fact in the case of (6–7) is as follows: If $E(t) = 0$, and if somehow a charge q_0 is placed on the capacitor at time $t = 0$, so that $q(0) = q_0$, $\dot{q}(0) = 0$, the charge $q(t)$ will diminish with increasing time and will approach zero. This behavior is of course due to the large value of R^2 relative to $4L/C$. A similar interpretation exists in the case of (6–8) when $E(t)$ is a constant. When $R^2 - 4L/C > 0$, the system is called *overdamped*; when $R^2 - 4L/C = 0$, it is called *critically damped*.

Case 2. $R \neq 0$, $R^2 - 4L/C < 0$. Define

$$\alpha = \frac{R}{2L}, \quad \beta = \frac{1}{2L}\sqrt{\frac{4L}{C} - R^2}.$$

The complementary function is

(6–10)
$$e^{-\alpha t}(C_1 \cos \beta t + C_2 \sin \beta t),$$

or

$$a e^{-\alpha t} \sin (\beta t - \phi_0).$$

It follows that, if $E(t) = 0$ in (6–7), then the charge q is zero for all t or oscillates with amplitude $ae^{-\alpha t}$ decreasing with limit zero as t increases indefinitely. Thus the free responses constitute a family of *damped* or *decaying* oscillations with frequency $\beta/(2\pi)$. This frequency is called the *natural frequency* of the system. The interpretation for (6–8) is evident.

Case 3. $R = 0$. A separate treatment of this case is not needed, since the system is equivalent to the undamped oscillating spring of Section 6–2 with $k = 1/C$, $m = L$. The free responses are simple harmonic with frequency $\dfrac{1}{2\pi\sqrt{LC}}$. Since they do not approach zero in this case, we refer to the system as *undamped*.

Let us now consider the non-homogeneous case and limit attention to (6–8), first assuming $R \neq 0$. The complete solution is the sum $I_{\dot{E}} + I_0$ of a particular solution $I_{\dot{E}}$ and the complementary function I_0. An important special case is that in which the applied e.m.f. is *simple harmonic* (alternating), that is,

$$(6\text{--}11) \qquad\qquad E(t) = E_0 \sin \omega t,$$

with amplitude E_0 and frequency $\omega/(2\pi)$. Differentiation of (6–11), substitution in (6–8), and use of undetermined coefficients to determine a particular solution yield

$$(6\text{--}12) \qquad I_{\dot{E}} = \frac{E_0}{Z^2}\left[-\left(\omega L - \frac{1}{\omega C}\right)\cos \omega t + R \sin \omega t \right],$$

where

$$Z = \sqrt{R^2 + \left(\frac{1}{\omega C} - \omega L\right)^2}.$$

If we introduce an angle ϕ by the equations

$$\cos \phi = \frac{1}{Z}\cdot R, \quad \sin \phi = \frac{1}{Z}\left(\omega L - \frac{1}{\omega C}\right),$$

then (6–12) becomes

$$(6\text{--}13) \qquad\qquad I_{\dot{E}} = \frac{E_0}{Z}\sin(\omega t - \phi).$$

It is clear from (6–13) that the current $I_{\dot{E}}$ is an alternating current with the same frequency as E. The amplitude of $I_{\dot{E}}$ is the amplitude of E_0 divided by the constant Z, called the *impedance* of the system.

The impedance clearly depends on the frequency and takes on its minimum value R when $\dfrac{1}{\omega C} - \omega L = 0$, that is, when

$$\omega = \frac{1}{\sqrt{LC}}.$$

The corresponding frequency $\dfrac{1}{2\pi\sqrt{LC}}$ is called the *resonant* frequency of the system.

The undamped case $R = 0$ may be briefly disposed of. Here the system is equivalent to the undamped spring oscillator of Section 6-2, since (6-8), for example, is identical to (6-4) if m is identified with L, k with $1/C$, $f(t)$ with $E(t)$, and y with I. When $E(t)$ is simple harmonic, as in (6-11), the treatment leading to equation (6-12) giving a particular solution applies except when $\omega^2 = \dfrac{1}{LC}$. (For a discussion of this case, see Example 6-4.) Since no circuit is entirely free of resistance, behavior of the system when $R = 0$ is of little practical interest.

When $R \neq 0$, it is customary to refer to the solution $I_{\dot{E}}$ in (6-13) as the *steady-state* solution and to I_0 as the *transient* solution, since, regardless of initial conditions, the contribution of I_0 to I rapidly becomes negligible and I is approximated by $I_{\dot{E}}$. The steady-state solution may be characterized as the only simple harmonic solution. However, when $R = 0$, I_0 no longer approaches zero, and so this terminology is not appropriate.

It is frequently important to solve (6-8) when $E(t)$ is a sum of terms each of which is of the form (6-11):

$$E(t) = \sum_{k=1}^{n} E_k \sin \omega_k t.$$

In this case one may find a particular solution of (6-8) corresponding to each term of the sum and add the results. (See exercise 9 of Section 4-4.) The solution $I_{\dot{E}}$ so obtained is a sum of terms of the type appearing in the right side of (6-12) when $R \neq 0$ or when each $\omega_k \neq \dfrac{1}{\sqrt{LC}}$ if $R = 0$. Here again $I_{\dot{E}}$ is called the *steady-state* solution if $R \neq 0$.

In this situation, the amplitudes of the various terms constituting $I_{\dot{E}}$ depend on the corresponding ω_k. If $R \neq 0$, and one of the ω_k, say ω_1, is equal to $\dfrac{1}{\sqrt{LC}}$, then the amplitude of the first term will be much greater relative to E_1 than those of the other terms relative to the corresponding E_k. The effect of this disparity is to emphasize the response at frequency $\omega_1/(2\pi)$ over others which may be present. This role of resonance as a device to provide for frequency discrimination is of utmost importance in electronics; thus it provides for "tone controls" in audio amplifiers, for tuning devices for radio and television, and for attenuation of signals at undesired frequencies.

Example 6–3. In the *LRC*-network theory of the text determine the frequency of an applied alternating e.m.f. for which the amplitude of the steady-state current is maximum. Evaluate this frequency if $L = 1$ henry and $C = 0.01$ microfarads.

Solution: If E_0/Z is to be a maximum, Z^2 must be a minimum. But this occurs at the resonant frequency $\dfrac{1}{2\pi\sqrt{LC}}$. In this case, $Z = R$, $\phi = 0$, and

$$I_{\dot{E}} = \frac{E_0}{R} \sin \omega t = \frac{E(t)}{R}.$$

The output at this frequency is then the same as it would be if the network included only the resistor R.

When $L = 1$ and $C = 0.01 \cdot 10^{-6}$, the resonant frequency is given by

$$\frac{1}{2\pi\sqrt{LC}} = \frac{1}{2\pi\sqrt{10^{-8}}} = \frac{10^4}{2\pi},$$

or approximately 1592 cycles per second.

Example 6–4. Assume in (6–8) that $R = 0$ and that $E(t) = E_0 \sin \omega t$, where $\omega^2 = \dfrac{1}{LC}$. Discuss the solution in general. Then find the solution if[3] $I = I_0$ and $\dot{I} = 0$ when $t = 0$.

Solution: Since $\cos \omega t$ and $\sin \omega t$ satisfy the associated homogeneous equation, we use $At \cos \omega t + Bt \sin \omega t$ as a trial solution. The method of undetermined coefficients yields $A = 0$, $B = E_0/(2L)$.

[3]Here I_0 means a particular value of I, not the complementary function.

The complete solution is

$$I = C_1 \cos \omega t + C_2 \sin \omega t + \frac{E_0}{2L} t \sin \omega t,$$

or

$$I = a \sin (\omega t - \phi_0) + \frac{E_0}{2L} t \sin \omega t.$$

As t increases, the first term in this latter expression for I oscillates between $\pm a$, while the second term oscillates between increasingly large limits. Here I exhibits oscillations which "build up" indefinitely. If this situation, again called *resonance*, could occur in practice, it would result in ultimate component destruction. Application of the initial conditions yields $C_1 = I_0$, $C_2 = 0$, so that

$$I = I_0 \cos \omega t + \frac{E_0}{2L} t \sin \omega t.$$

Mechanical Equivalent of the Electric Network. It was noted that the RLC network with $R = 0$ is equivalent to the spring system of Section 6–2. Similarly, the general RLC network is equivalent to a damped spring system in which a retarding (possibly frictional) force proportional to y is present. (See Figure 6–1). In this case, we have

(6–14) $$f(t) - ky - \gamma \dot{y} = m\ddot{y},$$

where the *damping constant* γ is positive in order to produce a retarding effect on the motion. Upon rewriting (6–14), we have

(6–15) $$m\ddot{y} + \gamma \dot{y} + ky = f(t).$$

The problem of treating (6–15) is precisely the problem which was discussed in this section, provided we identify m with L, γ with R, k with $1/C$. If (6–15) is to correspond to (6–7), then $f(t)$ is identified with $E(t)$ and y with q. Similar correspondence with (6–8) is also possible.

In particular, if the forcing function is harmonic, $f(t) = f_0 \cos \omega t$, then the motions of the spring are given by the responses found for the electrical system. There are concepts of resonant frequency, mechanical impedance, and so on. In the undamped case, if the forcing function is harmonic with frequency equal to the natural frequency of the system, oscillations increase indefinitely in amplitude, as shown in Example 6–4. This case of "mechanical resonance" would quickly result in destruction of the spring.

★**Use of Complex Functions; Transfer Functions.** It has been shown (see pages 138 and 139 and exercises 9 and 10 of Section 5–4) that a real linear equation $p(D)y = f(x)$ may be solved by first solving $p(D)z = f + ig$ and taking y as the real part of the solution z. In the case of (6–7) with $R \neq 0$, where $E = E_0 \cos \omega t$, let us consider the equation

$$p(D)z = L\ddot{q} + R\dot{q} + \frac{1}{C} q = E_0 (\cos \omega t + i \sin \omega t) = E_0 e^{i\omega t}.$$

We may refer to the *complex e.m.f.* $\mathcal{E} = E_0 e^{i\omega t}$ as the *complex input.* If we neglect the transient part of the solution, we obtain, by the method of undetermined coefficients,

$$\mathcal{Q} = \frac{E_0 e^{i\omega t}}{-L\omega^2 + R\omega i + 1/C} = \frac{E_0 e^{i\omega t}}{p(i\omega)} = \frac{\mathcal{E}}{p(i\omega)}.$$

Note that, since ω is real and $R \neq 0$, $p(i\omega) \neq 0$. If we call $\dfrac{1}{p(i\omega)}$ the *transfer function* of the system, and if the solution $\mathcal{Q}$ obtained is called the *complex steady-state output,* or simply the (*complex*) *output,* then we have

$$\text{output} = (\text{transfer function}) \cdot \text{input.}$$

Thus the transition from input to output is achieved by simple multiplication by a numerical function.

If this same procedure is applied to (6–8), input may be taken as

$$\dot{\mathcal{E}} = \frac{d}{dt} (E_0 e^{i\omega t}) = E_0 i\omega e^{i\omega t}.$$

The transfer function is then again $\dfrac{1}{p(i\omega)}$. The transition from $\mathcal{E}$ to the complex steady-state current $\mathcal{J}$ satisfying $p(D)\mathcal{J} = \dot{\mathcal{E}}$ is given by

$$\mathcal{J} = \frac{\mathcal{E}}{\mathcal{Z}},$$

where the quantity

$$\mathcal{Z} = \frac{p(i\omega)}{i\omega} = R + i\left(\omega L - \frac{1}{\omega C} \right)$$

is called the *complex impedance* of the system. The absolute value of $\mathcal{Z}$ is what we have called the impedance earlier and designated by Z. Expressing the complex impedance in polar form, we obtain

$\mathcal{Z} = Ze^{i\phi}$, where ϕ is the same angle as appears in (6–13). This angle is referred to as the *phase* angle of the system. When $1/C = 0$, ϕ may be chosen so that $0 \le \phi < \pi/2$, and the current in an LR-network "lags behind" the e.m.f. by ϕ; when $L = 0$, we choose ϕ so that $-\pi/2 < \phi \le 0$, and the current in an RC-network "leads" the e.m.f. by ϕ. (Note exercise 8 in the following group.) Generally, the sign of ϕ depends on the relative values of ωL and $\dfrac{1}{\omega C}$; at resonance, there is no phase shift, since $\phi = 0$. In electrical theory, $\cos \phi$ is called the *power factor* of the network.

The significance of the equation $\mathcal{J} = \mathcal{E}/\mathcal{Z}$ is that it generalizes to LRC-networks the familiar Ohm's law $I = E/R$, which applies to resistive networks. The generalization is valid only when $\mathcal{E}$ and $\mathcal{J}$ are simple harmonic; in that case it not only relates, as does the impedance Z, the amplitudes of input and output but also furnishes information concerning the phase relationship. Without essential use of the complex numbers, such a generalization would not be possible.

EXERCISES

1. Find the steady-state current in an LRC-network in which $L = 0.5$ henrys, $R = 500$ ohms, $C = 1$ microfarad, and $E = E_0 \sin \omega t$ and in which the frequency is 60 cycles per second.

2. Work exercise 1 assuming the frequency is 1000 cycles per second.

3. Find the impedance Z of the network of exercise 1 at the frequency of 60 cycles per second and at the frequency of 1000 cycles per second. Then find the natural and resonant frequencies.

4. Find the natural and resonant frequencies of an LRC-network in which $L = 3.125$ henrys, $R = 50,000$ ohms, $C = 0.004$ microfarads.

5. Find the steady-state current in an LRC-network in which $L = 0.005$ henrys, $R = 1000$ ohms, $C = 0.0004$ microfarads, and E is given as in exercise 1 with frequency equal to $1/(2\pi)$ megacycles per second.

6. In case $1/C = 0$, show that equation (6–7) becomes $L\dot{I} + RI = E(t)$. If $E(t)$ is given by (6–11), show directly that (6–12) gives the steady-state solution.

7. In exercise 6 assume that $L = 1$ henry and $R = 1$ ohm; plot a graph of the impedance as a function of ω.

8. In (6–8) let $L = 0$. Solve directly the resulting first-order equation when $E = E_0 \sin \omega t$. Show that the steady-state solution is again given by (6–12).

9. In exercise 8 assume that $C = 1$ farad and $R = 1$ ohm; plot a graph of the impedance as a function of ω.

10. Find the value of R so that a network with L in henrys equal to C in microfarads will be critically damped.

11. A spring lies on a horizontal table. One end is fixed, and the other is free to move along the line of the spring taken as the x-axis. A weight of 8 pounds is attached to the free end. The spring constant is 0.5 pounds per inch and the damping force is $2\dot{x}$, where $\dot{x}$ is measured in feet per second. Find the motion if at time $t = 0$ the spring is stretched 2 inches and released.

12. The spring in exercise 11 is suspended vertically. At $t = 0$, the amount of stretch is that due to the hanging weight and the initial velocity is 4 inches per second downward. Assume the same damping constant and find the motion. Also find the lowest point reached by the weight.

★13. In (6–13) find the two frequencies for which the amplitude of $I_{\dot{E}}$ is one-half its amplitude at resonance. Show that the difference of these frequencies is $\sqrt{3} \dfrac{R}{2\pi L}$; also show that one of these frequencies is greater than the resonant frequency and one is less than the resonant frequency.

★14. In exercise 13 show that the ratio of the difference found to the resonant frequency is $\sqrt{3}\,R/Q$, where $Q = \sqrt{\dfrac{L}{C}}$. (For a given value of R, Q measures the "sharpness" of the resonance. But for given Q, the sharpness decreases as R increases.)

★15. In an LRC-network, $C = 50 \cdot 10^{-12}$ farads. The resonant frequency is to be $10.7 \cdot 10^6$ cycles per second, and the *bandwidth* (difference of the frequencies in exercise 13) is to be $3 \cdot 10^5$ cycles per second. Find L and R.

★16. In exercise 1 replace the e.m.f. by a complex e.m.f. and find the complex impedance and hence the complex steady-state current. Hence find the solution to exercise 1.

★17. An RC-network has, at 60 cycles per second, a power factor of 0.5. Find R if $C = 0.1$ microfarads. Find the power factor of the same network at 120 cycles per second.

★18. In an LRC-network, the complex input is $\sum\limits_{k=1}^{n} \mathscr{E}_k$, where $\mathscr{E}_k$ $= E_k e^{i\omega_k t}$. Show that the complex steady-state current is given by

$$\mathscr{I} = \sum_{k=1}^{n} \frac{\mathscr{E}_k}{\mathscr{Z}_k},$$

where the $\mathscr{Z}_k$ are suitable complex impedances. Interpret these impedances and give a formula for them.

6–4. APPLICATIONS OF SYSTEMS OF EQUATIONS

When description of the behavior of an applied system requires more than one function, and several conditions define the relationship between stimulus and response, then $\mathscr{S}$ may consist of vectors $\mathbf{f}(t) = (f_1(t), \cdots, f_m(t))$, whose components are functions, and $\mathscr{R}$ may similarly consist of vectors $\mathbf{y}(t) = (y_1(t), \cdots, y_n(t))$. As in Section 6–1, one may refer to the set of pairs $(\mathbf{f}, \mathbf{y})$ for which $\mathbf{y}$ is a response associated with the stimulus $\mathbf{f}$ as an operator A. For the most part we shall limit attention to the case $m = n$ and assume that the operator A is such that $\mathbf{y} = A\mathbf{f}$ if and only if

$$(6\text{--}16) \qquad \sum_{j=1}^{n} p_{ij}(D)y_j = f_i(t)$$

for some choice of polynomials p_{ij}. The methods of Section 5–7 for the solution of linear systems apply here.

Multiple Spring Oscillators. Consider three springs with constants k_1, k_2, k_3 situated and connected as shown in Figure 6–5 and having

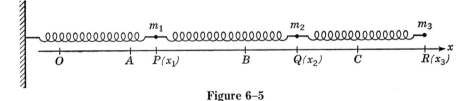

Figure 6–5

masses m_1, m_2, m_3 attached to their respective right ends. The left end of the first spring is fixed. The springs lie on a line, the x-axis, and are constrained to move on that line. It is assumed for simplicity that there are no damping forces. Designate the endpoints of the springs, assuming the springs neither extended nor compressed, by A, B, C. When the springs are stretched (or compressed), points A, B, C are displaced to P, Q, R, respectively. Denote by x_1, x_2, x_3 the respective algebraic lengths AP, BQ, CR. The deformations of the springs are then $x_1, x_2 - x_1, x_3 - x_2$.

When the springs take on a general configuration, the force on m_3 is

$$m_3 \ddot{x}_3 = -k_3(x_3 - x_2),$$

where the negative sign indicates that the force is negatively directed. The force on m_2 is the resultant of two forces oppositely directed: $k_3(x_3 - x_2)$, representing the tension in the third spring and directed positively, and $-k_2(x_2 - x_1)$, representing the tension in the middle spring and directed negatively. Hence

$$m_2 \ddot{x}_2 = k_3(x_3 - x_2) - k_2(x_2 - x_1).$$

Similarly,

$$m_1 \ddot{x}_1 = k_2(x_2 - x_1) - k_1 x_1.$$

Equations describing the motion are thus

$$
\begin{cases}
[m_1 D^2 + (k_1 + k_2)I\,]x_1 & -k_2 x_2 & = 0, \\
-k_2 x_1 + [m_2 D^2 + (k_2 + k_3)I\,]x_2 & -k_3 x_3 = 0, \\
-k_3 x_2 + [m_3 D^2 + k_3 I\,]x_3 = 0.
\end{cases}
$$

Upon elimination there will arise a linear equation of order 6 for each of x_1, x_2, x_3. Of the total of eighteen constants which appear, twelve will be expressible in terms of the others. Specification of initial conditions giving $x_1, x_2, x_3, \dot{x}_1, \dot{x}_2, \dot{x}_3$ for $t = 0$ leads to a unique solution, as may be shown by applying the theorem on page 120.

A similar method is applicable to the same problem with n springs. Also, introduction of damping leads to no serious complications.

Example 6–5. Solve the problem of the text for two springs, given $k_1 = 3$, $k_2 = 2$, $m_1 = m_2 = 1$ in suitable units. Assume that initially the second spring is stretched 1/2 unit and released.

Solution: The system analogous to (6–16) becomes

$$
\begin{cases}
(D^2 + 5I)x_1 - & 2x_2 = 0, \\
-2x_1 + (D^2 + 2I)x_2 = 0.
\end{cases}
$$

When $t = 0$, the mass m_1 is in equilibrium, so that $5x_1(0) = 2x_2(0)$. Thus, since $x_2 = 1/2$ initially, we have $x_1(0) = 1/5$, $x_2(0) = 1/2$, $\dot{x}_1(0) = \dot{x}_2(0) = 0$. Elimination yields

$$\Delta(D)x_1 = (D^4 + 7D^2 + 6I)x_1 = 0,$$
$$\Delta(D)x_2 = (D^4 + 7D^2 + 6I)x_2 = 0.$$

It follows that

$$x_1 = C_1 \cos t + C_2 \sin t + C_3 \cos \sqrt{6}\,t + C_4 \sin \sqrt{6}\,t,$$
$$x_2 = C_5 \cos t + C_6 \sin t + C_7 \cos \sqrt{6}\,t + C_8 \sin \sqrt{6}\,t.$$

Substitution in the given equations gives

$$C_5 = 2C_1, \quad C_6 = 2C_2, \quad C_3 = -2C_7, \quad C_4 = -2C_8.$$

Moreover, the initial conditions imply

$$C_1 = \frac{6}{25}, \quad C_3 = -\frac{1}{25}, \quad C_5 = \frac{12}{25}, \quad C_7 = \frac{1}{50},$$

$$C_2 = C_4 = C_6 = C_8 = 0.$$

The desired solution is thus given by

$$x_1 = \frac{6}{25} \cos t - \frac{1}{25} \cos \sqrt{6}\,t,$$

$$x_2 = \frac{12}{25} \cos t + \frac{1}{50} \cos \sqrt{6}\,t.$$

Although neither x_1 nor x_2 is a periodic function of t, since the periods of the separate terms are not commensurable, there are two periods present, namely, 2π and $2\pi/\sqrt{6}$. The corresponding frequencies, $1/(2\pi)$ and $\sqrt{6}/(2\pi)$, are called the *frequencies* of the system. Their relationship to the characteristic roots of $\Delta(D)$ should be noted.

Multiple Electric Networks. The single-branch network theory of Section 6–3 may be extended to the case of more branches. Here one has a number of vertices or junctions, certain ordered pairs of which are designated as joined. Each such pair is connected with a directed path consisting of one or more elements such as we have met, namely, inductors, capacitors, resistors, and generators, joined in series. The equations defining the relationship between input (impressed e.m.f.'s at the generators) and outputs (currents flowing in the branches) are derived in each instance by application of *Kirchhoff's laws*:

1. The sum of the currents entering a vertex is zero.
2. The sum of drops in e.m.f. around every closed loop is zero.

It is understood that in the first law, currents along paths directed away from the vertex must be prefixed with negative signs prior to the summation. Similarly, in the second law, when proceeding along a path in the direction opposite to that of the path, one attaches negative signs to the drops in e.m.f. before summation.

Example 6–6. Suppose a capacitor and resistor are connected in series and the combination is connected in parallel with an inductor. An e.m.f. $E(t)$ is impressed across the parallel combination. Set up a system of equations for the currents in the branches. Solve the system, given $E(t) = 0$. Refer to Figure 6–6.

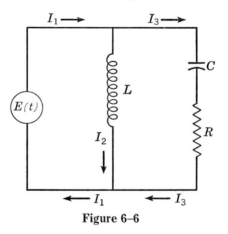

Figure 6–6

Solution: Assign arbitrary directions to the paths and indicate currents as shown. Assign also (arbitrarily) a direction to the generator $E(t)$ so that the downward drop across it is "positive." Using Kirchhoff's first law, we have $I_1 - I_2 - I_3 = 0$. From the second law applied to the left loop we have $-E(t) + L \dfrac{dI_2}{dt} = 0$; similarly, applying the second law to the large loop, we have

$-E(t) + RI_3 + \dfrac{1}{C} \displaystyle\int_0^t I_3 \, d\tau = 0$. These equations become, after differentiation of the last,

$$\begin{cases} I_1 - I_2 \quad - \quad I_3 = 0, \\ L\dot{I}_2 \qquad\qquad = E(t), \\ R\dot{I}_3 + \dfrac{1}{C} I_3 = \dot{E}(t). \end{cases}$$

The desired values of I_2 and I_3 are then given by

$$I_2 = \frac{1}{L} \int_0^t E(\tau)\, d\tau + c_2,$$

$$I_3 = c_3 e^{-t/(RC)} + e^{-t/(RC)} \int_0^t e^{\tau/(RC)} \frac{\dot{E}(\tau)}{R}\, d\tau,$$

while I_1 is their sum.

If $E(t) = 0$, then $I_2 = c_2$, $I_3 = c_3 e^{-t/(RC)}$. Thus, if at time $t = 0$ initial currents $I_2(0)$ and $I_3(0)$ are present, then

$$I_2 = I_2(0), \quad I_3 = I_3(0)e^{-t/(RC)}, \quad I_1 = I_2(0) + I_3(0)e^{-t/(RC)}.$$

(The reason for the decay in I_3 is the loss of energy in heat in the resistor as the capacitor discharges, while no such loss occurs to cause decay in I_2.)

In this system, the input may be regarded as the single function $E(t)$, while an output is a vector function $(I_1(t), I_2(t), I_3(t))$. Alternatively, the input could be thought of as the vector function $(0, E(t), \dot{E}(t))$, so as to bring the problem into harmony with the basic remarks at the beginning of this section.

The Two-Body Problem. An important problem in mechanics underlying the theory of the motions of planets, satellites, double-stars and the like is that of determining the relative motions of two particles subject to Newton's law of attraction. This problem actually leads to a non-linear system of equations; however, the solution employs the theory of linear equations. We shall formulate the problem mathematically and then carry out the solution in detail.

Select a coordinate system (see Figure 6–7) so that the origin remains coincident with one particle O with mass m_1. The other particle P, with mass m_2, is the point (x, y, z) at time t. The force on P is the vector $\mathbf{f}$ directed toward O, whose magnitude is $\dfrac{km_1m_2}{r^2}$, where k is the gravitational constant and $r = \sqrt{x^2 + y^2 + z^2}$. Denote the vector $\overrightarrow{OP}$ by $\mathbf{r}$. Then we have the vector equation

$$m_2 \ddot{\mathbf{r}} = \mathbf{f}.$$

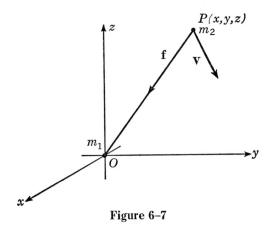

Figure 6–7

If this is written in component form, we have

$$
\left\{
\begin{array}{l}
m_2 \ddot{x} = -\dfrac{km_1m_2}{r^2} \cdot \dfrac{x}{r}, \\[2mm]
m_2 \ddot{y} = -\dfrac{km_1m_2}{r^2} \cdot \dfrac{y}{r}, \\[2mm]
m_2 \ddot{z} = -\dfrac{km_1m_2}{r^2} \cdot \dfrac{z}{r},
\end{array}
\right.
$$

or

(6–17)
$$
\left\{
\begin{array}{l}
\ddot{x} = -\dfrac{km_1x}{r^3}, \\[2mm]
\ddot{y} = -\dfrac{km_1y}{r^3}, \\[2mm]
\ddot{z} = -\dfrac{km_1z}{r^3}.
\end{array}
\right.
$$

Suppose that the coordinate system is so chosen that at $t = 0$ P is the point $(a, 0, 0)$, where $a \neq 0$, and so that the velocity vector **v** lies in the xy-plane. The theorem on page 120 shows that the system (6–17) has a unique solution $(x(t), y(t), z_1(t))$ defined for t in an interval about 0 satisfying the indicated initial conditions. By these conditions, we have $z_1(0) = \dot{z}_1(0) = 0$. We shall prove first that the motion takes place in the xy-plane, that is, that $z_1(t)$ is the zero function.

Suppose that $z_1(t) \neq 0$, and substitute $(x(t), y(t), z_1(t))$ into the third equation in (6–17). Since r becomes a function of t, we may write the result as

$$\ddot{z}_1(t) + F(t)z_1(t) = 0.$$

Consider now the equation

(6–18) $$\ddot{z} + F(t)z = 0.$$

This equation is linear, and so it possesses a unique solution $z(t)$ such that $z(0) = \dot{z}(0) = 0$; moreover, this function $z(t)$ is the zero function (see page 121). But we have seen that $z_1(t)$ also satisfies (6–18) together with the same initial conditions. Hence $z_1(t) = 0$, contrary to the assumption.

Since $z = 0$, we may delete the last equation in (6–17) and treat the problem in the xy-plane, using the simplified system

(6–19)
$$\begin{cases} \ddot{x} = -\dfrac{km_1 x}{r^3}, \\[2ex] \ddot{y} = -\dfrac{km_1 y}{r^3}. \end{cases}$$

The presence of r suggests transformation of (6–19) into polar coordinate form by

(6–20)
$$\begin{cases} x = r\cos\theta, \\ y = r\sin\theta. \end{cases}$$

Two differentiations of (6–20), followed by substitution into (6–19), yield

(6–21)
$$\begin{cases} \ddot{r}\cos\theta - 2\dot{r}\sin\theta\,\dot{\theta} - r\cos\theta\,\dot{\theta}^2 - r\sin\theta\,\ddot{\theta} = -\dfrac{km_1\cos\theta}{r^2}, \\[2ex] \ddot{r}\sin\theta + 2\dot{r}\cos\theta\,\dot{\theta} - r\sin\theta\,\dot{\theta}^2 + r\cos\theta\,\ddot{\theta} = -\dfrac{km_1\sin\theta}{r^2}. \end{cases}$$

Multiplication of these equations by $\cos\theta$, $\sin\theta$, respectively, followed by addition, and similar procedure using the multipliers $-\sin\theta$, $\cos\theta$, respectively, yield

(6–22) $$\ddot{r} - r\dot{\theta}^2 = -\frac{km_1}{r^2},$$

(6–23) $$2\dot{r}\dot{\theta} + r\ddot{\theta} = 0.$$

Actually, similar combinations of (6–22) and (6–23) lead to (6–21), whence (6–21) is equivalent to the pair (6–22), (6–23). It is assumed that P remains outside a region about the origin.

Integration of (6–23) is immediate, since (6–23) is equivalent to $\dfrac{d}{dt}(r^2\dot{\theta}) = 0$. The result is

$$(6\text{--}24) \qquad\qquad r^2\frac{d\theta}{dt} = h.$$

If A represents the area bounded by the x-axis, the path of P, and the segment OP, then (6–24) states

$$(6\text{--}25) \qquad\qquad \frac{dA}{dt} = \frac{1}{2}h.$$

Kepler's famous law of areas, that OP "sweeps out" equal areas in equal time intervals, is contained in (6–25). We shall assume $h \neq 0$.

Substitution from (6–24) into (6–22) gives

$$(6\text{--}26) \qquad\qquad \ddot{r} - \frac{h^2}{r^3} = -\frac{km_1}{r^2}.$$

Now (6–26) may be integrated readily to give r as a function of t. The result may then be substituted into (6–24) to provide an equation for θ as a function of t. Parametric equations for r and θ as functions of t so obtained would describe the motion fully. (See exercises 18, 19 in the group which follows.) We shall content ourselves with a determination of the relationship between r and θ along the path.

To this end, we transform (6–26) with the help of (6–24) in order to make θ the independent variable. We have

$$\dot{r} = \frac{dr}{d\theta}\cdot\frac{d\theta}{dt} = \frac{dr}{d\theta}\cdot\frac{h}{r^2},$$

$$\ddot{r} = \frac{d\dot{r}}{d\theta}\cdot\frac{d\theta}{dt} = \left[\frac{d^2r}{d\theta^2}\cdot\frac{h}{r^2} - \frac{2h}{r^3}\left(\frac{dr}{d\theta}\right)^2\right]\frac{h}{r^2},$$

and so (6–26) becomes

$$(6\text{--}27) \qquad \frac{h}{r^2}\cdot\frac{d^2r}{d\theta^2} - \frac{2h}{r^3}\left(\frac{dr}{d\theta}\right)^2 - \frac{h}{r} = -\frac{km_1}{h}.$$

Substituting $r = 1/u$ in (6–27) gives

$$(6\text{--}28) \qquad\qquad \frac{d^2u}{d\theta^2} + u = \frac{km_1}{h^2}.$$

The complete solution of (6–28) is given by

(6–29) $$u = C \cos (\theta - \alpha) + \frac{km_1}{h^2} ;$$

hence

(6–30) $$r = \frac{h^2/(km_1)}{1 + [Ch^2/(km_1)] \cos (\theta - \alpha)} ,$$

and it follows from analytic geometry that the path is a conic with the origin as one focus. The eccentricity is

(6–31) $$e = \frac{|C| h^2}{km_1} ,$$

and the (major or transverse) axis of the conic makes an angle α with the x-axis. The constants C and α are determined by imposing the initial conditions.

In order to determine the constants C, α, h in (6–30), it is simpler to use (6–29) and the following equations relating a $[=x(0) = r(0)]$ and the components v_x, v_y of the initial velocity vector $\mathbf{v_0}$:

(6–32)
$$\begin{cases} v_y = \dfrac{dy}{dt} = \dfrac{dr}{dt} \sin \theta + r \cos \theta \dfrac{d\theta}{dt} = \dfrac{h}{a} & \text{(at } t = 0), \\[2ex] v_x = \dfrac{dx}{dt} = \dfrac{dr}{dt} \cos \theta - r \sin \theta \dfrac{d\theta}{dt} = \dfrac{dr}{dt} & \text{(at } t = 0), \\[2ex] \dfrac{du}{d\theta} = \dfrac{du}{dt} \Big/ \dfrac{d\theta}{dt} = -\dfrac{1}{r^2} \cdot \dfrac{dr}{dt} \Big/ \dfrac{h}{r^2} = -\dfrac{1}{h} v_x = -\dfrac{1}{a} \cdot \dfrac{v_x}{v_y} \\[1ex] & \text{(at } t = 0). \end{cases}$$

It is found that $h = av_y$, and

(6–33)
$$C \sin \alpha = -\frac{1}{a} \cdot \frac{v_x}{v_y} ,$$
$$C \cos \alpha = \frac{1}{a} - \frac{km_1}{a^2 v_y^2} ,$$

from which C and α may be determined.

It is thus seen that the orbit (path) of the one particle P about the other particle O is an ellipse, a hyperbola, or a parabola. If one neglects gravitational attractions of other bodies in the universe, and if one assumes that the sun, planets, and satellites behave as particles, then one may conclude that the orbit of a planet is an ellipse with the sun at the focus. A satellite moves about its planet in similar fashion. If a non-returning comet may be regarded as a particle, it will move in a hyperbolic orbit.

Example 6–7. In the two-body problem find the path if $v_x = 0$.

Solution: When $v_x = 0$, the initial velocity vector is perpendicular to the x-axis. From (6–33) we have

$$\alpha = 0, \quad C = \frac{1}{a} - \frac{km_1}{a^2 v_y^2}.$$

The initial position of P is that of a vertex. Except in the parabolic case, this vertex is the one nearer to O if

$$\frac{km_1}{a} < v_y^2,$$

since then $C > 0$; it is the one farther from O if

$$\frac{km_1}{a} > v_y^2.$$

Equation (6–30) may be written

$$r = \frac{a^2 v_y^2/(km_1)}{1 \pm e \cos \theta}.$$

By (6–31) and the fact that $h = av_y$, we have

$$e = \left| \frac{av_y^2}{km_1} - 1 \right|.$$

Now if $av_y^2 < km_1$, then $e = 1 - av_y^2/(km_1) < 1$, so that the orbit is an ellipse; in other words, if the initial position of P is at the vertex farther from O, then the path is an ellipse. Thus, if the orbit is hyperbolic, it must lie on the branch near to O.

On the other hand, if $av_y^2 > km_1$, then $e = av_y^2/(km_1) - 1$; in this case the orbit is elliptic, parabolic, or hyperbolic according as

$$v_y^2 < \frac{2km_1}{a}, \quad v_y^2 = \frac{2km_1}{a} \quad \text{or} \quad v_y^2 > \frac{2km_1}{a}.$$

Note that the elliptic case above is included here also. The special case $av_y^2 = km_1$ evidently leads to a circular orbit.

Example 6–8. Discuss the possibility of a circular motion in the two-body problem.

Solution: If the motion of P is to be circular, the origin will be the center and the initial conditions of Example 6–7 apply. Moreover, $e = 0$ if and only if

$$av_y^2 = km_1.$$

Since r is constant and equal to a, it follows from (6–24) and (6–32) that $\dfrac{d\theta}{dt}$ is constant and equal to v_y/a. Hence $\theta = (v_y/a)t$ (since $\theta = 0$ when $t = 0$). But $v_y = \sqrt{\dfrac{km_1}{a}}$, so that polar parametric equations of the motion are given by

$$\begin{cases} r = a \\ \theta = \sqrt{\dfrac{km_1}{a^3}}\, t. \end{cases}$$

The period of motion is $2\pi\sqrt{\dfrac{a^3}{km_1}}$. From this result, it follows that the period of P depends not on the mass of P but on that of O and on the distance $|OP|$. It is also clear that the square of the period is proportional to the cube of the radius a; this is a special case of Kepler's third law.

EXERCISES

1. Solve the problem of Example 6–5 with modified initial conditions as follows: the right end of the second spring is held fixed at its normal position, while its left end is moved to the left $1/2$ unit. At $t = 0$ both ends are released.

2. Solve the problem of Example 6–5 with modified spring constants $k_1 = 5$, $k_2 = 6$. Find the frequencies of the system.

3. Solve the problem of exercise 1 using $k_1 = 5$, $k_2 = 6$.

4. Solve the problem of Example 6–5 if both springs are initially pulled to the right $1/2$ unit and released.

5. In the spring problem of the text designate the frequencies of the system by $\omega_1/(2\pi)$, $\omega_2/(2\pi)$, $\omega_3/(2\pi)$. Find an algebraic equation satisfied by ω_1, ω_2, ω_3 and find an expression for $\omega_1^2 \cdot \omega_2^2 \cdot \omega_3^2$ in terms of the system parameters m_1, m_2, m_3, k_1, k_2, k_3.

6. In the network of Figure 6–6 find I_2, I_3, I_1 if $E(t) = E_0 \sin \omega t$, $I_2(0) = -E_0/(\omega L)$, $I_3(0) = 0$. Find also the ratio Z of the amplitudes of E and the steady-state current I_1.

7. An inductor L and a capacitor C are connected in parallel; a generator $E(t)$ and a resistor R are connected in series. The two combinations are connected in parallel. Set up a system of differential equations for the currents and find the complete solution in the case $E(t) = 0$.

8. An inductor L, a resistor R, a capacitor C, and a generator $E(t)$ are all connected in parallel. Set up a system of differential equations for the currents, and find the complete solution in the case $E(t) = 0$.

9. In exercise 8 assume $E(t) = E_0 \cos \omega t$. When $t = 0$, the current in the branch containing the inductor is 0. Find the total current I in the branch containing the generator.

10. In exercise 9 plot a graph of the amplitude of I as a function of ω. (Assume $L = R = C = 1$ for convenience.) In the general case, determine ω so that this amplitude is a minimum.

11. Two inductors L_1 and L_2 are connected in parallel, and across the combination is connected a generator $E(t)$. Find the value L of a single inductor which may replace the given pair so as to produce the same current in the branch containing the generator.

12. Work exercise 11 for capacitors.

13. In the theory of the two-body problem it was assumed that $h \neq 0$. Show that this means $v_y \neq 0$. If $v_y = 0$, show that in (6–17) $y = 0$, so that only the first equation is needed to determine the motion, and P moves along the x-axis.

14. Transform (6–24) to rectangular coordinates.

In exercises 15 to 17 regard the earth as a particle and take $km_1 = 1.5 \cdot 10^{16}$ in fps (foot, pound, second) units. Use 4000 miles as the earth's radius.

15. A satellite revolves about the earth in an elliptic orbit of eccentricity 0.1. At perihelion (nearest vertex), it is 500 miles from the earth's surface. Find the speed of the satellite at the perihelion.

16. A satellite travels about the earth in a circular orbit. Its speed is 20,000 feet per second. Find its height above the earth's surface.

17. How fast would a satellite have to travel in a circular orbit about the earth if it just skimmed the surface of the earth?

★18. In the theory of the two-body problem, carry through an integration of (6-26). Use the method of Example 2-15.

★19. Integrate (6-24) to relate θ and t in the elliptic case. Use (6-30).

★20. Carry through a development of the two-body problem, assuming an attractive force with magnitude directly proportional to the distance between the particles. In particular, discuss the possibility of circular motions.

★21. Set up differential equations for a plane motion of P about the origin, assuming a force on P directed toward the origin, with magnitude equal to a function of r. Transform to polar coordinates and prove the areal property $r^2\dot{\theta} = $ constant.

MISCELLANEOUS EXERCISES

1. A substance A is changing into a substance B and is losing mass at a unit rate proportional to the amount of A present. The substance B is radioactive and losing mass at a unit rate proportional to the amount of B present. Find the masses of A, B as functions of time.

2. Solve exercise 1 assuming that B is stable.

3. It takes Jupiter 11.9 years to complete a revolution about the sun. Find its distance from the sun. (Assume circular orbits for Jupiter and the earth.)

4. The impedance of an RC network at 15,000 cycles per second is 500 ohms. At 50 cycles per second it is 10,000 ohms. Find R and C.

5. A damped spring oscillator as in Figure 6-1 has mass 1, spring constant 1, and damping constant 4, all in suitable units. When $t = 0$, the spring is stretched 3 units beyond its natural length and released. Find the displacement. Assume no external forces.

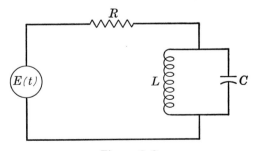

Figure 6-8

6. Work exercise 5 assuming a gravitational force $mg = g$. Let units be so chosen that $g = 2$.

7. Find the steady-state current through R if $E(t) = E_0 \cos \omega t$, where $R = 1000$ ohms, $L = 5$ henrys, $C = 0.01$ microfarads, and $\omega = 2\pi \cdot 120$. See Figure 6–8.

8. In case of the plane motion (6–19) show that the difference of the kinetic energy $(1/2)m_2(\dot{x}^2 + \dot{y}^2)$ and the potential of the field is a constant.

9. A particle moves in the xy-plane so that $\ddot{x} = -k^2x$, $\ddot{y} = -k^2y$, $x(0) = a$, $y(0) = 0$, $\dot{x}(0) = 0$, $\dot{y}(0) = v$. Find the motion and identify the path. Determine whether Kepler's law of areas holds.

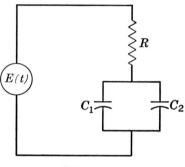

Figure 6–9

10. By analyzing the network of Figure 6–9 show that the parallel-connected capacitors C_1 and C_2 may be replaced by a single capacitor C to obtain an equivalent system. Prove that $C = C_1 + C_2$.

11. In the theory of planetary motion, assume an elliptic orbit and prove that the period of the motion is $2\pi\sqrt{\dfrac{\delta^3}{km_1}}$, where δ is the average of the greatest and least distances of P from O. [HINT: Use (6–25) and the fact that the area of an ellipse is $\pi\alpha\beta$, where α, β are the semi-axes.]

12. Generalize exercise 8 to the case of an arbitrary conservative plane force field.

13. Set up a system of differential equations for the currents in the branches of the bridge network shown in Figure 6–10. Assume an alternating e.m.f. $E(t)$ and show that the steady-state current through R is zero if and only if $R_1/R_2 = C_2/C_1$. This is the case of balance of the bridge.

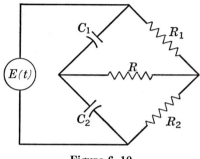

Figure 6-10

14. In the network shown in Figure 6-11, each box A indicates a network consisting of L, R, C as shown, the four networks being identical. Show that if one network A is connected between P and Q, replacing the combination of four, the resulting system is equivalent to the original.

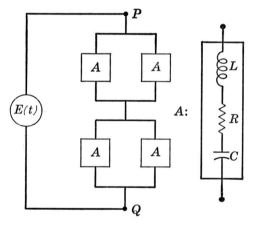

Figure 6-11

7

Series Methods

7-1. PRELIMINARIES

The possibility of expressing solutions of differential equations by infinite series was explored by Newton as early as 1676. It is the purpose of this chapter to provide an introduction to this subject. Also, in Section 7-6, a somewhat different approach to approximate solution of differential equations is developed.

It has been seen that determination of solutions of differential equations "in closed form," that is, in a simple way in terms of elementary functions, is possible only in a relatively limited number of cases. For example, the equation $y' = e^{-x^2}$ does not possess a solution expressible in a form involving only a finite number of operations on simple elementary functions.[1] Since the existence theorem of Section 1-4 guarantees that a solution of this equation exists, it is important to find some way of representing such a solution.

That it is reasonable to search for solutions of differential equations in series form is indicated by the theory of algebraic numerical equations. An equation of second (or higher) degree with rational coefficients may be known to have a real root, though such real root need not be rational. It is clear that irrational numbers cannot be expressed in terms of rational numbers by a finite number of applications of the "rational" operations—addition, multiplication, subtraction, and division. While various representations are possible, the most common and best known representation is that by series. Thus

$$\pi = 3.14159 \cdots = 3. + 0.1 + 0.04 + 0.001$$
$$+ 0.0005 + 0.00009 + \cdots$$

is a series representation of the irrational number π. In an analogous way we may expect that solutions of $y' = e^{-x^2}$ and many other

---

[1] Included here are the algebraic operations, composition (taking functions of functions) and inversion. The elementary functions referred to are the algebraic, trigonometric, and exponential functions.

equations may be found in series form. Also, it may happen that an equation for which no other mode of solution is known will be found to have series solutions which are recognizable as representing elementary functions.

There are many types of series in use, the best known kinds being *power series* and *Fourier series*. The latter type will be considered in Section 7–7, but most of our attention will center about power series.

If a power series $\sum_{n=0}^{\infty} a_n(x - x_0)^n$, or possibly $\sum_{n=0}^{\infty} a_n(x - x_0)^{n+\alpha}$ with α real, is to be constructed so as to satisfy a given differential equation, three questions arise. First, how are the a_n determined; secondly, for what values of x does the series converge; and thirdly, is the function so defined actually a solution of the given equation, relative to a domain consisting of the interval of convergence of the series, or possibly a smaller interval?

We recall here for reference an important theorem from calculus which bears on power series representation of functions.

Taylor's Theorem. If a function $f(x)$ and its first $n - 1$ derivatives are continuous for $x_1 \leqq x \leqq x_2$, and if the nth derivative exists for $x_1 < x < x_2$, then, for every a and x such that $x_1 < a < x_2$ and $x_1 \leqq x \leqq x_2$, there exists a number u, with $a < u < x$ or $x < u < a$, such that

$$(7\text{–}1) \qquad f(x) = \sum_{k=0}^{n-1} \frac{f^{(k)}(a)}{k!}(x - a)^k + \frac{f^{(n)}(u)}{n!}(x - a)^n,$$

where $f^{(0)}(x)$ as usual means $f(x)$.

Taylor's theorem provides a way of approximating the value of a function at a point of its domain by means of its value and the values of its first $n - 1$ derivatives at a neighboring point. It also suggests that if all of the derivatives of a function f are continuous on a certain interval, then it may be possible to represent the function by the *Taylor series*

$$(7\text{–}2) \qquad \sum_{k=0}^{\infty} \frac{f^{(k)}(a)}{k!}(x - a)^k.$$

Whether or not this is the case depends on whether the last term in the right side of (7–1) approaches zero. This term is called the *remainder after n terms*. In case $a = 0$, the series (7–2) is called a *Maclaurin series*.

Power series in $x - a$, such as that in (7–2), are known to converge either for all x or for all x such that $-h < x - a < h$ (possibly also for $x - a = h$ or $-h$ or both). The case $h = 0$ can occur, but we shall agree that use of the term *Taylor series* or *Maclaurin series* always implies $h \neq 0$.

7–2. FIRST SERIES METHOD

Let us apply the ideas of the last section to the problem of solving a differential equation of order n of the form

(7–3) $$y^{(n)}(x) = F(x, y, y', \cdots, y^{(n-1)}),$$

in which $F(x, u_0, \cdots, u_{n-1})$ is a function defined over a suitable domain and satisfying differentiability conditions adequate for the following considerations.[2] Initial conditions of the form

(7–4) $$y(a) = a_0, \quad y'(a) = a_1, \cdots, y^{(n-1)}(a) = a_{n-1},$$

with $(a, a_0, a_1, \cdots, a_n)$ in the domain of F, are appended to (7–3).

Suppose $y(x)$ is a solution (with a suitable domain) satisfying (7–3) and (7–4). Then, by (7–3),

(7–5) $$y^{(n)}(a) = F(a, a_0, a_1, \cdots, a_{n-1}).$$

To obtain $y^{(n+1)}(a)$, we differentiate (7–3); the result is

(7–6) $$y^{(n+1)}(x) = F_x + \sum_{k=0}^{n-1} F_{y^{(k)}} \, y^{(k+1)}(x),$$

in which we have written $F_{y^{(k)}}$ for $F_{u_k}(x, y(x), \cdots, y^{(n-1)}(x))$. Substituting $x = a$ into (7–6), and using (7–4) and (7–5), we obtain $y^{(n+1)}(a)$. Repeating this process, we compute the value at $x = a$ of each succeeding derivative of $y(x)$.

The given and computed values of $y(a)$, $y'(a)$, $\cdots$, $y^{(n-1)}(a)$, $y^{(n)}(a)$, $\cdots$ may be used as coefficients in a Taylor series (7–2). It is to be hoped that the function represented by this series in its interval of convergence will prove to be the solution function. The argument completed shows that a necessary condition for a solution of (7–4) and (7–5) to be represented by a Taylor series is that the

---

[2] The domain of F should be a *connected open* set of vectors $(x, u_0, u_1, \cdots, u_{n-1})$. It is required also that at each point of its domain F shall have differentials of all orders.

coefficients in this series be those found. No claim has been made that this condition is sufficient for the series to be a solution. The sufficiency must be verified in each case.

Example 7–1. Find the solution of $y' = y$, $y(a) = a_0$ in Taylor series form.

Solution: Successive differentiation of the given equation yields $y^{(k)}(x) = y(x)$. It follows that $y^{(k)}(a) = a_0$ ($k = 0, 1, 2, \cdots$). The desired series is thus given by

$$z(x) = \sum_{k=0}^{\infty} \frac{a_0(x - a)^k}{k!} = a_0 \sum_{k=0}^{\infty} \frac{(x - a)^k}{k!}.$$

It is easy to show by the Cauchy ratio test that this series converges for all x; in fact, it is the Taylor series for the function $a_0 e^{x-a}$, and so there is no difficulty in demonstrating that for every choice of a_0 the series is a solution of the given equation.

Without reference to the closed form of the representation for the function we can show directly that the series is a solution in the following manner. If a series $\sum_{k=0}^{\infty} a_k(x - a)^k$ converges to a function $g(x)$ for $|x| < b$, then $\sum_{k=1}^{\infty} k a_k(x - a)^{k-1}$ converges to g' for $|x| < b$, as may be proved.[3] Therefore, if

$$z(x) = \sum_{k=0}^{\infty} a_0 \frac{(x - a)^k}{k!},$$

then

$$z'(x) = \sum_{k=1}^{\infty} a_0 \frac{(x - a)^{k-1}}{(k - 1)!} = z,$$

and $z(x)$ is a solution of the given equation. Since $z(a) = a_0$, we have shown that the desired solution $y(x)$ coincides with $z(x)$.

Finally, note that, if $a_0 = 0$, then the obvious solution $y = 0$ is obtained. It is of course clear that the solutions of this equation could have been obtained by several other and simpler methods.

---

[3] We cannot say more than that the derivative series converges in the interior of the interval of convergence of the given series, even though the latter converges at one or both endpoints. Proofs of this theorem may be found in books on advanced calculus.

Example 7-2. Solve $y' = e^{-x^2}$ by means of Maclaurin series.

Solution: For any solution $y(x)$ we must have

$$y'' = -2xe^{-x^2} = -2xy',$$
$$y''' = -2xy'' - 2y',$$
$$y^{iv} = -2xy''' - 4y'',$$
$$y^v = -2xy^{iv} - 6y'''.$$

One may reasonably conjecture that

$$(7\text{-}7) \qquad y^{(n)} = -2xy^{(n-1)} - 2(n-2)y^{(n-2)} \qquad (n \geqq 3).$$

It is easy to substantiate (7-7) by induction. Equation (7-7) is known to be true for $n = 3$. If $k \geqq 3$, and if (7-7) holds for $n = k$, then

$$y^{(k)} = -2xy^{(k-1)} - 2(k-2)y^{(k-2)}.$$

Hence

$$y^{(k+1)} = \frac{d}{dx}\, y^{(k)} = -2xy^{(k)} - 2y^{(k-1)} - 2(k-2)y^{(k-1)}$$
$$= -2xy^{((k+1)-1)} - 2((k+1)-2)y^{((k+1)-2)},$$

so that (7-7) is true for $n = k + 1$. Hence (7-7) holds for all $n \geqq 3$.

Now if we seek a solution in powers of x such that $y(0) = a_0$, we observe that, by the given equation and (7-7),

$$y'(0) = e^0 = 1, \quad y''(0) = (-2)\cdot 0 \cdot y'(0) = 0.$$

Again by (7-7),

$$y^{(n)}(0) = (-2)(n-2)y^{(n-2)} \qquad (n \geqq 3).$$

It follows that $y^{iv}(0) = y^{vi}(0) = \cdots = y^{(2k)}(0) = 0$. Moreover, for $k \geqq 1$,

$$y^{(2k+1)}(0) = (-2)(2k-1)y^{(2k-1)}(0)$$
$$= (-2)(2k-1)(-2)(2k-3)y^{(2k-3)}(0)$$
$$= (-2)(2k-1)(-2)(2k-3)(-2)(2k-5)y^{(2k-5)}(0)$$
$$= \cdots = (-1)^k 2^k (2k-1)(2k-3) \cdots 3 \cdot 1.$$

The Maclaurin series becomes

$$z(x) = a_0 + x + \sum_{k=1}^{\infty} \frac{(-1)^k \cdot 2^k \cdot 1 \cdot \cdots \cdot (2k-1)}{(2k+1)!}\, x^{2k+1}$$

$$= a_0 + x + \sum_{k=1}^{\infty} \frac{(-1)^k x^{2k+1}}{k!(2k+1)}.$$

This series $z(x)$ is readily shown to converge for all x and is in fact simply the series obtained by integrating term by term the Maclaurin series for e^{-x^2}; clearly, then, $z'(x) = e^{-x^2}$, so that $y = z(x)$ is the desired solution of the equation.

Example 7–3. Find a Maclaurin series solution of $y' = xy$ such that $y(0) = 1$.

Solution: From the given equation it is easy to show that $y'(0) = 0$ and

$$y^{(n)} = xy^{(n-1)} + (n-1)y^{(n-2)} \qquad (n \geq 2).$$

Then $y''(0) = 1 \cdot y(0) = 1$. Furthermore, since

$$y^{(n)}(0) = 0 \cdot y^{(n-1)}(0) + (n-1)y^{(n-2)}(0),$$

it is clear that $y^{(n)}(0) = 0$ if n is odd. If n is even, then it must be true that $y^{(n)}(0) = (n-1)(n-3) \cdots 5 \cdot 3 \cdot 1$.

Hence, consider the series

$$z(x) = 1 + \sum_{k=1}^{\infty} \frac{1 \cdot 3 \cdot \cdots \cdot (2k-1)}{(2k)!} x^{2k} = \sum_{k=0}^{\infty} \frac{x^{2k}}{2^k k!}.$$

The ratio test shows that this series converges for all x. Finally,

$$z'(x) = \sum_{k=1}^{\infty} \frac{2k x^{2k-1}}{2^k k!} = x \sum_{k=1}^{\infty} \frac{x^{2(k-1)}}{2^{k-1}(k-1)!} = x \sum_{k=0}^{\infty} \frac{x^{2k}}{2^k k!} = x f(x),$$

and so $y = z(x)$ is the desired solution.

Difficulties arise in the attempt to find by this method the Taylor coefficients for a solution $y(x)$ of the equation of Example 7–3 subject to the condition that $y(1) = 1$. From the relationship

$$y^{(n)}(1) = 1 \cdot y^{(n-1)}(1) + (n-1)y^{(n-2)}(1) \qquad (n = 2, 3, \cdots),$$

the value which each derivative must have at $x = 1$ may be obtained from the value of the preceding derivatives at $x = 1$. Unfortunately, $y^{(n)}(1)$ is not a simple function of n. Since the recursion relationship is expressed in terms of three derivatives, it appears to be difficult, or perhaps impossible, to exhibit the Taylor coefficients in a form useful for the consideration of questions of the convergence of the series. This kind of difficulty, met here in a simple equation, seriously limits the scope of this method. (Again it should be noted that solutions of this equation can be obtained easily by the methods of Chapter 2.)

EXERCISES

In each of the following exercises, find the general solution of the equation by obtaining solutions in Maclaurin series form. Determine the interval of convergence of each series and verify that the solution obtained satisfies the equation for every x in this interval.

1. $4y'' + x^2y' - xy = 0.$

2. $y'' - 2xy' + y = 0.$

3. $(1 - x^2)y' + 3xy = 0.$

4. $(1 - x^2)y'' - 2xy' + 20y = 0.$ [NOTE: This equation and those in exercises 5 and 6 are special cases of Legendre's equation $(1 - x^2)y'' - 2xy' + a(a + 1) = 0.$]

5. $(1 - x^2)y'' - 2xy' + 56y = 0.$

6. $4(1 - x^2)y'' - 8xy' + 3y = 0.$

7. $(x^2 + 2)y'' + 3xy' - y = 0.$

8. $y'' + 3x^3y' + x^2y = 0.$

9. $(8 + x^3)y'' + 3x^2y' + xy = 0.$

10. $(x^3 - 8)y'' - 4xy = 0.$

11. $y''' - x^2y'' - 2y = 0.$

12. $(1 - x^4)y''' - 24xy = 0.$

7–3. SECOND SERIES METHOD

Another method for obtaining power series solutions of differential equations (7–3), which often proves more efficient than the method of Section 7–2, will now be developed. Instead of constructing the series by Taylor's formula, we use a technique of undetermined coefficients.

Example 7–4. Find a Maclaurin series solution of the equation $y' = xy$ of Example 7–3 such that $y(0) = a_0$.

Solution: Let us assume that the desired solution takes the form $y(x) = \sum\limits_{n=0}^{\infty} a_n x^n$, where the a_n $(n = 0, 1, \cdots)$ are to be determined, and the series converges in a suitable interval. The derivative series $\sum\limits_{n=0}^{\infty} na_n x^{n-1}$ converges in the same interval to $y'(x)$. The condition that $y(x)$ is a solution becomes

(7-8) $$\sum_{n=1}^{\infty} na_n x^{n-1} = x \sum_{n=0}^{\infty} a_n x^n$$

$$= \sum_{n=0}^{\infty} a_n x^{n+1} = \sum_{n=2}^{\infty} a_{n-2} x^{n-1}.$$

[Note that the last expression in (7-8) is obtained from the preceding one by a mere shift of index according to the following:

$$\sum_{n=0}^{\infty} a_n x^n = \sum_{n=k}^{\infty} a_{n-k} x^{n-k} \qquad (k = 0, 1, 2, \cdots).$$

The shift is made so that the comparison of coefficients of like powers of x may be more easily made.] In order that (7-8) hold, it is necessary and sufficient that each coefficient in the first expression be equal to the corresponding coefficient in the final expression. (See exercise 13 of the group at the end of this section.) Thus $a_1 = 0$, and $na_n = a_{n-2}$ for all $n \geq 2$. Therefore we have

$$a_1 = a_3 = \cdots = a_{2k-1} = 0,$$

and

$$a_2 = 2^{-1}a_0, \quad a_4 = 4^{-1}a_2, \quad a_6 = 6^{-1}a_4, \cdots ,$$
$$a_{2k} = (2k)^{-1}a_{2k-2} \qquad (k = 1, 2, \cdots).$$

Eliminating $a_2, a_4, \cdots , a_{2k-2}$, we have

$$a_{2k} = (2^k k!)^{-1} a_0.$$

It follows that the series

$$y(x) = a_0 \sum_{k=0}^{\infty} \frac{x^{2k}}{2^k k!}$$

gives a solution whose domain is at least the interior of the interval of convergence. It was noted in the solution of Example 7-3 that the series converges for all values of x.

It should be observed that, in attempting to solve the equation of Example 7-4 in the form $\sum_{n=0}^{\infty} a_n(x - 1)^n$, the same difficulty as appeared in Section 7-3 arises. The equation may be rewritten as $y' = (x - 1)y + y$. Conditions on the a_n are obtained from the relationship

$$\sum_{n=0}^{\infty} na_n(x-1)^{n-1} = \sum_{n=0}^{\infty} a_n(x-1)^{n+1} + \sum_{n=0}^{\infty} a_n(x-1)^n,$$

or

$$\sum_{n=1}^{\infty} na_n(x-1)^{n-1} = \sum_{n=2}^{\infty} a_{n-2}(x-1)^{n-1} + \sum_{n=1}^{\infty} a_{n-1}(x-1)^{n-1}.$$

These requirements are met if $a_1 = a_0$ and $na_n = a_{n-2} + a_{n-1}$ ($n \geq 2$). While the a_n are determined by these conditions, the question of the interval of convergence of the series is still open. The difficulty, as in the use of the first method on this problem, lies in the three-term recursion formula.

Henceforth we shall restrict our attention to series in powers of x. When series in powers of $(x - a)$ are desired, the translation $X = x - a$ is employed. Since $\dfrac{d^n y}{dx^n} = \dfrac{d^n y}{dX^n}$, the original equation is easily replaced by one in y and X, and solutions of this equation can be sought in powers of X.

Example 7–5. Solve

(7–9) $$(x^2 - 4)y'' - 3xy' + 4y = 0.$$

Solution: For comparison we present both methods to obtain power series solutions.

Method 1. Let $y = \sum_{n=0}^{\infty} a_n x^n$. In order that y be a solution of the equation, it is necessary and sufficient that

$$\sum_{n=0}^{\infty} n(n-1)a_n x^n = \sum_{n=0}^{\infty} 4n(n-1)a_n x^{n-2}$$

$$- \sum_{n=0}^{\infty} 3na_n x^n + \sum_{n=0}^{\infty} 4a_n x^n = 0,$$

or

$$\sum_{n=2}^{\infty} [(n-2)(n-3) - 3(n-2) + 4] a_{n-2} x^{n-2}$$

$$= \sum_{n=0}^{\infty} 4n(n-1)a_n x^{n-2}.$$

Equating coefficients of x^0 gives $4 \cdot 0 \cdot (-1)a_0 = 0$, and so a_0 may be chosen arbitrarily. Similarly, equating coefficients of x gives $4 \cdot 1 \cdot 0 \cdot a_1 = 0$, and a_1 also may be chosen arbitrarily. Finally, equating coefficients of x^n for $n \geq 2$, we have

$$[(n-2)(n-3) - 3(n-2) + 4]a_{n-2} = 4n(n-1)a_n,$$

or

$$(n-4)^2 a_{n-2} = 4n(n-1)a_n.$$

It follows that

$$a_2 = \frac{(-2)^2}{4 \cdot 2 \cdot 1} a_0, \quad a_4 = 0, \quad 0 = a_6 = \cdots = a_{2k} = \cdots \quad (k \geq 3);$$

$$4 \cdot 3 \cdot 2a_3 = (-1)^2 a_1, \quad 4 \cdot 5 \cdot 4a_5 = 1^2 a_3, \quad 4 \cdot 7 \cdot 6a_7 = 3^2 a_5, \quad \cdots,$$

$$4(2k+1)2ka_{2k+1} = (2k-3)^2 a_{2k-1} \quad (k = 1, 2, \cdots),$$

so that

$$a_{2k+1} = \frac{[(-1) \cdot 1 \cdot 3 \cdot \cdots \cdot (2k-3)]^2}{4^k (2k+1)!} a_{2k-1} \quad (k = 1, 2, \cdots).$$

Hence

$$(7\text{-}10) \quad y = a_0 + a_1 x + \frac{a_0}{2} x^2$$

$$+ a_1 \sum_{k=1}^{\infty} \frac{[(-1) \cdot 1 \cdot 3 \cdot \cdots \cdot (2k-3)]^2 x^{2k+1}}{4^k (2k+1)!}.$$

Choosing successively $a_0 = 1$, $a_1 = 0$, and $a_0 = 0$, $a_1 = 1$, we obtain two solutions,

$$y_1 = 1 + \frac{1}{2} x^2, \quad y_2 = x + \sum_{k=1}^{\infty} \frac{[(-1) \cdot 1 \cdot 3 \cdot \cdots \cdot (2k-3)]^2 x^{2k+1}}{4^k (2k+1)!},$$

such that $y = a_0 y_1 + a_1 y_2$. The theory of series tells us that the series for y converges if those for y_1 and y_2 do. If $a_0, a_1 \neq 0$, the domain of y is the common part of those of y_1 and y_2; here y_1 is a polynomial, and so the domain of y is that of y_2, namely, $|x| < 2$. If $a_0 \neq 0$, $a_1 = 0$, then y converges for all values of x, and the same is of course true if $a_0 = a_1 = 0$. If $a_0 = 0$, $a_1 \neq 0$, then again the domain of y is that of y_1. The presence of two arbitrary coefficients corresponds to the fact that $y(0)$ and $y'(0)$ may be arbitrarily prescribed, since, by (7-10), $a_0 = y(0)$, $a_1 = y'(0)$.

Method 2. We sketch the results, leaving details to the reader. Successive differentiation of (7-9) gives, by induction,

$$(x^2 - 4)y^{(n)} + (2n - 7)xy^{(n-1)} + (n-4)^2 y^{(n-2)} = 0 \quad (n \geq 2).$$

Setting $x = 0$, we obtain

$$4y^{(n)}(0) = (n - 4)^2 y^{(n-2)}(0),$$

whence $y''(0) = y(0)$, $y^{(2k)}(0) = 0$ $(k \geq 2)$. Moreover,

$$y^{(2k+1)}(0) = 4^{-k}[(-1) \cdot 1 \cdot 3 \cdot \cdots \cdot (2k - 3)]^2 y'(0) \quad (k = 1, 2, \cdots).$$

Evidently the desired Maclaurin series becomes (7–10), where $a_0 = y(0)$, $a_1 = y'(0)$.

Example 7-6. Solve the non-homogeneous linear equation

(7–11)　　　　　$y'' + x^2 y' + 2xy = 3 - x + x^3,$

using undetermined coefficients.

Solution: Substitution into (7–11) of $y = \sum\limits_{n=0}^{\infty} a_n x^n$ gives

$$\sum_{n=0}^{\infty} n(n - 1)a_n x^{n-2} + \sum_{n=3}^{\infty} (n - 1)a_{n-3} x^{n-2} = 3 - x + x^3.$$

This condition will be satisfied if we choose a_0 and a_1 arbitrarily and a_n for $n \geq 2$ so that

$$2 \cdot 1 \cdot a_2 = 3, \quad 3 \cdot 2a_3 + 2a_0 = -1, \quad 4 \cdot 3a_4 + 3a_1 = 0,$$

$$5 \cdot 4a_5 + 4a_2 = 1, \quad \cdots, \quad a_n = -\frac{1}{n} a_{n-3} \quad (n \geq 6).$$

Thus

$$a_2 = \frac{3}{2}, \quad a_3 = -\frac{2a_0 + 1}{6}, \quad a_4 = -\frac{1}{4} a_1, \quad a_5 = -\frac{1}{4},$$

and, for $k \geq 2$,

$$a_{3k} = \frac{(-1)^{k-1}}{6 \cdot 9 \cdot \cdots \cdot 3k} a_3, \quad a_{3k+1} = \frac{(-1)^{k-1}}{7 \cdot 10 \cdot \cdots \cdot (3k + 1)} a_4,$$

$$a_{3k+2} = \frac{(-1)^{k-1}}{8 \cdot 11 \cdot \cdots \cdot (3k + 2)} a_5.$$

In writing the series for y, we find it convenient to make some rearrangement of terms. The result is

$$y = \frac{3}{2} x^2 - \frac{1}{6} x^3 - \frac{1}{4} x^5$$

$$+ \frac{1}{6} \sum_{k=2}^{\infty} \frac{(-1)^k x^{3k}}{6 \cdot 9 \cdot \cdots \cdot 3k} + \frac{1}{4} \sum_{k=2}^{\infty} \frac{(-1)^k x^{3k+2}}{8 \cdot 11 \cdot \cdots \cdot (3k + 2)}$$

$$+ a_0\left[1 + \sum_{k=1}^{\infty} \frac{(-1)^k x^{3k}}{3 \cdot 6 \cdot \ \cdots \ \cdot 3k}\right]$$

$$+ a_1\left[x + \sum_{k=1}^{\infty} \frac{(-1)^k x^{3k+1}}{4 \cdot 7 \cdot \ \cdots \ \cdot (3k+1)}\right],$$

in which the part involving a_0 and a_1 represents the complete solution of the associated homogeneous equation and the remainder is a particular solution.

An argument justifying splitting the portion involving a_0 and a_1 into two series can be given as in the solution of Example 7–5. However, writing the remainder as we have done is justified only because the two series involved converge for all x. Otherwise, it would be necessary to write them as a single power series.

The two methods for determining series solutions of differential equations are not always effective. The equations most readily solved are linear equations in which the coefficients of y and its derivatives are simple polynomials in x. The simplicity of the recursion relationship, which depends on these coefficients, is crucial; if this relationship is one involving together more than two of the series coefficients, then, as we have seen, it is usually not possible to exhibit the series coefficients in a simple form.

If the coefficient functions in the equation are not polynomials in x but are analytic at $x = 0$, that is, have a Maclaurin series, or if the equation is not linear, difficulties arise in the multiplication of one series by another (second method) or in the computation of derivatives (first method). For example, if the first method is used on the equation $y' = x^2 + y^2$, a formula of Leibnitz is useful:

$$\frac{d^n}{dx^n}(y^2) = \sum_{r=0}^{n} \frac{n!}{r!(n-r)!} \cdot \frac{d^{n-r}y}{dx^{n-r}} \cdot \frac{d^r y}{dx^r}.$$

Nevertheless, the determination of the $y^{(n)}(0)$ in any simple form appears to be very difficult or impossible. The representation of $\left(\sum_{n=0}^{\infty} a_n x^n\right)^2$ as a power series in x, which must be accomplished in the work by the second method, introduces a similarly complicated sort of summation.

EXERCISES

1 to 12. Work exercises 1 to 12 of Section 7–2, page 202, by the method of the present section.

⋆**13.** Prove that two series $\sum_{n=0}^{\infty} a_n x^n$ and $\sum_{n=0}^{\infty} b_n x^n$ cannot represent the same function for $|x| < b'$, where $b' \neq 0$, unless $a_n = b_n$ ($n = 0, 1, 2, \cdots$). (HINT: First show that a Maclaurin expansion of a function is unique; then apply this result to the zero function.)

7–4. EQUATIONS POSSESSING SINGULAR POINTS

The equation $xy' + y = 0$ can be solved by writing it as $xy' + y = \dfrac{d}{dx}(xy) = 0$. All solutions are given by $y = cx^{-1}$, where the domain of y consists of either all x such that $x > 0$ or all x such that $x < 0$, except when $c = 0$, in which case $y(x) = 0$ for all values of x. Therefore no solution of this equation, except the trivial $y = 0$, is represented by a Maclaurin series, and attempts to find a solution by either of our series methods are bound to fail. This is clear because a Maclaurin series solution has $x = 0$ interior to its domain, and no solution has this property.

Because of the difficulties encountered in this example at $x = 0$, we call 0 a *singular point* of the differential equation. More generally, a point $x = h$ is called a singular point of a linear homogeneous equation

$$(7\text{–}12) \qquad \sum_{j=0}^{n} t_{n-j}(x) y^{(j)} = 0$$

of order n if $t_0(h) = 0$. (Note the relationship between this concept of singular point and that discussed in Section 1–6 for equations of the first order. In this section we shall study solutions of a linear equation in an interval about a singular point. It suffices to consider the case in which the singular point is $x = 0$, because the point $x = h$ becomes $X = 0$ under the translation $x - h = X$.

In the example $xy' + y = 0$, it is clear that a solution of the form $y = x^{-1}z$ exists, where z does have a Maclaurin series representation. [Here $z(x) = 1$.] It is reasonable in general to seek solutions of the form $x^{\alpha}z(x)$, where $\alpha \neq 0$ and $z(x)$ has a Maclaurin series form. This method, employing undetermined coefficients for finding the series for $z(x)$, will be found effective for many equations.

Example 7-7. Apply the suggested method to the equation $xy' + y = 0$.

Solution: The zero solution is of no interest. Hence let $y = \sum_{n=0}^{\infty} a_n x^{n+\alpha}$, where the leading coefficient $a_0 \neq 0$, and α and the a_n are to be found such that

$$\sum_{n=0}^{\infty} (n + \alpha)a_n x^{n+\alpha} + \sum_{n=0}^{\infty} a_n x^{n+\alpha} = 0,$$

or

$$(7\text{-}13) \qquad \sum_{n=0}^{\infty} (n + \alpha + 1)a_n x^{n+\alpha} = 0.$$

It is not difficult to show that two series of the type appearing in (7-13) are equal if and only if coefficients of like powers agree. (See exercise 14 of the group which follows.) Hence (7-13) gives

$$(7\text{-}14) \qquad (n + \alpha + 1)a_n = 0 \qquad (n = 0, 1, 2, \cdots).$$

But (7-14) yields, since $a_0 \neq 0$, that $\alpha + 1 = 0$ and $a_n = 0 \ (n \neq 0)$. There results the solution

$$y = a_0 x^{-1}$$

with a_0 arbitrary. Since the series here terminates, no convergence question arises, and the domain of y consists of all $x > 0$ or of all $x < 0$. We shall see that in general α is not expected to be unique, and that different choices, where possible, may lead to different families of solutions.

Example 7-8. Solve the equation $2xy'' + 3y' - 2xy = 0$.

Solution: The reader may show that assumption of a Maclaurin series leads only to a one-parameter family of solutions

$$y_1 = \sum_{n=0}^{\infty} a_0 \frac{x^{2n}}{n! \cdot 1 \cdot 5 \cdot \ \cdots \ \cdot (4n + 1)}.$$

We now try $y = \sum_{n=0}^{\infty} a_n x^{n+\alpha} \ (a_0 \neq 0)$ and choose the a_n so that

$$\sum_{n=0}^{\infty} 2(n + \alpha)(n + \alpha - 1)a_n x^{n+\alpha-1} + \sum_{n=0}^{\infty} 3(n + \alpha)a_n x^{n+\alpha-1}$$

$$= \sum_{n=0}^{\infty} 2a_n x^{n+\alpha+1},$$

that is,

$$\sum_{n=0}^{\infty} (n + \alpha)(2n + 2\alpha + 1)a_n x^{n+\alpha-1} = \sum_{n=2}^{\infty} 2a_{n-2}\, x^{n+\alpha-1}.$$

Hence

$$\alpha(2\alpha + 1)a_0 = 0, \quad (1 + \alpha)(2 + 2\alpha + 1)a_1 = 0,$$
$$(n + \alpha)(2n + 2\alpha + 1)a_n = 2a_{n-2} \qquad (n \geq 2).$$

The first of these equations leads to

$$(7\text{–}15) \qquad\qquad \alpha(2\alpha + 1) = 0,$$

which is called the *indicial equation*. The root $\alpha = 0$ of (7–15) leads to the solution already obtained. The root $\alpha = -1/2$ yields $a_1 = 0$ and

$$n(2n - 1)a_n = 2a_{n-2}.$$

From this recursion formula we have $a_{2k+1} = 0$ and

$$a_{2k} = \frac{1}{k! \cdot 3 \cdot 7 \cdot \,\cdots\, \cdot (4k - 1)}\, a_0 \qquad (k = 1, 2, \cdots).$$

Solutions arising from $\alpha = -1/2$ are therefore given by

$$y = \frac{a_0}{\sqrt{x}}\left[1 + \sum_{k=1}^{\infty} \frac{x^{2k}}{k! \cdot 3 \cdot 7 \cdot \,\cdots\, \cdot (4k - 1)}\right].$$

The series converges for all x, and so y has domain consisting of all $x > 0$.

In view of Example 7–7, in which solutions were found defined for all $x > 0$ or all $x < 0$, it is natural to ask whether solutions defined for $x < 0$ exist in the present case. The answer lies in a simple observation. While

$$\frac{d}{dx}\left(|x|^\alpha x^n\right) = (n + \alpha)\,|x|^\alpha\, x^{n-1}$$

is evident for $x > 0$, the same is also true for $x < 0$, as the reader may show. Hence, if

$$\sum_{n=0}^{\infty} a_n x^{\alpha+n} = x^\alpha \sum_{n=0}^{\infty} a_n x^n$$

satisfies a linear differential equation with polynomial coefficients for $x > 0$, then the same is true of $|x|^\alpha \sum_{n=0}^{\infty} a_n x^n = (-x)^\alpha \sum_{n=0}^{\infty} a_n x^n$ for $x < 0$. In the present case, we therefore have the solution

$$y = \frac{a_0}{\sqrt{-x}} \left[1 + \sum_{k=1}^{\infty} \frac{x^{2k}}{k! \cdot 3 \cdot 7 \cdot \ \cdots \ \cdot (4k - 1)} \right] \qquad (x < 0).$$

Henceforth, in view of the remarks just concluded, we shall seek solutions of the form

$$(7\text{–}16) \qquad\qquad y = |x|^{\alpha} \sum_{n=0}^{\infty} a_n x^n \qquad\qquad (a_0 \neq 0).$$

Example 7–9. Solve $2x^2 y'' + 5xy' + (1 - 2x^2)y = 0$.

Solution: The zero solution is of no interest. Let y be given by (7–16). Substitution into the given equation yields, after simplification and division by $|x|^{\alpha}$,

$$\sum_{n=0}^{\infty} [2(n + \alpha)(n + \alpha - 1) + 5(n + \alpha) + 1] a_n x^n = \sum_{n=2}^{\infty} 2a_{n-2} x^n.$$

The indicial equation is

$$(7\text{–}17) \qquad\qquad (\alpha + 1)(2\alpha + 1) = 0.$$

Moreover, we have $a_1 = 0$ and the recursion formula

$$[2(n + \alpha)(n + \alpha - 1) + 5(n + \alpha) + 1] a_n = 2a_{n-2} \qquad (n > 1).$$

For the root $\alpha = -1$ of (7–17), we obtain $a_{2k+1} = 0$ $(k = 0, 1, \cdots)$ and

$$a_{2k} = \frac{1}{k! \cdot 3 \cdot 7 \cdot \ \cdots \ \cdot (4k - 1)} a_0 \qquad (k = 1, 2, \cdots).$$

There results the family

$$y_1 = \frac{c_1}{|x|} \left[1 + \sum_{k=1}^{\infty} \frac{x^{2k}}{k! \cdot 3 \cdot 7 \cdot \ \cdots \ \cdot (4k - 1)} \right],$$

with c_1 arbitrary. The series converges for all values of x, and so we have a family of solutions for all $x > 0$ or all $x < 0$.

For the root $\alpha = -1/2$, we obtain in similar manner the family

$$y_2 = \frac{c_2}{\sqrt{|x|}} \left[1 + \sum_{k=1}^{\infty} \frac{x^{2k}}{k! \cdot 5 \cdot 9 \cdot \ \cdots \ \cdot (4k + 1)} \right]$$

of solutions for all $x > 0$ or all $x < 0$, in which c_2 is arbitrary.

From the general theory of linear equations, we expect that the complete solution of the given equation is $y_1 + y_2$, although this depends on the linear independence of y_1 and y_2 (with $c_1 = c_2 = 1$).

It is clear that the method of solution illustrated in the foregoing examples will fail in cases where no solutions of the type (7–16) exist. For example, the reader may show (see exercise 5 of the following group) that $x^2y' = y$, whose solution is $y = ce^{-1/x}$, is a case in point. It may also happen that the indicial equation has no real roots.

An important class of singular points, to be studied in Section 7–5, is the class of *regular* singular points. Assume that the linear equation (7–12) has been written (rewritten if necessary) in a form so that $t_0(x) = (x - h)^n r(x)$, where $r(h) \neq 0$ and $r(x)$ has a Taylor series expansion about $x = h$. Then $x = h$ is a *regular* singular point if $t_{n-j}(x) = (x - h)^j r_{n-j}(x)$, where $r_{n-j}(x)$ has a Taylor series expansion about $x = h$ ($j = 0, \cdots, n - 1$). For example, $x = 0$ is a regular singular point of $xy' + y = 0$. But $x = 0$ is a non-regular singular point of $x^2y' + y = 0$. For if this equation is written in the form $xy' + (1/x)y = 0$, we have $t_1(x) = r_1(x) = 1/x$, and $r_1(x)$ fails to have a Taylor series expansion about $x = 0$. The reader may show that $x = 0$ is a regular singular point of

(7–18) $$x^2y'' + x^3y' + 5(\sin x)y = 0,$$

but not of

(7–19) $$x^2y'' - y' + xy = 0.$$

EXERCISES

1. Prove that $x = 0$ is a regular singular point of (7–18), but not of (7–19), as stated in the text.

2. Show that $x = 0$ is a singular point of each of the following equations. Identify those for which $x = 0$ is a regular singular point.

    a. $x^2y'' + 3xy' + (x^2 + 1)y = 0$;

    b. $xy'' + y' - x^2y = 0$;

    c. $x^2y''' - y' + y = 0$;

    d. $x^4y''' + \dfrac{x^2}{1 + x} y'' - (1 + x)y = 0$;

    e. $x^4y''' - \dfrac{x^2}{1 + x} y' + y = 0$;

    f. $x^2y'' + (\sin x)y' - 2y = 0$.

3. Show that

$$\frac{d}{dx} (|x|^\alpha x^n) = (n + \alpha) |x|^\alpha x^{n-1}$$

for $x < 0$, as stated in the text.

4. Find the one-parameter family of Maclaurin series solutions of the equation of Example 7–8.

5. Show that the equation $x^2y' - y = 0$ has no solutions of the form (7–16) by attempting to find such a solution and arriving at a contradiction.

In each of exercises 6 to 12 find the general solution of the given equation.

6. $xy' + (1 + x)y = 0$.

7. $x^2y'' + 5xy' - 5y = 0$. (This equation is an example of Cauchy's equation, $ax^2y'' + bxy' + cy = 0$.)

8. $2xy'' + y' + y = 0$.

9. $25x^2y'' + (4 + 2x)y = 0$.

10. $x^2y'' - (5x + 3x^4)y' + (5 + 6x^3)y = 0$.

11. $6x^2y'' + (11x + x^3)y' + (1 - 2x^2)y = 0$.

12. $x^2(1 + x)y'' - 3xy' + (3 - 2x)y = 0$.

★13. The solution of Example 7–6 suggests that no polynomial is a solution of the equation $y'' + x^2y' + 2xy = 3 - x + x^3$. Prove this conjecture directly by showing that it is impossible to choose constants $a_0, \cdots, a_n$ so that $a_0x^n + \cdots + a_n$ is a solution. (HINT: For $n \geq 2$ consider only the constant term and the term in x^3 in $y'' + x^2y' + 2xy$.)

★14. Prove that if two series $x^\alpha \sum_{n=0}^{\infty} a_nx^n$ and $x^\beta \sum_{n=0}^{\infty} b_nx^n$ are equal for $0 < x < b'$, where $b' \neq 0$ and $a_0, b_0 \neq 0$, then $\alpha = \beta$ and $a_n = b_n$ ($n = 0, 1, 2, \cdots$).

7–5. REGULAR SINGULAR POINTS

We shall devote this section to special equations having $x = 0$ as a regular singular point. Examples 7–10 and 7–12 will show that solutions of a linear homogeneous equation (7–12) are not exclusively of the form (7–16) and that (7–12) may have solutions of the form $y_1 \ln |x| + y_2$, where y_1 is a solution of (7–12) and y_2 is of the form (7–16). Assume that the Maclaurin expansion for r_{n-j} converges for all x ($j = 0, \cdots, n - 1$). Then the Maclaurin series in (7–16) converges in an interval $|x| < R$, where R is the smallest absolute value of the non-zero (real or non-real) roots of $t_0(x) = 0$, and the solutions are valid for all x such that $0 < x < R$ or $-R < x < 0$. When $t_0(x) \neq 0$ for $x \neq 0$, convergence occurs for all (real) values of x and the solutions are valid for all x such that $x > 0$ or $x < 0$.

When the indicial equation has a multiple real root, it is not clear how one can get more than one solution (linearly independent of the first) from this root. On the other hand, if the roots of the indicial equation are all distinct, one expects to get n linearly independent solutions by the methods of Section 7–4. However, this expectation is not always realized; if two roots differ by an integer, difficulties can arise. From these two situations come solutions in which $\ln |x|$ appears. We investigate these matters briefly in the next three examples.

Example 7–10. Solve $xy'' + y' + y = 0$.

Solution: If $y = |x|^\alpha \sum\limits_{n=0}^{\infty} a_n x^n$ is to satisfy the given equation, then

$$\sum_{n=0}^{\infty} (n + \alpha)^2 a_n x^{n-1} + \sum_{n=1}^{\infty} a_{n-1} x^{n-1} = 0.$$

The indicial equation, obtained by setting the coefficient of a_0 equal to 0, is $\alpha^2 = 0$; zero is a double root. By choosing $\alpha = 0$, we obtain only one family of solutions of the equation, all of which are constant multiples of a particular one.

For $n \geq 1$, the coefficients in the series are connected by the equation $(n + \alpha)^2 a_n = -a_{n-1}$, so that

$$[(\alpha + 1)(\alpha + 2) \cdots (\alpha + n)]^2 a_n = (-1)^n a_0.$$

If α is not a negative integer, and if we define

$$y(x, \alpha) = a_0 |x|^\alpha \left[1 + \sum_{n=1}^{\infty} (-1)^n [(\alpha + 1)(\alpha + 2) \cdots (\alpha + n)]^{-2} x^n \right],$$

then the series in brackets converges for all values of x, and

$$x \frac{\partial^2}{\partial x^2} [y(x, \alpha)] + \frac{\partial}{\partial x} [y(x, \alpha)] + y(x, \alpha) = \alpha^2 a_0 |x|^\alpha \qquad (x \neq 0).$$

If $\alpha = 0$, then $\alpha^2 a_0 |x|^\alpha = 0$, and $y_1 = y(x, 0)$, where

$$y_1 = a_0 \sum_{n=0}^{\infty} (-1)^n (n!)^{-2} x^n$$

gives the solution family already found. We also note that, because of the factor α^2, $\dfrac{\partial}{\partial \alpha} (\alpha^2 a_0 |x|^\alpha)$ will have the value zero when

$\alpha = 0$. Suppose now that $y(x, \alpha)$ is a function such that the order of partial differentiations with regard to x and to α can be interchanged. Then it follows that, for $x \neq 0$,

$$x \frac{\partial^2}{\partial x^2}\left(\frac{\partial}{\partial \alpha}[y(x, \alpha)]\right) + \frac{\partial}{\partial x}\left(\frac{\partial}{\partial \alpha}[y(x, \alpha)]\right) + \frac{\partial}{\partial \alpha}[y(x, \alpha)]$$

$$= \frac{\partial}{\partial \alpha}\left[\left[x \frac{\partial^2}{\partial x^2}[y(x, \alpha)] + \frac{\partial}{\partial x}[y(x, \alpha)] + y(x, \alpha)\right]\right]$$

$$= \frac{\partial}{\partial \alpha}(\alpha^2 a_0 \mid x \mid^\alpha) = a_0[2\alpha \mid x \mid^\alpha + \alpha^2(\ln \mid x \mid) \mid x \mid^\alpha].$$

Hence a second solution family of the given equation is given by $y_2 = y_\alpha(x, 0)$.

To find $\dfrac{\partial}{\partial \alpha}[y(x, \alpha)]$, we must compute

$$\frac{\partial}{\partial \alpha}[(\alpha + 1)(\alpha + 2) \cdots (\alpha + n)]^{-2}.$$

If $\alpha > -1$, then $\alpha + 1, \cdots, \alpha + n$ are all positive and

$$\ln[(\alpha + 1) \cdots (\alpha + n)]^{-2}$$

is defined. Hence we have

$$\frac{\partial}{\partial \alpha}[(\alpha + 1) \cdots (\alpha + n)]^{-2}$$

$$= [(\alpha + 1) \cdots (\alpha + n)]^{-2} \frac{\partial}{\partial \alpha} \ln[(\alpha + 1) \cdots (\alpha + n)]^{-2}$$

$$= [(\alpha + 1) \cdots (\alpha + n)]^{-2} \frac{\partial}{\partial \alpha}\left[-2 \sum_{k=1}^{n} \ln(\alpha + k)\right]$$

$$= -2[(\alpha + 1) \cdots (\alpha + n)]^{-2} \sum_{k=1}^{n} \frac{1}{\alpha + k}.$$

Therefore it follows that

$$y_\alpha(x, \alpha) = a_0 \mid x \mid^\alpha \left[\ln \mid x \mid + \sum_{n=1}^{\infty}(-1)^n \left\{(x^n \ln \mid x \mid)\sum_{k=1}^{n}(\alpha + k)^{-2}\right.\right.$$

$$\left.\left. - \left(2x^n \prod_{k=1}^{n}(\alpha + k)^{-2}\right)\sum_{k=1}^{n}(\alpha + k)^{-1}\right\}\right].$$

Hence

$$y_2 = y_\alpha (x, 0)$$

$$= y_1 \ln |x| - 2a_0 \sum_{n=1}^{\infty} (-1)^n (n!)^{-2} \left(1 + \frac{1}{2} + \cdots + \frac{1}{n} \right) x^n.$$

Without proving the differentiability assumption concerning $y(x, \alpha)$ we simply verify that y_2 is a solution of the given equation. If $h_n = \sum_{k=1}^{n} \frac{1}{k}$, then

$$y_2' = y_1' \ln |x| + x^{-1} y_1 - 2a_0 \sum_{n=1}^{\infty} (-1)^n n (n!)^{-2} h_n x^{n-1},$$

$$y_2'' = y_1'' \ln |x| + 2x^{-1} y_1' - x^{-2} y_1$$

$$- 2a_0 \sum_{n=1}^{\infty} (-1)^n n(n-1)(n!)^{-2} h_n x^{n-2}.$$

Hence

$$xy_2'' + y_2' + y_2 = (xy_1'' + y_1' + y_1) \ln |x| + 2y_1' + x^{-1} y_1 - x^{-1} y_1$$

$$- 2a_0 \sum_{n=1}^{\infty} [(-1)^n (n!)^{-2} h_n x^{n-1} (x + n^2)]$$

$$= 2a_0 \left[\sum_{n=1}^{\infty} (-1)^n (n!)^{-2} n x^{n-1} - \sum_{n=1}^{\infty} (-1)^n (n!)^{-2} h_n x^{n-1} (x + n^2) \right]$$

$$= 2a_0 \left[\sum_{n=1}^{\infty} (-1)^n (n!)^{-2} (n - n^2 h_n) x^{n-1} \right.$$

$$\left. - \sum_{n=2}^{\infty} (-1)^{n-1} [(n-1)!]^{-2} h_n x^{n-1} \right]$$

$$= 2a_0 (-1) \cdot 1^{-2} (1 - 1 \cdot 1) x^0 + 2a_0 \sum_{n=2}^{\infty} \left[(-1)^n (n!)^{-2} n (1 - n h_n) \right.$$

$$\left. - (-1)^{n-1} [(n-1)!]^{-2} h_{n-1} \right] x^{n-1}$$

$$= 2a_0 \sum_{n=2}^{\infty} (-1)^n x^{n-1} \left[(n!)^{-2} n (1 - n h_n) + [(n-1)!]^{-2} h_{n-1} \right]$$

$$= 2a_0 \sum_{n=2}^{\infty} (-1)^n x^{n-1} (n!)^{-2} [n - n^2 h_n + n^2 h_{n-1}] = 0.$$

It may be readily shown that y_1 and y_2 are linearly independent.

In some cases, in the search for a solution of the form (7–16) one or more roots of the indicial equation must be discarded because they lead to duplication among solutions, or to violation of the assumption $a_0 \neq 0$. Sometimes, but not always, it is possible, even in such situations, to obtain the requisite number of linearly independent solutions without special devices. The next two examples illustrate some possibilities.

Example 7-11. Solve

$$x^2 y'' - (4x + x^2)y' - (24 - 3x)y = 0.$$

Solution: Having observed that $x = 0$ is a regular singular point, we substitute into the given equation $y = |x|^\alpha \sum_{n=0}^{\infty} a_n x^n$ and find

$$\sum_{n=0}^{\infty} [(n + \alpha)(n + \alpha - 1) - 4(n + \alpha) - 24] a_n x^n$$
$$= \sum_{n=1}^{\infty} (n + \alpha - 4)a_{n-1} x^n.$$

The indicial equation is $\alpha^2 - 5\alpha - 24 = (\alpha - 8)(\alpha + 3) = 0$. If we choose $\alpha = -3$, then

$$n(n - 11)a_n = (n - 7)a_{n-1} \qquad (n \geq 1).$$

By means of this relationship we determine $a_1, a_2, \cdots, a_6$ in terms of a_0. For $n = 7$ we obtain $7 \cdot 4a_7 = 0 \cdot a_6 = 0$, and so $a_7 = 0$ $= a_8 = a_9 = a_{10}$. However, for $n = 11$ we have $11 \cdot 0 \cdot a_{11} = 4a_{10}$ $= 0$, whence a_{11} is arbitrary. All a_n for $n > 11$ can then be found in terms of a_{11}. Therefore we have two linearly independent families of solutions of the equation. One is

$$y = |x|^{-3}(a_0 + a_1 x + \cdots + a_6 x^6),$$

and the other is

$$y = |x|^{-3}(a_{11}x^{11} + \cdots).$$

The reader should try $\alpha = 8$ and show that this choice leads to a duplication of one family of solutions obtained from $\alpha = -3$.

Example 7-12. Solve

$$xy'' + (x^2 - 1)y' + 2xy = 0.$$

Solution: Evidently $x = 0$ is a regular singular point. We substitute $y = |x|^\alpha \sum_{n=0}^{\infty} a_n x^n$ into the given equation to obtain

$$(7\text{–}20) \quad \sum_{n=0}^{\infty} (n + \alpha)(n + \alpha - 2)a_n x^{n-1} + \sum_{n=2}^{\infty} (n + \alpha)a_{n-2}\, x^{n-1} = 0.$$

The indicial equation is $\alpha(\alpha - 2) = 0$. Let us choose $\alpha = 2$, so that $a_1 = 0$ and

$$(n + 2)na_n + (n + 2)a_{n-2} = 0 \qquad (n \geq 2).$$

There results the solution family

$$y = a_0 x^2 \sum_{k=0}^{\infty} \frac{(-1)^k x^{2k}}{2^k k!}.$$

Here $\alpha = 0$ violates the requirement $a_0 \neq 0$.

A procedure similar to that of Example 7–10 may be used here to yield a second family of solutions. From (7–20), we have

$$(\alpha + 1)(\alpha - 1)a_1 = 0,$$
$$(n + \alpha)(n + \alpha - 2)a_n = -(n + \alpha)a_{n-2} \qquad (n \geq 2).$$

We choose $a_1 = 0$ and $a_n = -(n + \alpha - 2)^{-1}a_{n-2}$ $(n \geq 2)$, provided that α is not chosen to be equal to 0 or any negative integer. For such choices, $a_{2k+1} = 0$ and

$$a_{2k} = (-1)^k[\alpha(\alpha + 2) \cdots (\alpha + 2k - 2)]^{-1}a_0.$$

Suppose that we now choose $a_0 = \alpha$, so that $a_2 = -1$, and, for $k \geq 2$,

$$a_{2k} = (-1)^k[(\alpha + 2) \cdots (\alpha + 2k - 2)]^{-1}.$$

Let

$$y(x, \alpha) = |x|^{\alpha}\left[\alpha - x^2 + \sum_{k=2}^{\infty} (-1)^k[(\alpha + 2)(\alpha + 4) \right.$$
$$\left. \cdots (\alpha + 2k - 2)]^{-1}x^{2k}\right],$$

where α is subject to the restrictions already mentioned, and $x \neq 0$. Moreover, define

$$y(x, 0) = \lim_{\alpha \to 0} y(x, \alpha) = \sum_{k=1}^{\infty} (-1)^k\, [2^{k-1}(k - 1)!]^{-1}x^{2k}.$$

Evidently $y(x, 0)$ gives the solutions already obtained. Furthermore,

$$x\frac{\partial^2}{\partial x^2}[y(x, \alpha)] + (x^2 - 1)\frac{\partial}{\partial x}[y(x, \alpha)] + 2xy(x, \alpha) = \alpha^2(\alpha - 2)\,|x|^{\alpha},$$

and we expect that $y_\alpha(x, 0)$ will also be a solution of the equation if $y_\alpha(x, \alpha)$ exists and the order of second partial differentiation of $y(x, \alpha)$ is immaterial. We find that

$$y_\alpha (x, \alpha) = (|x|^\alpha \ln |x|) \left[\alpha - x^2 \right.$$

$$+ \sum_{k=2}^\infty (-1)^k [(\alpha + 2) \cdots (\alpha + 2k - 2)]^{-1} x^{2k} \Bigg]$$

$$+ |x|^\alpha \left[1 + \sum_{k=2}^\infty (-1)^k [(\alpha + 2) \right.$$

$$\cdots (\alpha + 2k - 2)]^{-1} c(k)(-1) x^{2k} \Bigg],$$

where $c(k) = \dfrac{1}{\alpha + 2} + \cdots + \dfrac{1}{\alpha + 2k - 2} \cdot$ Therefore

$$y_\alpha (x, 0) = (\ln |x|) y(x, 0) + 1$$

$$+ \sum_{k=2}^\infty (-1)^{k+1} \left[\frac{1}{2} + \cdots + \frac{1}{2(k-1)} \right] \frac{x^{2k}}{2^{k-1}(k-1)!} \cdot$$

The reader should verify that this function is a solution of the equation.

In general, suppose the indicial equation is $(\alpha - r)(\alpha - s) = 0$, $r < s$, and suppose that r and s differ by an integer. If the two roots do not directly yield two independent solutions, then one may choose $a_0 = \alpha - r$ and form $y(x, \alpha)$ as in the solution of Example 7-12. The desired linearly independent solutions are $y(x, r)$ and $y_\alpha(x, r)$.

Bessel's Equation. An important equation arising in many applications of mathematics is

(7-21) $$x^2 y'' + xy' + (x^2 - b^2)y = 0.$$

Evidently $x = 0$ is a regular singular point, and solutions of the equation can be found in the form $y = |x|^\alpha \sum_{n=0}^\infty a_n x^n$. The indicial equation is $\alpha^2 = b^2$, and the solutions obtained, when b is a nonnegative integer, by choosing $\alpha = b$, are of special interest. The a_n are to be determined so that

$$\sum_{n=0}^\infty [(n + \alpha)^2 - b^2] a_n x^n + \sum_{n=2}^\infty a_{n-2} x^n = 0.$$

Hence, if $\alpha = b$, we have

$$1(1 + 2b)a_1 = 0, \quad \text{and} \quad n(n + 2b)a_n = -a_{n-2} \quad (n \geq 2).$$

We find $a_{2k+1} = 0$ for $k = 1, 2, \cdots$, and

$$a_{2k} = \frac{(-1)^k a_0}{2^{2k} k!(1 + b) \cdots (k + b)} \quad (k = 1, 2, \cdots),$$

and thus have the solutions

$$y = a_0 \mid x \mid^b \sum_{k=0}^{\infty} \frac{(-1)^k x^{2k}}{2^{2k} k!(1 + b) \cdots (k + b)}.$$

Since b is here a non-negative integer, we may write x^b for $\mid x \mid^b$. The particular solution obtained by taking $a_0 = (2^b b!)^{-1}$ is customarily called the Bessel function of order b of the first kind and denoted by $J_b(x)$:

$$J_b(x) = \sum_{k=0}^{\infty} \frac{(-1)^k x^{2k+b}}{2^{2k+b} k!(k + b)!}.$$

These functions and their derivatives satisfy many interesting identities.

EXERCISES

In each of exercises 1 to 10, find two linearly independent families of solutions, and hence the complete solution.

1. $x^2 y'' + (x - 4x^3)y' - x^2 y = 0$.

2. $x^2 y'' - 5xy' + (9 - x^2)y = 0$.

3. $x^2 y'' + (x^2 - x)y' + y = 0$.

4. $x^2 y'' + 5xy' + (4 + 2x)y = 0$.

5. $xy'' + (1 - x)y' + 2y = 0$.

6. $xy'' + 2y' - 3y = 0$.

7. $x^2 y'' + 2x^4 y' - 2y = 0$.

8. $4x^2 y'' + 8xy' + (2x - 3)y = 0$.

9. $9x^2 y'' + (x^2 - 15x)y' + 7y = 0$.

10. $x^2 y'' + (x^2 - 5x)y' + (5 - 6x)y = 0$.

11. Solve $xy' + ky = 0$ by the substitution $y = x^\alpha v$, determining α so that v has a Maclaurin series.

★12. Determine a second family of solutions of Bessel's equation (7–21).

7-6. METHOD OF SUCCESSIVE APPROXIMATIONS

When a differential equation has a series solution, the partial sums of the series may be regarded as approximating the solution, with accuracy as great as desired by taking sufficiently many terms.

It is desirable to obtain successive approximations to a solution under more general circumstances. For example, there are many equations whose solutions do not possess for any values of x derivatives of arbitrarily high order. This section is devoted to a brief explanation of such a method, known as the *method of Picard*. We begin with an equation whose solutions are known.

Consider the first-order equation $y' = xy$. Suppose we wish to find a solution of this equation such that $y(0) = 1$. An equivalent formulation of the problem is that we wish to find a function $y(x)$ satisfying

$$(7\text{-}22) \qquad y(x) = 1 + \int_0^x ty(t)\, dt,$$

obtained by simply integrating the given differential equation. The idea of the method is to substitute into the right side of (7-22) a function which is thought to be an approximation y_0 to the desired solution. Thus we have

$$y_1(x) = 1 + \int_0^x ty_0(t)\, dt.$$

If y_0 satisfies the given equation, then $y_1 = y_0$. Otherwise, y_1 is not the same function as y_0. The same step is repeated with y_1 replacing y_0, and so on. It is to be noted that, if y_0 is a polynomial, then y_1 is also such with degree one more than that of y_0.

Suppose $y_0 = 1$. Then we obtain

$$y_1 = 1 + \int_0^x t\, dt = 1 + \frac{1}{2}x^2,$$

$$y_2 = 1 + \int_0^x ty_1\, dt = 1 + \int_0^x \left(t + \frac{1}{2}t^3\right) dt$$

$$= 1 + \frac{1}{2}x^2 + \frac{1}{8}x^4,$$

$$y_3 = 1 + \int_0^x ty_2\, dt = 1 + \int_0^x \left(t + \frac{1}{2}t^3 + \frac{1}{2\cdot 4}t^5\right) dt$$

$$= 1 + \frac{x^2}{2} + \frac{x^4}{2\cdot 4} + \frac{x^6}{2\cdot 4\cdot 6}.$$

Note that the terms of y_3 agree with the first terms in the series form of the solution obtained in Example 7–3. An inductive argument shows that

$$(7\text{--}23) \qquad\qquad y_n = \sum_{k=0}^{n} \frac{x^{2k}}{2^k k!} \qquad\qquad (n = 0, 1, 2, \cdots).$$

Indeed, if (7–23) is assumed true for a particular value of n, then

$$y_{n+1} = 1 + \int_0^x t y_n \, dt = 1 + \sum_{k=0}^{n} \int_0^x \frac{t^{2k+1}}{2^k k!} \, dt$$

$$= 1 + \sum_{k=0}^{n} \frac{x^{2k+2}}{2^k k!(2k + 2)} = \sum_{k=0}^{n+1} \frac{x^{2k}}{2^k k!},$$

and (7–23) holds for $n + 1$.

The limit y of y_n as $n \to \infty$ clearly exists for all values of x, since the infinite series based on (7–23) converges. It is easy to show that y is the desired solution. (See the starred subsection on pages 224 and 225.)

In general, to find a solution $y(x)$ of the equation

$$(7\text{--}24) \qquad\qquad y' = F(x, y)$$

such that $y(0) = a$, we let $y_0 = a$ and

$$(7\text{--}25) \qquad\qquad y_n(x) = a + \int_0^x F(t, y_{n-1}) \, dt \qquad (n = 1, 2, \cdots).$$

With slight restrictions on F it can be shown that the functions y_n converge in some interval about $x = 0$ to a function y which is a solution of (7–25) such that $y(0) = a$, and that this solution is unique. (See the starred subsection on pages 224 and 225.)

It is interesting to note that the Picard method corrects some small errors or poor initial guesses. Suppose we take $y_0 = a$ instead of $y_0 = 1$ in the example. Then

$$y_1 = 1 + \int_0^x at \, dt = 1 + \frac{ax^2}{2},$$

$$y_2 = 1 + \int_0^x \left(t + \frac{a}{3} t^3 \right) dt = 1 + \frac{1}{2} x^2 + \frac{a}{2 \cdot 4} x^4,$$

and we can prove by induction that

$$y_n = 1 + \frac{1}{2} x^2 + \frac{1}{2 \cdot 4} x^4 + \cdots + \frac{x^{2n-2}}{2 \cdot 4 \cdot \,\cdots\, \cdot (2n - 2)} + \frac{ax^{2n}}{2 \cdot \,\cdots\, \cdot 2n}.$$

The absolute value of the difference of this polynomial and that given by (7–23) is $\dfrac{|\,a-1\,|\,x^{2n}}{2^n n!}$. For every x and every a this difference approaches zero as $n \to \infty$, and consequently both sequences of polynomials approach $\sum\limits_{k=0}^{\infty} \dfrac{x^{2k}}{2^k k!}$.

Suppose that for some reason we had erroneously computed y_2 as $1 + ax^2 + \dfrac{x^4}{2 \cdot 4}$ with $a \neq 1/2$. Then

$$y_3 = 1 + \int_0^x \left(t + at^3 + \frac{1}{2 \cdot 4} t^5 \right) dt = 1 + \frac{x^2}{2} + \frac{ax^4}{4} + \frac{x^6}{2 \cdot 4 \cdot 6},$$

$$y_4 = 1 + \int_0^x \left(t + \frac{t^3}{2} + \frac{at^5}{4} + \frac{t^7}{2 \cdot 4 \cdot 6} \right) dt$$

$$= 1 + \frac{x^2}{2} + \frac{x^4}{2 \cdot 4} + \frac{x^6}{4 \cdot 6} + \frac{x^8}{2 \cdot 4 \cdot 6 \cdot 8},$$

and again we can prove by induction that

$$y_n = \sum_{k=0}^{n-2} \frac{x^{2k}}{2^k k!} + \frac{ax^{2n-2}}{4 \cdot 6 \cdot \,\cdots\, \cdot (2n-2)} + \frac{1}{2 \cdot 4 \cdot \,\cdots\, \cdot 2n} x^{2n} \quad (n \geq 3).$$

It is clear that this sequence of polynomials also converges to the solution previously found, irrespective of the value of a.

It is unfortunate that it is usually quite difficult to exhibit y_n in a polynomial form even when $F(x, y)$ is a polynomial in x and y. If we try to find a solution of $y' = xy^2 + 1$ such that $y(0) = 1$, we meet with computational difficulties. The function $y_0 = 1 + x$ has the value 1 when $x = 0$ and $y_0' = 0 \cdot 1^2 + 1 = 1$ when $x = 0$, and appears to be a good initial choice. Then

$$y_1 = 1 + \int_0^x (1 + t + 2t^2 + t^3) \, dt = 1 + x + \frac{x^2}{2} + \frac{x^3}{3} + \frac{x^4}{4},$$

$$y_2 = 1 + \int_0^x \left[1 + t \left(1 + \frac{t^2}{2} + \frac{t^3}{3} + \frac{t^4}{4} \right)^2 \right] dt.$$

It is clear from this that the method is of no practical value in determining a series expansion for y, but may be most useful if y_k with k small is an adequate approximation to y for a specific purpose.

*The Convergence Question.** It was asserted in the text that the sequence y_n converges to the desired solution of (7–24) under suitable circumstances. If one assumes that $F(x, y)$ satisfies the hypotheses of the existence theorem in Section 1–4, the proof may be carried out as follows.

By (7–25), we have, for x in a suitable closed interval S including $x = 0$,

$$y_{n+1}(x) - y_n(x) = \int_0^x [F(t, y_n) - F(t, y_{n-1})] \, dx \quad (n = 1, 2, \cdots).$$

Hence, by well-known properties of integrals,

(7–26) $\left| y_{n+1} - y_n \right| \le \left| \int_0^x | F(t, y_n) - F(t, y_{n-1}) | \, dt \right|$

$$\le A \left| \int_0^x | y_n(t) - y_{n-1}(t) | \, dt \right|,$$

where A is a Lipschitz constant for F. Since $y_1(t)$ and hence $y_2(t)$ are continuous, they are bounded for t in S. Thus $| y_2(t) - y_1(t) | \le B$ for some number $B > 0$. Repeated applications of (7–26) yield

$$| y_3 - y_2 | \le AB \, | x |,$$

$$| y_4 - y_3 | \le A^2 B \frac{| x |^2}{2},$$

$$\cdot \quad \cdot \quad \cdot \quad \cdot \quad \cdot \quad \cdot \quad \cdot \quad \cdot$$

$$| y_{n+1} - y_n | \le A^{n-1} B \frac{| x |^{n-1}}{(n-1)!} \le \frac{A^{n-1} B h^{n-1}}{(n-1)!},$$

where h is the width of S, so that $| x | \le h$.

Now

$$y_n - y_1 = \sum_{k=2}^n (y_k - y_{k-1}),$$

so that $y_n - y_1$ is the nth partial sum of the series $\sum_{k=2}^\infty (y_k - y_{k-1})$.

The terms of this series are in absolute value less than or equal to the respective terms of

$$ABh + A^2 B \frac{h^2}{2} + \cdots + \frac{A^{n-1} B h^{n-1}}{(n-1)!} + \cdots .$$

This series converges to $ABhe^{Ah}$. It follows from the comparison test for series that $y_n(x)$ converges uniformly in S to a limit function $y(x)$.

To show that $y(x)$ satisfies (7–24) together with $y(0) = a$, it suffices to show that $y(x) = a + \int_0^x F(t, y(t))\, dt$. But

$$\left| y - a - \int_0^x F(t, y)\, dt \right| = \left| y - y_n + \int_0^x [F(t, y_{n-1}) - F(t, y)]\, dt \right|$$

$$\leqq |y - y_n| + A \left| \int_0^x |y_{n-1} - y|\, dt \right|.$$

If $\epsilon > 0$, then there exists $n_0 = 1, 2, \cdots$ such that $|y - y_{n-1}| < \epsilon$ for $n - 1 > n_0$. Hence the sum above is less than

$$\epsilon + A\epsilon \left| \int_0^x dx \right| \leqq \epsilon(1 + Ah).$$

The desired result then follows.

Finally, to prove uniqueness, suppose z is any solution, so that

$$z = a + \int_0^x F(t, z)\, dt.$$

Then

$$|z - y| \leqq \left| \int_0^x |F(t, z) - F(t, y)|\, dt \right|$$

$$\leqq A \left| \int_0^x |z - y|\, dt \right| \leqq AB_1 |x|,$$

where B_1 is an upper bound of $|z - y|$ in S. It follows that $AB_1 |x|$ is also an upper bound of $|z - y|$. Hence, applying the same argument, we have

$$|z - y| \leqq A^2 B_1 \frac{|x|^2}{2};$$

by induction, we have

$$|z - y| \leqq A^n B_1 \frac{|x|^n}{n!}.$$

As $n \to \infty$ the right side approaches zero; hence $z - y = 0$.

It should be noted that, with small notational changes, the argument just presented yields a proof of the existence theorem in Section 1–4.

EXERCISES

Use Picard's method to solve each of the equations in exercises 1 to 5. Solve each by another method and compare the results.

    1. $y' = 2y$ $[y(0) = 1]$.

    2. $y' = x + 2y$ $[y(0) = 2]$.

    3. $y' - y = 1 + x^2$ $[y(0) = 1]$.

    4. $y' - y = 1 + x^2$ $[y(0) = -3]$.

    5. $y' - 7y = 2 - x^4$ $[y(0) = a]$.

In each of exercises 6 to 11 find approximations y_1, y_2, y_3 using $y_0 = y(0)$.

    6. $y' = x^2 + y^2$ $[y(0) = 0]$.

    7. $y' = 1 + y^2$ $[y(0) = 0]$.

    8. $y' = 1 - x^2 - y^2$ $[y(0) = 0]$.

    9. $y' = xy^2 + 1$ $[y(0) = 1]$.

    10. $y' = 3 + x + x^2 y$ $[y(0) = 1]$.

    11. $y' = 1 + xy$ $[y(1) = 0]$.

7–7. FOURIER SERIES

It is possible to represent functions as limits of sequences of functions other than polynomials. We shall examine briefly a method due to Fourier for representing, by a series of sine functions or cosine functions or both, a function which is defined on a closed interval. Such series are useful in the study of many physical problems, notably periodic phenomena and conduction of heat.

Let f be a function defined over a closed interval S which we may take without loss of generality to be the set of all x such that $0 \leq x \leq 2g$ with $g > 0$. We try to determine coefficients a_n such that, for x in S, except possibly at a finite number of points,

$$(7\text{–}27) \qquad\qquad f(x) = \sum_{n=1}^{\infty} a_n \sin \frac{n\pi x}{2g}.$$

[That exceptional values of x must be allowed is clear, since, unless $f(0) = 0$ or $f(2g) = 0$, (7–27) cannot hold for $x = 0$ or $x = 2g$.]

The coefficients a_n are determined by the following device. If the series represents f, then for every $k = 1, 2, \cdots$,

$$f(x) \sin \frac{k\pi x}{2g} = \sin \frac{k\pi x}{2g} \sum_{n=1}^{\infty} a_n \sin \frac{n\pi x}{2g},$$

and

$$(7\text{-}28) \quad \int_0^{2g} f(x) \sin \frac{k\pi x}{2g} \, dx = \int_0^{2g} \sin \frac{k\pi x}{2g} \sum_{n=1}^\infty a_n \sin \frac{n\pi x}{2g} \, dx,$$

$$= \sum_{k=1}^\infty a_n \int_0^{2g} \sin \frac{k\pi g}{2g} \sin \frac{n\pi x}{2g} \, dx,$$

under appropriate assumptions. [We shall not now be concerned with investigation of precise conditions of validity of (7–28) or the formal processes to follow. See the theorem at the end of the discussion.]

If $n \neq k$, then

$$\int_0^{2g} \sin \frac{k\pi x}{2g} \sin \frac{n\pi x}{2g} \, dx = \frac{1}{2} \int_0^{2g} \left[\cos \frac{(k-n)\pi x}{2g} - \cos \frac{(k+n)\pi x}{2g} \right] dx$$

$$= \frac{1}{2} \left[\frac{2g}{(k-n)\pi} \sin \frac{(k-n)\pi x}{2g} - \frac{2g}{(k+n)\pi} \sin \frac{(k+n)\pi x}{2g} \right]_0^{2g} = 0.$$

If $n = k$, we have

$$\int_0^{2g} \sin^2 \left(\frac{n\pi x}{2g} \right) dx = \frac{1}{2} \int_0^{2g} \left(1 - \cos \frac{2n\pi x}{2g} \right) dx$$

$$= \frac{1}{2} \left[x - \frac{2g}{2n\pi} \sin \frac{2n\pi x}{2g} \right]_0^{2g} = g.$$

Thus

$$\int_0^{2g} f(x) \sin \frac{k\pi x}{2g} = ga_k,$$

and

$$(7\text{-}29) \quad a_n = \frac{1}{g} \int_0^{2g} f(x) \sin \frac{n\pi x}{2g} \, dx \qquad (n = 1, 2, \cdots).$$

Similarly, to find coefficients b_n such that

$$(7\text{-}30) \quad f(x) = \sum_{n=0}^\infty b_n \cos \frac{n\pi x}{2g}$$

(except possibly for a finite number of values of x), we compute

$$\int_0^{2g} f(x) \cos \frac{k\pi x}{2g} \, dx = \int_0^{2g} \cos \frac{k\pi x}{2g} \sum_{n=0}^\infty b_n \cos \frac{n\pi x}{2g} \, dx$$

$$= \sum_{n=0}^\infty b_n \int_0^{2g} \cos \frac{k\pi x}{2g} \cos \frac{n\pi x}{2g} \, dx$$

$$= gb_k \qquad (k = 1, 2, \cdots).$$

Thus

(7–31) $$b_n = \frac{1}{g} \int_0^{2g} f(x) \cos \frac{n\pi x}{2g} \, dx \qquad (n = 1, 2, \cdots).$$

The computation is parallel to that employed to determine the a_n, except that, for $n = 0$,

$$b_0 \int_0^{2g} \cos \frac{k\pi x}{2g} \, dx = \frac{2g}{k\pi} \left(\sin \frac{2k\pi g}{2g} - \sin \frac{k\pi \cdot 0}{2g} \right) b_0 = 0.$$

To obtain b_0, consider

$$\int_0^{2g} f(x) \, dx = \int_0^{2g} b_0 \, dx + \int_0^{2g} \sum_{n=1}^{\infty} b_n \cos \frac{n\pi x}{2g} \, dx = 2g b_0.$$

Hence

(7–32) $$b_0 = \frac{1}{2g} \int_0^{2g} f(x) \, dx.$$

If, as is customary, we select the notation so that f is represented by the series

(7–33) $$\frac{1}{2} B_0 + \sum_{n=1}^{\infty} B_n \cos \frac{n\pi x}{2g},$$

then we can write

(7–34) $$B_n = \frac{1}{g} \int_0^{2g} f(x) \cos \frac{n\pi x}{2g} \, dx \qquad (n = 0, 1, 2, \cdots).$$

If we wish to represent f by a series containing both sines and cosines, then we consider the interval on which f is defined to be that from $-g$ to g and try to determine numbers c_n and d_n so that

(7–35) $$f(x) = \frac{1}{2} d_0 + \sum_{n=1}^{\infty} \left(c_n \sin \frac{n\pi x}{g} + d_n \cos \frac{n\pi x}{g} \right).$$

As before, we have, for $k = 1, 2, \cdots$,

$$\int_{-g}^{g} f(x) \sin \frac{k\pi x}{g} \, dx = \frac{1}{2} d_0 \int_{-g}^{g} \sin \frac{k\pi x}{g} \, dx$$

$$+ \int_{-g}^{g} \sin \frac{k\pi x}{g} \sum_{n=1}^{\infty} \left(c_n \sin \frac{n\pi x}{g} + d_n \cos \frac{n\pi x}{g} \right) dx$$

$$= \frac{1}{2} d_0 \int_{-g}^{g} \sin \frac{k\pi x}{g} \, dx$$

$$+ \sum_{n=1}^{\infty} \left[c_n \int_{-g}^{g} \sin \frac{k\pi x}{g} \sin \frac{n\pi x}{g} \, dx + d_n \int_{-g}^{g} \sin \frac{k\pi x}{g} \cos \frac{n\pi x}{g} \, dx \right].$$

If $k = n$, then

$$\int_{-g}^{g} \left(\sin \frac{n\pi x}{g} \right)^2 dx = \frac{1}{2} \int_{-g}^{g} \left(1 - \cos \frac{2n\pi x}{g} \right) dx$$

$$= \frac{1}{2} \left[x - \frac{g}{2n\pi} \sin \frac{2n\pi x}{g} \right]_{-g}^{g} = g.$$

The remaining integrals may be easily evaluated with the help of some information about odd and even functions. A function f is called *odd* if $f(-x) = -f(x)$, and a function g is called *even* if $g(-x) = g(x)$, for every x in the respective domains of the functions. Then clearly

(7–36) $\displaystyle\int_{-a}^{a} f(x)\, dx = 0,$ and $\displaystyle\int_{-a}^{a} g(x)\, dx = 2 \int_{0}^{a} g(x)\, dx$

for odd functions f and even functions g. If f is odd and g even, then the product of f and g is odd, whereas, if both are odd or both even, their product is even.

Since $\sin rx$ and $\cos rx$ are, respectively, odd and even functions for every real number r,

(7–37) $\displaystyle\int_{-g}^{g} \sin \frac{k\pi x}{g} \cos \frac{n\pi x}{g}\, dx = 0.$

Therefore

$$\int_{-g}^{g} f(x) \sin \frac{k\pi x}{g}\, dx = g c_k \,,$$

and we have

(7–38) $c_k = \dfrac{1}{g} \displaystyle\int_{-g}^{g} f(x) \sin \dfrac{k\pi x}{g}\, dx$ $(k = 1, 2, \cdots).$

Now we compute, again for $k = 1, 2, \cdots$,

$$\int_{-g}^{g} f(x) \cos \frac{k\pi x}{g}\, dx = \frac{1}{2} d_0 \int_{-g}^{g} \cos \frac{k\pi x}{g}\, dx$$

$$+ \int_{-g}^{g} \cos \frac{k\pi x}{g} \sum_{n=1}^{\infty} \left(c_n \sin \frac{n\pi x}{g} + d_n \cos \frac{n\pi x}{g} \right) dx$$

$$= \frac{1}{2} d_0 \int_{-g}^{g} \cos \frac{k\pi x}{g}\, dx$$

$$+ \sum_{n=1}^{\infty} \left[c_n \int_{-g}^{g} \cos \frac{k\pi x}{g} \sin \frac{n\pi x}{g}\, dx + d_n \int_{-g}^{g} \cos \frac{k\pi x}{g} \cos \frac{n\pi x}{g}\, dx \right].$$

First, note that, by (7–36),

$$\int_{-g}^{g} \cos \frac{k\pi x}{g}\, dx = 2\int_{0}^{g} \cos \frac{k\pi x}{g}\, dx = 0.$$

By (7–37),

$$\int_{-g}^{g} \cos \frac{k\pi x}{g} \sin \frac{n\pi x}{g}\, dx = 0,$$

and, if $k \neq n$,

$$\int_{-g}^{g} \cos \frac{k\pi x}{g} \cos \frac{n\pi x}{g}\, dx = 0.$$

If $k = n$, we have

$$\int_{-g}^{g} \cos^2 \frac{n\pi x}{g}\, dx = \int_{0}^{g}\left(1 + \cos \frac{2n\pi x}{g}\right) dx = g.$$

Therefore it follows that

(7–39) $$d_k = \frac{1}{g}\int_{-g}^{g} f(x) \cos \frac{k\pi x}{g}\, dx \qquad (k = 1, 2, \cdots).$$

Since

$$\int_{-g}^{g} \sin \frac{n\pi x}{g}\, dx = 0 = \int_{-g}^{g} \cos \frac{n\pi x}{g}\, dx \quad (n = 1, 2, \cdots),$$

we may find d_0 from

$$\int_{-g}^{g} f(x)\, dx = \frac{1}{2}d_0 \int_{-g}^{g} dx = g d_0;$$

thus

(7–40) $$d_0 = \frac{1}{g}\int_{-g}^{g} f(x)\, dx.$$

It remains, of course, to show in what sense the representations (7–27), (7–30), and (7–35) are valid, with the coefficients as determined. We shall state without proof a typical theorem containing sufficient conditions for (7–35) to be true. Similar results hold for (7–27) and (7–30).

Theorem. Let $f(x)$ be defined for $-g \leq x \leq g$. Suppose f has a finite number of finite discontinuities and a finite number of relative maxima and minima. Define

$$c_n = \frac{1}{g}\int_{-g}^{g} f(x) \sin \frac{n\pi x}{g}\, dx \qquad (n = 1, 2, \cdots),$$

$$d_n = \frac{1}{g}\int_{-g}^{g} f(x) \cos \frac{n\pi x}{g}\, dx \qquad (n = 0, 1, \cdots).$$

Then, for every point x' with $-g < x' < g$ such that $f(x)$ is continuous at $x = x'$,

$$f(x') = \frac{1}{2} d_0 + \sum_{n=1}^{\infty} \left(c_n \sin \frac{n \pi x'}{g} + d_n \cos \frac{n \pi x'}{g} \right).$$

Moreover, if f is not continuous at $x = x'$, then the right side of this equation converges to

$$\frac{1}{2} \left[\lim_{\substack{x \to x' \\ x > x'}} f(x) + \lim_{\substack{x \to x' \\ x < x'}} f(x) \right].$$

Example 7–13. Given $f(x) = x - 3$ for $0 \leqq x \leqq 4$, find expansions (7–27) and (7–30) for f. Then find a representation of f of the form (7–35).

Solution: By (7–29),

$$a_n = \frac{1}{2} \int_0^4 (x - 3) \sin \frac{n \pi x}{4} \, dx$$

$$= \frac{1}{2} \left[-\frac{4(x-3)}{n} \cos \frac{n \pi x}{4} + \frac{16}{n^2 \pi^2} \sin \frac{n \pi x}{4} \right]_0^4$$

$$= -\frac{2}{n \pi} (\cos n \pi + 3).$$

Then

(7–41) $$f(x) = \sum_{n=1}^{\infty} \left[-\frac{2(\cos n \pi + 3)}{n \pi} \sin \frac{n \pi x}{4} \right]$$

$$= -\frac{4}{\pi} \sin \frac{\pi x}{4} - \frac{4}{\pi} \sin \frac{\pi x}{2} - \cdots,$$

except at $x = 0$ and $x = 4$.

Next, by (7–31) and (7–32),

$$b_0 = \frac{1}{4} \int_0^4 (x - 3) \, dx = -1,$$

and

$$b_k = \frac{1}{2} \int_0^4 (x - 3) \cos \frac{k \pi x}{4} \, dx = \frac{8}{k^2 \pi^2} (\cos k \pi - 1) \quad (k = 1, 2, \cdots).$$

Then, except possibly at $x = 0$ and $x = 4$,

$$(7\text{-}42) \quad f(x) = -1 + \sum_{n=1}^{\infty} \frac{8}{n^2\pi^2} (\cos n\pi - 1) \cos \frac{n\pi x}{4}$$

$$= -1 - \sum_{k=1}^{\infty} \frac{16}{(2k-1)^2\pi^2} \cos \frac{(2k-1)\pi x}{4}$$

$$= -1 - \frac{16}{\pi^2} \cos \frac{\pi x}{4} - \frac{16}{9\pi^2} \cos \frac{3\pi x}{4} - \frac{16}{25\pi^2} \cos \frac{5\pi x}{4} - \cdots.$$

Finally, to represent $f(x)$ in the form (7-35), it is necessary to replace f by a function defined for $-g \leq x \leq g$. This may be done by defining $F(x) = f(x+2) = x - 1$. Then $F(x)$ is defined for $-2 \leq x \leq 2$, and it follows that $f(x) = F(x-2)$. Applying (7-35), together with (7-38), (7-39), (7-40), we have

$$c_n = \frac{1}{2} \int_{-2}^{2} (x-1) \sin \frac{n\pi x}{2} \, dx = -\frac{8}{n\pi} \cos n\pi \quad (n = 1, 2, \cdots),$$

$$d_n = \frac{1}{2} \int_{-2}^{2} (x-1) \cos \frac{n\pi x}{2} \, dx = 0 \qquad (n = 1, 2, \cdots),$$

$$d_0 = \frac{1}{2} \int_{-2}^{2} (x-1) \, dx = -2;$$

hence, except possibly at $x = -2$ and $x = 2$,

$$F(x) = -1 + \sum_{n=1}^{\infty} -\frac{8}{n\pi} \cos n\pi \sin \frac{n\pi x}{2}$$

$$= -1 + \sum_{n=1}^{\infty} \frac{(-1)^{n+1} \cdot 8}{n\pi} \sin \frac{n\pi x}{2}.$$

Therefore

$$(7\text{-}43) \qquad f(x) = -1 + \sum_{n=1}^{\infty} \frac{(-1)^{n+1} \cdot 8}{n\pi} \sin \frac{n\pi(x-2)}{2}.$$

It is worth noting certain simplifications in evaluation of the integrals leading to c_n and d_n that result from properties of even and odd functions. Thus, for example,

$$\int_{-2}^{2} (x-1) \sin \frac{n\pi x}{2} \, dx = \int_{-2}^{2} x \sin \frac{n\pi x}{2} \, dx = 2 \int_{0}^{2} x \sin \frac{n\pi x}{2} \, dx,$$

and

$$\int_{-2}^{2} (x-1) \cos \frac{n\pi x}{2} \, dx = -\int_{-2}^{2} \cos \frac{n\pi x}{2} \, dx = -2 \int_{0}^{2} \cos \frac{n\pi x}{2} \, dx.$$

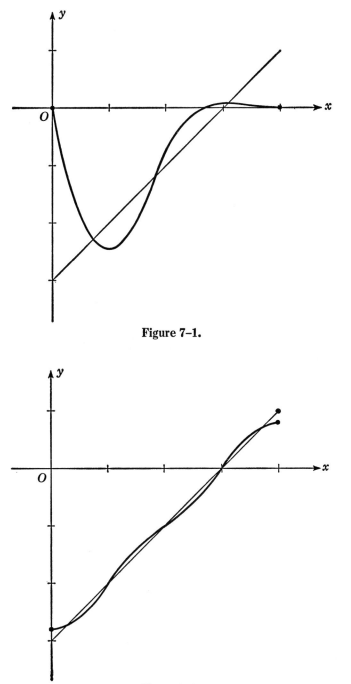

Figure 7-1.

Figure 7-2.

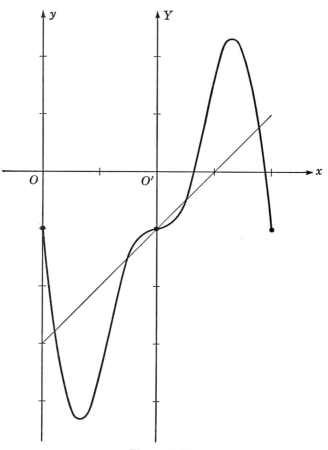

Figure 7–3.

That the integral of cos $(n\pi x/2)$ from -2 to 2 equals zero might have been predicted from the fact that the length of the interval, four units, is a multiple of the period of cos $(n\pi x/2)$ and from the fact that the integral of sin rx or cos rx over a complete period is zero. These remarks should be kept in mind in dealing with functions more complicated than that of our present example. That no cosine terms appear in (7–43) is merely a reflection of the fact that, if the graph of this function were translated one unit upward, it would represent an odd function. The sketches in Figures 7–1, 7–2, and 7–3 show the function approximated by the first three terms of the respective series (7–41), (7–42), and (7–43).

The Fourier sine and cosine series have period $4g$, and the mixed series containing both sines and cosines has period $2g$. Considered

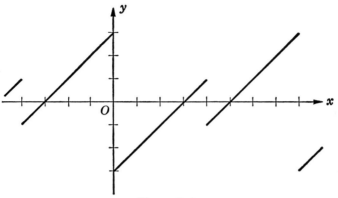

Figure 7–4.

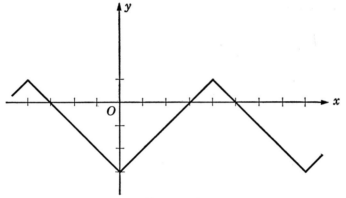

Figure 7–5.

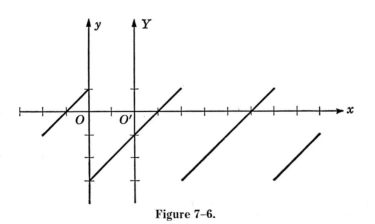

Figure 7–6.

beyond the original intervals, the three series represent periodic extensions of f. The sine series represents the extension of f, with period $4g$, which is an odd function. The cosine series represents the extension of f, with period $4g$, which is an even function. The third series represents the extension with period $2g$. Figures 7–4, 7–5, and 7–6 illustrate these extensions in connection with the function f of Example 7–13.

Example 7–14. Given

$$f(x) = \begin{cases} x & (0 \leqq x \leqq 2), \\ 1 & (2 < x \leqq 4). \end{cases}$$

Find representations (7–27), (7–30), and (7–35) for f.

Solution: The discontinuity of $f(x)$ at $x = 2$ requires that integrals from 0 to 4 be evaluated in two parts. Thus

$$2a_n = \int_0^2 f(x) \sin \frac{n\pi x}{4} \, dx + \int_2^4 f(x) \sin \frac{n\pi x}{4} \, dx$$

$$= \left[-\frac{4x}{n\pi} \cos \frac{n\pi x}{4} + \frac{16}{n^2\pi^2} \sin \frac{n\pi x}{4} \right]_0^2 - \frac{4}{n\pi} \left[\cos \frac{n\pi x}{4} \right]_2^4$$

$$= -\frac{4}{n\pi} \cos \frac{n\pi}{2} + \frac{16}{n^2\pi^2} \sin \frac{n\pi}{2} - \frac{4}{n\pi} \cos n\pi;$$

$$a_n = -\frac{2}{n\pi} \cos \frac{n\pi}{2} + \frac{8}{n^2\pi^2} \sin \frac{n\pi}{2} - \frac{2}{n\pi} \cos n\pi \quad (n = 1, 2, \cdots).$$

Hence, except for $x = 2$ and possibly $x = 0$ and $x = 4$,

$$f(x) = \sum_{n=1}^\infty \left[-\frac{2}{n\pi} \cos \frac{n\pi}{2} + \frac{8}{n^2\pi^2} \sin \frac{n\pi}{2} - \frac{2}{n\pi} \cos n\pi \right] \sin \frac{n\pi x}{4}$$

$$= \left(\frac{8}{\pi^2} + \frac{2}{\pi} \right) \sin \frac{\pi x}{4} + \left(\frac{2}{3\pi} - \frac{8}{9\pi^2} \right) \sin \frac{3\pi x}{4} - \frac{1}{\pi} \sin \pi x + \cdots .$$

Likewise, we find that

$$2b_n = \int_0^4 f(x) \cos \frac{n\pi x}{4} \, dx = \int_0^2 x \cos \frac{n\pi x}{4} \, dx + \int_2^4 \cos \frac{n\pi x}{4} \, dx$$

$$= \frac{8}{n\pi} \sin \frac{n\pi}{2} + \frac{16}{n^2\pi^2} \cos \frac{n\pi}{2} - \frac{16}{n^2\pi^2} - \frac{4}{n\pi} \sin \frac{n\pi}{2} \quad (n = 1, 2, \cdots),$$

$$4b_0 = \int_0^4 f(x) \, dx = \int_0^2 x \, dx + \int_2^4 dx = 4.$$

Thus we obtain the representation, except for $x = 2$ and possibly $x = 0$ and $x = 4$,

$$f(x) = 1 + \sum_{n=1}^{\infty} \left[\frac{2}{n\pi} \sin \frac{n\pi}{2} + \frac{8}{n^2\pi^2} \cos \frac{n\pi}{2} - \frac{8}{n^2\pi^2} \right] \cos \frac{n\pi x}{4}$$

$$= 1 + \left(\frac{2}{\pi} - \frac{8}{\pi^2} \right) \cos \frac{\pi x}{4} - \frac{4}{\pi^2} \cos \frac{\pi x}{2} - \left(\frac{2}{3\pi} + \frac{8}{9\pi^2} \right) \cos \frac{3\pi x}{4} + \cdots.$$

Finally, define $F(x) = f(x + 2)$, so that

$$F(x) = \begin{cases} x + 2 & (-2 \leqq x \leqq 0), \\ 1 & (0 < x \leqq 2). \end{cases}$$

For $F(x)$, we find

$$d_0 = 2, \quad c_n = -\frac{1}{n\pi} (\cos n\pi + 1), \quad d_n = \frac{2}{n^2\pi^2} (1 - \cos n\pi)$$

$$(n = 1, 2, \cdots).$$

There results the representation

$$F(x) = 1 + \sum_{n=1}^{\infty} \left[-\frac{1}{n\pi} (1 + \cos n\pi) \sin \frac{n\pi x}{2} \right.$$

$$\left. + \frac{2}{n^2\pi^2} (1 - \cos n\pi) \cos \frac{n\pi x}{2} \right]$$

$$= 1 + \frac{4}{\pi^2} \cos \frac{\pi x}{2} - \frac{1}{\pi} \sin \pi x + \frac{4}{9\pi^2} \cos \frac{3\pi x}{2}$$

$$- \frac{1}{2\pi} \sin 2\pi x + \cdots,$$

for $-2 < x < 2$, $x \neq 0$.

Fourier Series and Differential Equations. The most significant uses of Fourier series in the field of differential equations occur in connection with partial differential equations. These equations may possess infinitely larger families of solutions than ordinary equations; the problem of singling out from among all solutions of such an equation those which are periodic may be treated by Fourier series in a way similar to our use of power series in solving ordinary differential equations.

There is, however, one manner worth noting in which Fourier series can be used in the theory of ordinary linear equations

$p(D)y = f$. If f is periodic and represented by a sine, cosine, or mixed series, $f = \sum_{n=0}^{\infty} f_n$, one may first solve $p(D)y = f_n$, obtaining a solution y_n $(n = 1, 2, \cdots)$, and then form the series $y = \sum_{n=0}^{\infty} y_n$. Under appropriate conditions, y so obtained will satisfy the given equation. This technique is especially important in connection with mechanical or electrical vibrations; it extends in a natural way the ideas developed in Section 6–3 just before Example 6–3. We illustrate the technique in one example.

Example 7–15. Find the complete solution of $(D^2 - I)y = g$, where $g(x)$ is the Fourier sine series (7–41) of the function f of Example 7–13.

Solution: We have $g(x) = \sum_{n=1}^{\infty} g_n(x)$, where

$$g_n(x) = a_n \sin \frac{n\pi x}{4}.$$

Using undetermined coefficients, we find that

$$y_n = -\frac{16a_n}{n^2\pi^2 + 16} \sin \frac{n\pi x}{4}$$

is a particular solution of $(D^2 - I)y_n = g_n$. Hence the complete solution is

$$y = c_1 e^x + c_2 e^{-x} - 16 \sum_{n=1}^{\infty} \frac{a_n}{n^2\pi^2 + 16} \sin \frac{n\pi x}{4},$$

where $a_n = \dfrac{2}{n\pi} (\cos n\pi + 3)$, as found in Example 7–13.

EXERCISES

1. Find the Fourier sine series and cosine series for $f(x) = 1$ $(0 \leq x \leq 2)$ and the mixed series for $F(x) = f(x + 1)$ $(-1 \leq x \leq 1)$.

2. Find the sine and cosine series for $f(x) = 1 - 2x$ $(0 \leq x \leq 2)$ and the mixed series for $F(x) = f(x + 1) = -1 - 2x$ $(-1 \leq x \leq 1)$.

3. Find the sine and cosine series for
$$f(x) = \begin{cases} 1 & (0 \leq x \leq 1), \\ x - 2 & (1 < x \leq 3); \end{cases}$$
also find the mixed series for
$$F(x) = f\left(x + \frac{3}{2}\right) = \begin{cases} 1 & \left(-\frac{3}{2} \leq x \leq -\frac{1}{2}\right), \\ x - \frac{1}{2} & \left(-\frac{1}{2} < x \leq \frac{3}{2}\right). \end{cases}$$

4. Find the sine and cosine series for
$$f(x) = \begin{cases} 1 & (0 \leq x \leq 1), \\ 2 & (1 < x \leq 2), \\ -1 & (2 < x \leq 4); \end{cases}$$
also find the mixed series for
$$F(x) = f(x + 2) = \begin{cases} 1 & (-2 \leq x \leq -1), \\ 2 & (-1 < x \leq 0), \\ -1 & (0 < x \leq 2). \end{cases}$$

5. Find the sine and cosine series for $f(x) = x^2 - 3x + 2$ $(0 \leq x \leq 4)$, and the mixed series for $F(x) = f(x + 2) = x^2 + x$ $(-2 \leq x \leq 2)$.

6. Find the sine and cosine series for $f(x) = \sin \pi x$ $(0 \leq x \leq 1)$.

7. Find the complete solution of $(D^2 + I)y = f_1$, where f_1 is the Fourier sine series for the function f in exercise 3.

8. Let
$$f(x) = \begin{cases} -1 & (-2 \leq x \leq 0), \\ 1 & (0 < x \leq 2). \end{cases}$$
Let f_1 be the mixed Fourier series for f and find the complete solution of $(D + I)y = f_1$.

9. Let $f_1(t)$ be the periodic extension of $f(t) = t$ $(-1 \leq t < 1)$. Let $E(t)$ be the Fourier sine series for $f_1(t)$. An electric network as in Figure 6–4 has $L = 1$ henry, $R = 1$ ohm, and $C = 1$ farad. Express formally the steady-state value of the charge on the capacitor as a trigonometric series, given that the input is $E(t)$. (This is the case of an applied *saw-tooth* e.m.f.)

10. Solve the same problem as in exercise 9, using $E(t) = f_1(t)$, where f_1 is the function of exercise 8. (This is the case of a *square-wave* input.)

Appendix

1

Laplace Transforms

GENERAL RELATIONSHIPS

The parameters a, b, c are real constants.

(1) $L(f_1 + f_2) = Lf_1 + Lf_2$.

(2) $L^{-1}(F_1 + F_2) = L^{-1}F_1 + L^{-1}F_2$.

(3) $L(cf) = cLf$.

(4) $L^{-1}(cF) = cL^{-1}F$.

(5) If $F = Lf, f_1(t) = f(bt), F_1(x) = F\left(\dfrac{x}{b}\right)$, then $F_1 = bLf_1$.

(6) If $F = Lf, f_1(t) = e^{at}f(t), F_1(x) = F(x - a)$, then $F_1 = Lf_1$.

(7) If $F = Lf, f_1(t) = -tf(t)$, then $F' = Lf_1$.

TABLE OF TRANSFORMS OF SPECIAL FUNCTIONS

The domain of f is the set of all non-negative real numbers; the domain of F is the set of all $x \geq k$ for some real k. The parameters are real constants.

	$f(t)[=(L^{-1}F)(t)]$	$F(x)[=(Lf)(x)]$
(8)	0	0
(9)	1	$\dfrac{1}{x}$
(10)	t	$\dfrac{1}{x^2}$
(11)	t^2	$\dfrac{2!}{x^3}$
(12)	$t^n \quad (n = 0, 1, 2, \cdots)$	$\dfrac{n!}{x^{n+1}}$
(13)	$\dfrac{1}{\sqrt{t}}$	$\sqrt{\dfrac{\pi}{x}}$

$f(t)[=(L^{-1}F)(t)]$	$F(x)[=(Lf)(x)]$
(14) $\sqrt{t}$	$\dfrac{\sqrt{\pi}}{2x^{3/2}}$
(15) $t^c \quad (c>0)$	$\dfrac{\Gamma(c+1)}{x^{c+1}}$
(16) e^{at}	$\dfrac{1}{x-a}$
(17) $t\,e^{at}$	$\dfrac{1}{(x-a)^2}$
(18) $t^2 e^{at}$	$\dfrac{2!}{(x-a)^3}$
(19) $t^n e^{at} \quad (n=1,2,\cdots)$	$\dfrac{n!}{(x-a)^{n+1}}$
(20) $t^c e^{at} \quad (c>0)$	$\dfrac{\Gamma(c+1)}{(x-a)^{c+1}}$
(21) $\dfrac{e^{at}-e^{bt}}{a-b} \quad (a\neq b)$	$\dfrac{1}{(x-a)(x-b)}$
(22) $\dfrac{ae^{at}-be^{bt}}{a-b} \quad (a\neq b)$	$\dfrac{x}{(x-a)(x-b)}$
(23) $e^{at}(1+at)$	$\dfrac{x}{(x-a)^2}$
(24) $1-(1-at)e^{at}$	$\dfrac{a^2}{x(x-a)^2}$
(25) $\dfrac{(c-b)e^{at}+(a-c)e^{bt}+(b-a)e^{ct}}{(a-b)(b-c)(c-a)}$ $(a\neq b\neq c\neq a)$	$\dfrac{1}{(x-a)(x-b)(x-c)}$
(26) $\sin bt$	$\dfrac{b}{x^2+b^2}$
(27) $\cos bt$	$\dfrac{x}{x^2+b^2}$
(28) $\sinh bt \left(=\dfrac{e^{bt}-e^{-bt}}{2}\right)$	$\dfrac{b}{x^2-b^2}$
(29) $\cosh bt \left(=\dfrac{e^{bt}+e^{-bt}}{2}\right)$	$\dfrac{x}{x^2-b^2}$
(30) $e^{at}\sin bt$	$\dfrac{b}{(x-a)^2+b^2}$
(31) $e^{at}\cos bt$	$\dfrac{x-a}{(x-a)^2+b^2}$

	$f(t)[=(L^{-1}F)(t)]$	$F(x)[=(Lf)(x)]$
(32)	$e^{at} \sinh bt$	$\dfrac{b}{(x-a)^2 - b^2}$
(33)	$e^{at} \cosh bt$	$\dfrac{x-a}{(x-a)^2 - b^2}$
(34)	$1 - \cos bt$	$\dfrac{b^2}{x(x^2+b^2)}$
(35)	$bt - \sin bt$	$\dfrac{b^2}{x^2(x^2+b^2)}$
(36)	$t \sin bt$	$\dfrac{2bx}{(x^2+b^2)^2}$
(37)	$t \cos bt$	$\dfrac{x^2-b^2}{(x^2+b^2)^2}$
(38)	$\sin bt - bt \cos bt$	$\dfrac{2b^3}{(x^2+b^2)^2}$
(39)	$\sin bt + bt \cos bt$	$\dfrac{2bx^2}{(x^2+b^2)^2}$
(40)	$t^2 \sin bt$	$\dfrac{2b(3x^2-b^2)}{(x^2+b^2)^3}$
(41)	$t^2 \cos bt$	$\dfrac{2x(x^2-3b^2)}{(x^2+b^2)^3}$
(42)	$t^n \sin bt \quad (n = 0, 1, 2, \cdots)$	$(-1)^n \dfrac{d^n}{dx^n}\left(\dfrac{b}{x^2+b^2}\right)$
(43)	$t^n \cos bt \quad (n = 0, 1, 2, \cdots)$	$(-1)^n \dfrac{d^n}{dx^n}\left(\dfrac{x}{x^2+b^2}\right)$
(44)	$(3 - b^2 t^2) \sin bt - 3bt \cos bt$	$\dfrac{8b^5}{(x^2+b^2)^3}$
(45)	$t \sin bt - bt^2 \cos bt$	$\dfrac{8b^3 x}{(x^2+b^2)^3}$
(46)	$\begin{cases} \dfrac{e^{at} - e^{bt}}{t} & (t > 0) \\ a - b & (t = 0) \end{cases}$	$\ln\left(\dfrac{x-b}{x-a}\right)$
(47)	$\begin{cases} \dfrac{\sin bt}{t} & (t > 0) \\ b & (t = 0) \end{cases}$	$\operatorname{arc\,cot} \dfrac{x}{b}$

2

Some Results from Calculus

CONCEPT OF FUNCTION

If A, B are sets, a *relation* is a set R of pairs (x, y) with x in A and y in B. The *domain* of R is the set of all first elements x, and the *range* is the set of all second elements y. If for every x in the domain of R there is only one y such that (x, y) is in R, then R is a (*single-valued*) *function*, and y is denoted by $R(x)$. (See also Section 4–5.) Sometimes the function also is written $R(x)$.

CONTINUITY

A real- or complex-valued function f of a real number x is continuous over its domain D if, for every c in D, $\lim\limits_{x \to c} f(x) = f(c)$, where the limit is taken over D. If

$$\lim_{\substack{x \to c \\ x > c}} f(x) \neq \lim_{\substack{x \to c \\ x < c}} f(x),$$

where the one-sided limits exist and are finite, then f has a *finite discontinuity* at c.

SERIES

A *series* $a_1 + a_2 + \cdots$ is a sequence of partial sums

$$\left(a_1, a_1 + a_2, \cdots, \sum_{k=1}^{n} a_k, \cdots \right),$$

where the a_i are numbers or functions. It *converges* to S if

$$\lim_{n \to \infty} \sum_{k=1}^{n} a_k = S.$$

It *diverges* when no finite S exists.

L'HOPITAL'S RULE

Let f, g be continuous over $I: a \leqq x \leqq b$, let c be in I, let $f'(x)$, $g'(x)$ exist for x in I, $x \neq c$, and suppose $g(x)$, $g'(x) \neq 0$ for x in I, $x \neq c$. If $f(c) = g(c) = 0$, then

$$\lim_{x \to c} \frac{f(x)}{g(x)} = \lim_{x \to c} \frac{f'(x)}{g'(x)},$$

provided the limit on the right exists. (Many variations and extensions of the rule are found in books on advanced calculus or function theory.)

FUNDAMENTAL THEOREM OF INTEGRAL CALCULUS

If f is real-valued and continuous over its domain $I: a \leqq x \leqq b$, and if F is an anti-derivative of f so that $F'(x) = f(x)$ for x in I, then

$$\int_a^b f(x)\, dx = F(b) - F(a).$$

DIFFERENTIATION OF INTEGRALS

Under suitable hypotheses (see advanced calculus books for details),

$$\frac{\partial}{\partial x} \int_{a(x)}^{b(x)} f(x, t)\, dt = \int_{a(x)}^{b(x)} \frac{\partial}{\partial x} f(x, t)\, dt + f(x, b(x))b'(x)$$
$$- f(x, a(x))a'(x).$$

In particular,

$$\frac{d}{dx} \int_a^x f(t)\, dt = f(x).$$

DIFFERENTIATION OF DETERMINANTS

If the elements of a determinant $\Delta(x)$ are differentiable functions of x, then $\Delta'(x)$ is the sum of all determinants obtainable from $\Delta(x)$ by replacing all entries in a column by the derivatives of those elements, but making no other changes. Thus, if

$$\Delta = \begin{vmatrix} f_{11} & f_{12} & f_{13} \\ f_{21} & f_{22} & f_{23} \\ f_{31} & f_{32} & f_{33} \end{vmatrix},$$

then

$$\Delta' = \begin{vmatrix} f'_{11} & f_{12} & f_{13} \\ f'_{21} & f_{22} & f_{23} \\ f'_{31} & f_{32} & f_{33} \end{vmatrix} + \begin{vmatrix} f_{11} & f'_{12} & f_{13} \\ f_{21} & f'_{22} & f_{23} \\ f_{31} & f'_{32} & f_{33} \end{vmatrix} + \begin{vmatrix} f_{11} & f_{12} & f'_{13} \\ f_{21} & f_{22} & f'_{23} \\ f_{31} & f_{32} & f'_{33} \end{vmatrix}$$

MEAN VALUE THEOREM OF DIFFERENTIAL CALCULUS

See Section 1–1.

SOME SPECIAL FUNCTIONS

Hyperbolic functions:

$$\sinh x = \frac{e^x - e^{-x}}{2}, \qquad \cosh x = \frac{e^x + e^{-x}}{2},$$

$$\tanh x = \frac{\sinh x}{\cosn x}, \qquad \coth x = \frac{\cosh x}{\sinh x},$$

$$\text{sech } x = \frac{1}{\cosh x}, \qquad \text{csch } x = \frac{1}{\sinh x};$$

$$\cosh^2 x - \sinh^2 x = 1, \qquad \tanh^2 x + \text{sech}^2 x = 1,$$

$$\frac{d}{dx} \sinh x = \cosh x, \qquad \frac{d}{dx} \cosh x = \sinh x,$$

$$\frac{d}{dx} \tanh x = \text{sech}^2 x.$$

Inverse functions are $\sinh^{-1} x$, $\cosh^{-1} x$, etc.

Inverse trigonometric functions:

$$y = \sin^{-1} x \; (-1 \leq x \leq 1) \text{ means } x = \sin y, \; -\frac{\pi}{2} \leq y \leq \frac{\pi}{2};$$

$$y = \cos^{-1} x \; (-1 \leq x \leq 1) \text{ means } x = \cos y, \; 0 \leq y \leq \pi;$$

$$y = \tan^{-1} x \text{ means } x = \tan y, \; -\frac{\pi}{2} < y < \frac{\pi}{2}.$$

Appendix

3

Notations

SOME SYMBOLS POSSESSING PERMANENT OR SEMI-PERMANENT MEANINGS IN THIS BOOK

π	$3.14159265\cdots$
e	$2.7182818\cdots$
D	derivative operator (see Chapter 4)
I	identity operator; current in electric networks
Z	impedance
E	electromotive force
d	differential symbol
L	Laplace operator
A^{-1}	inverse of operator A

SUM AND PRODUCT SYMBOLS

If $a_1, \cdots, a_n$ are given numbers or functions, their sum is designated by $\sum_{k=1}^{n} a_k$, where the symbol k may be replaced by any other free symbol without changing the meaning. Properties:

$$\sum_{k=p}^{p} a_k = a_p;$$

$$\sum_{k=1}^{p} a_k + a_{p+1} = \sum_{k=1}^{p+1} a_k;$$

$$\sum_{k=1}^{n} a_k = \sum_{j=1-p}^{n-p} a_{p+j}.$$

Similarly, the product of $a_1, \cdots, a_n$ is written $\prod_{k=1}^{n} a_k$. If $a_k = k$, then $\prod_{k=1}^{n} a_k$ is also written $n!$. By agreement, $0! = 1$. In finite sums, the order of summation is immaterial:

$$\sum_{j=1}^{n} \sum_{i=1}^{m} a_{ij} = \sum_{i=1}^{m} \sum_{j=1}^{n} a_{ij};$$

similarly for products.

GREEK ALPHABET

A, α	Alpha		N, ν	Nu
B, β	Beta		Ξ, ξ	Xi
Γ, γ	Gamma		O, o	Omicron
Δ, δ	Delta		Π, π	Pi
E, ϵ	Epsilon		P, ρ	Rho
Z, ζ	Zeta		Σ, σ	Sigma
H, η	Eta		T, τ	Tau
Θ, θ	Theta		Υ, υ	Upsilon
I, ι	Iota		Φ, ϕ	Phi
K, κ	Kappa		X, χ	Chi
Λ, λ	Lambda		Ψ, ψ	Psi
M, μ	Mu		Ω, ω	Omega

4

Answers to Odd-Numbered Exercises

1. $x = -2, 0, 4$.

3. $x = \pm 1$.

5. $x = 2, 3$.

7. $x = -1$.

9. All values of x, except $x = n\pi$ ($n = 0, \pm 1, \pm 2, \cdots$).

11. Infinitely many solutions; every interval $(2n - 1)(\pi/2)$ $< x < (2n + 1)(\pi/2)$ ($n = 0, \pm 1, \pm 2, \cdots$) contains exactly one solution.

13. Exactly one solution, $x = \log_e b$, if $b > 0$; no solution if $b \leqq 0$.

15. $y = -1/t; y = -1/t + c$.

17. $y_1 = \dfrac{1}{3} \ln |t - 1| - \dfrac{1}{6} \ln (t^2 + t + 1) - \dfrac{1}{\sqrt{3}} \tan^{-1} \dfrac{2t + 1}{\sqrt{3}}$; $y = y_1 + c$.

19. $y = \ln |t + 1 + \sqrt{t^2 + 2t}|; y = \ln |t + 1 + \sqrt{t^2 + 2t}| + c$.

21. $y_1 = t - (1/2) \ln |t| + (5/2) \ln |t - 2|$; $y = y_1 + c$.

23. 1.

25. 2.

27. $y(x) = e^{ax}$ is a solution for every real number a.

29. $y(x) = \sin (x + c)$ is a solution for every real number c.

31. Ex. 18: function: all real t; solution: all real t. Ex. 20: function: all $t > 0$; solution: all $t > 0$. Ex. 21: function: all real t such that $t \neq 0$, $t \neq 2$; solution: all t such that $t > 2$, or all t such that $0 < t < 2$, or all t such that $t < 0$.

1. $ty' = y$.

3. $ty' + 2y = 0$.

PAGE 12, SECTION 1–2 (Continued)

5. $y + ty' \ln y' = 0.$

7. $y' = y\left(1 + \dfrac{2}{t}\right).$

9. $(1 - y')(xy' - y) = y'.$

11. $y'' + 2y' + y = 0.$

13. $2yy'' = y'^2.$

15. $ty'^2 - 2yy' - 4y = 0.$

17. $n^{n+1}y^n = tn^n y^{n-1}y' - (y')^{n+1}.$

19. $y = 0$ and $y = -4t.$

PAGE 16, SECTION 1–3

5. $x^2 + y^2 = s$ if $s \geq 0.$

7. All points (x, y) for which $1 - x + y > 0$; i.e., all points "above" the line $y = x - 1.$

9. $6\sqrt{5}/25.$

11. Every solution has a minimum value at any intersection with $y = -|x|$ except $(0, 0)$; it has a maximum at any intersection with $y = |x|$ except $(0, 0)$.

PAGE 19, SECTION 1–4

1. Any $A \geq |k|.$
3. Any $A \geq 1.$

PAGE 22, SECTION 1–5

1. $\dfrac{dy}{du} = 1$, if $u = $ principal arc $\sin x$ $(-1 < x < 1)$;   no restrictions.

3. $v\left(vx\dfrac{dv}{dx} + v^2 - 1\right) = 0$; $x = 0$ may be excluded.

5. $x(v + 1)\dfrac{dv}{dx} + v^3 - 2v^2 - v = 0$; $x \neq 0$, and $y \neq 0$ for all $x.$

7. $3\dfrac{dy}{dt} + 4y = e^{et}$; $x > 0.$

9. $\dfrac{d^2y}{dt^2} + y = 0$; $x > 0.$

PAGE 25, SECTION 1–6

1. $dx - dy = 0.$
3. $3x \, dx + 2y \, dy = 0.$
5. $2xy \, dx - 3(x^2 + 1) \, dy = 0.$
7. $(x - 3y - 1) \, dx + (3x - y + 1) \, dy = 0.$
9. $(xy' - y)(x + yy') = (a^2 - b^2)y'.$
11. $64 = 9(y')^2[9x(y')^2 - 9y(y')^2 + 4]^2.$
15. $(y - xy')y''' + 3x(y'')^2 = 0.$

PAGE 29, SECTION 1–7

1. $y = x^2$, or $x = c$, $y = c^2.$
3. $y = -x^2 + \dfrac{1}{4}$, or $x = \dfrac{1}{2}\cot c$, $y = -\dfrac{1}{4}\csc^2 c + \dfrac{1}{2}.$
5. No envelope.
7. $y = xy' + x^2 + (2y - xy')^2.$

PAGE 33, SECTION 2–2

1. $y^2 = cx^{-1}.$
3. $y = \dfrac{c}{x + 1} \cdot e^{x - (1/2)x^2}; \ y = \dfrac{2}{x + 1} \cdot e^{x - (1/2)x^2 - (1/2)}.$
5. $2y^2(c + \sin^{-1} x) = 1.$
7. $2x^3 - 6x + 3y^2 + 6\ln |y| + c = 0.$
9. $6y^{-1} + \ln (x + 1)^2 - \ln (x^2 - x + 1)$
$$-2\sqrt{3}\tan^{-1}\left(\frac{2x - 1}{\sqrt{3}}\right) = c.$$

PAGE 35, SECTION 2–3

1. $x^6 + y^2 = cx^4.$
3. $\ln |y - x^2| = x^3 - 2x + c.$
5. $2(x^2 + y^2)^{3/2} = y^2 - x^2 + c(x^2 + y^2).$
7. $\ln y[3\ln^2 x + \ln^2 y] = c.$

PAGE 38, SECTION 2–4

1. $2y^2 + 2xy - 3x^2 = c.$
3. $x + x\cos (y/x) = c\sin (y/x).$
5. Not homogeneous.
7. $y + x + xe^{y/x}\ln (cx) = 0.$

PAGE 38, SECTION 2–4 (Continued)

9. $\ln(cx) = \sin^{-1}(y/x)$.

11. $cx^2(y - x) = (y - 2x)^2$.

13. $2 \tan^{-1}\dfrac{y - 2}{x + 1} = \ln[(x + 1)^2 + (y - 2)^2] + c$.

PAGE 41, SECTION 2–5

1. $x^3y - 3x^2 + y^3 = c$.

3. $\cos(2xy) - 6xy^2 = c$.

5. $x^2 + 5xy^3 + y^4 - 2x^2y = cy$.

7. $e^{x^3} + xe^{2y} - 3y = c$; $e^{x^3} + xe^{2y} - 3y = 1$.

9. $x^4y + \ln|2x + 3y| = c$.

11. (d) $x^3 - x^2y + x^2y^2 = c$.

PAGE 44, SECTION 2–6

1. x^3; $5x^4y - 4x^5y^2 = c$.

3. $x + 1$; $20(x + 1)^2y + 4x^5 + 5x^4 = c$.

5. y^{-3}; $x + 3x^2y^2 - 4xy^3 = cy^2$.

7. $(\ln y)/y$; $(\ln y)^2(x^3 + y^3) = c$.

9. No integrating factor of the specified form exists.

11. $x^{-6/5}y^{-7/5}$; $x^{14/5}y^{-7/5} - 7x^{-1/5}y^{-2/5} = c$.

PAGE 48, SECTION 2–7

1. $y = \dfrac{1}{3}x + \dfrac{2}{9} + ce^{-3x}$.

3. $y = 2xe^x + ce^x$.

5. $y = e^x + ce^{-x^3/3}$.

7. $y = \dfrac{1}{2}\sin x \tan x + c \sec x$;

$\qquad y = \dfrac{1}{2}\sin x \tan x + \dfrac{1}{4}(2\sqrt{2} - 1)\sec x$.

9. $y = -\dfrac{1}{2}\csc x + c \sin x$.

13. $y^3 = \dfrac{1}{3}x^3 + cx^{-6}$.

15. $1 = y^4 + cy^4e^{2x^2}$.

PAGE 52, SECTION 2–8

1. $y = c_1\sqrt{|1 + 2x|} + c_2.$

3. $y = c_1 x + (1 + c_1^2) \ln |x - c_1| + c_2.$

5. $\ln \left| \dfrac{c_1 + y}{c_1 - y} \right| = 3c_1 x + c_2$, and $y(3x + c) = 2$, and

$\quad y = c_1 \tan \left[-(3/2) c_1 x + c_2 \right]$, and $y = c.$

7. $y = 2x + c_1 [x\sqrt{1 - x^2} + \sin^{-1} x] + c_2$ if $1 - x^2 > 0$, and

$\quad y = 2x + c_1 [x\sqrt{x^2 - 1} - \ln |x + \sqrt{x^2 - 1}|] + c_2$
$\qquad\qquad\qquad\qquad\qquad\qquad\qquad$ if $x^2 - 1 > 0.$

9. $y = (1/2) + c_1 e^{-x/2} + c_2 e^{-4x/3}.$

PAGE 54, SECTION 2–9

1. $y = c_1 - 2x, \quad z = \dfrac{1}{2} e^{c_1} x^2 + c_2.$

3. $y = c_1 e^x - c_2 e^{-x}, \quad z = c_1 e^x + c_2 e^{-x}.$

5. $y = c_1 x, \quad 16c_1^2 x^3 = 3z^2 + c_2.$

7. $y = 2c_1 e^x + c_2 e^{-2x} - \dfrac{7}{2} x - \dfrac{9}{4}, \quad z = c_1 e^x - c_2 e^{-2x} - \dfrac{1}{2} x - \dfrac{7}{4}.$

9. $y = \dfrac{1}{6} x^3 + x^2 + c_1 x + c_2,$

$\quad z = -\dfrac{1}{6} x^3 - \dfrac{1}{2} x^2 + (1 - c_1)x - c_2 + c_1.$

PAGE 55, CHAPTER 2, MISCELLANEOUS

1. $y = ce^{x^3/3}.$

3. $y = c_1 e^{2t} + c_2 e^{-2t} + c_3 t + c_4.$

5. $y = c_1 x, z = c_2 x; \quad y = x, z = 2x.$

7. $cx^4 e^{-2y^2} - 4x^4 e^{-2y^2} \displaystyle\int_{y_0}^{y} e^{2t^2} dt = 1.$

9. $3x^2 - 2x(y + 1) - 2(y + 1)^2 = c.$

11. $2e^x \cos y + x^2 - y^2 = c.$

13. $y = c_1 x, \quad 2z = (3c_1 - 1)x^2 + c_2.$

15. $xy + \tan^{-1}(y/x) = c; \quad xy + \tan^{-1}(y/x) = \sqrt{3} + \dfrac{\pi}{3}.$

17. $x + y + y^3 = cy^2.$

19. $2x + 2\ln|x - 1| - 4\ln|y - 1| - (y + 1)^2 = c.$

21. $xy^2 + 2x^2 = c.$

23. $x(x + y) = cy.$

25. $4e^{-2x} + e^{-8y} = c.$

27. $y^2 = 2x^2 + cx^3.$

29. $y = \dfrac{1}{3} u$

$$+ \frac{1}{\sqrt{|u|}} \left[c_1 \cos\left(\frac{\sqrt{3}}{2} \ln|u|\right) + c_2 \sin\left(\frac{\sqrt{3}}{2} \ln|u|\right) \right],$$

$$z = \frac{1}{3} u + \frac{1}{2} \cdot \frac{1}{\sqrt{|u|}} \left[-(\sqrt{3}c_1 + c_2) \sin\left(\frac{\sqrt{3}}{2} \ln|u|\right) \right.$$

$$\left. + (\sqrt{3}c_2 - c_1) \cos\left(\frac{\sqrt{3}}{2} \ln|u|\right) \right],$$

where $u = x + y + z.$

PAGE 63, SECTION 3–2

1. (a) $M = 100(0.98)^{t/18}$;   617.6 years.

   (b) $M = 100(0.87)^{t/10}$;   49.8 years.

3. Continuously: 13.86 years;   quarterly: 13.95 years.

5. a) \$1050.00; b) \$1050.97; c) \$1051.16; d) \$1051.25;
e) \$1051.26;   f) \$1051.27.

7. 65.8 minutes;   371.3 minutes.

9. 180.7 grams.

11. 2.063 days; 10 days.

13. 13.69 seconds.

15. $u = u_0 e^{-kt} + U(1 - e^{-kt}).$

17. $U = 210.29 \cdot 10^6$; $u = \dfrac{1472}{7 + 361\,(3/19)^{t/60}} \cdot 10^6.$

19. 23.10 years.

PAGE 69, SECTION 3–3

1. $x = 6t + 12 - 28e^{(t/2)-1}$; maximum $x = 12(1 + \ln 3 - \ln 7)$

$$= 1.8324.$$

3. $y = -\dfrac{g}{2v_0^2 \cos^2 \alpha} x^2 + x \tan \alpha.$

5. $x = (3/2) \sin 2t,$ $y = -2e^t + t^2 + 2t + 7.$

7. $\theta = \sin t$; smallest $\theta_0 = \pi$ for full coverage of circle; suggests
clock escapement or (if θ is small) pendulum.

PAGE 69, SECTION 3–3 (Continued)

9. $40/\sqrt{33} = 6.95$ miles per second.

11. $x = -u_0 t + \dfrac{m_0 u_0}{k}\left(1 - \dfrac{k}{m_0}t\right)\ln\left(1 - \dfrac{k}{m_0}t\right).$

PAGE 73, SECTION 3–4

1. $y = ce^{-3x} + \dfrac{2}{3}x - \dfrac{2}{9}.$

3. $xy - x^3 y + \dfrac{y^3}{3} - \dfrac{x^2}{2} = c.$

5. $y = (x+1)^4.$

7. $y = ce^{2x} + \dfrac{1}{2}x + \dfrac{1}{4}.$

9. $xy = c.$

11. $x = -ay + c.$

13. $x^2 + ny^2 = c.$

15. $ay^2 + 2x = c.$

17. $y^2 + 4cx = 4c^2$ (a *self-orthogonal* family).

PAGE 79, SECTION 3–5

3. $M = -kx/r, N = -ky/r$, where $r = \sqrt{x^2 + y^2}; V = -kr;$ circles $r = c.$

5. $V = \int M\,dx + \int N\,dy.$

7. $(\pm xf(r)/r, \pm yf(r)/r).$

9. Components $kx/r^2, ky/r^2.$

11. They are orthogonal trajectories of each other.

15. The fields of exercise 9, with $f(r) = k/r, k \geqq 0.$

17. Part of locus: $y = 0$; if $q_1 q_2 < 0$, no additional locus; if $q_1 = q_2$, additional locus is $x = 0$; if $q_1 q_2 > 0, q_1 \neq q_2$, additional locus is the circle $(1 - \mu^2)(x^2 + y^2) + 2(1 + \mu^2)x + 1 - \mu^2 = 0$, where $\mu = (q_1/q_2)^{1/3}.$

PAGE 81, CHAPTER 3, MISCELLANEOUS

1. $3y^2 + 2x^2 = c.$

3. 4.08 per cent.

5. $r = ks + r_0.$ (HINT: Let $\dfrac{dm}{ds}$ be proportional to surface area.)

7. 45.46 pounds.

PAGE 81, CHAPTER 3, MISCELLANEOUS (Continued)

9. $2x^2 - y^2 = c$.

11. Tank never empties. As $t \to \infty$, V approaches 0.058 cubic feet.

13. \$27,000;   in 1.7 weeks;   in 6.9 weeks.

15. Conjugate: $(e^x \sin y, \ e^x \cos y)$;   potential: $e^x \sin y$.

PAGE 86, SECTION 4–2

1. $y = ce^{2x} - \dfrac{1}{4}(2x^2 + 2x - 1)$.

3. $y = ce^{5x} - \left(\dfrac{3}{5}x^3 + \dfrac{9}{25}x^2 + \dfrac{118}{125}x + \dfrac{118}{625}\right)$.

5. $y = ce^{x^2/2} + x^4$.

7. Same as exercise 1.

PAGE 93, SECTION 4–3

1. $y = c_1 e^{m_1 x} + c_2 e^{m_2 x}$, where $m_1 = \dfrac{5 + \sqrt{29}}{2}$, $m_2 = \dfrac{5 - \sqrt{29}}{2}$.

3. $y = c_1 e^{m_1 x} + c_2 e^{m_2 x}$, where $m_1 = 1 + \sqrt{5}$, $m_2 = 1 - \sqrt{5}$.

5. $y = c_1 \cos x + c_2 \sin x$.

7. $y = c_1 e^{m_1 x} + c_2 e^{m_2 x}$, where $m_1 = -\dfrac{k}{2} + \dfrac{1}{2}\sqrt{k^2 - 4l}$,

$$m_2 = -\dfrac{k}{2} - \dfrac{1}{2}\sqrt{k^2 - 4l}.$$

PAGE 97, SECTION 4–4

1. $y = c_1 e^x + c_2 e^{-6x} - \left(\dfrac{1}{6}x^3 + \dfrac{5}{12}x^2 + \dfrac{31}{36}x + \dfrac{185}{216}\right)$.

3. $y = c_1 \cos 2x + c_2 \sin 2x + \dfrac{1}{4}(1 - x)$;

$$y = -\dfrac{1}{4}\cos 2x + \dfrac{1}{8}\sin 2x + \dfrac{1}{4}(1 - x).$$

5. $y = e^{-x/2}\left(c_1 \cos \dfrac{\sqrt{3}}{2}x + c_2 \sin \dfrac{\sqrt{3}}{2}x\right) + \dfrac{1}{3}e^x$.

7. $y = c_1 e^{3x} + c_2 e^{-3x} - \dfrac{1}{8}e^x - \dfrac{1}{2}xe^{-3x}$.

PAGE 97, SECTION 4–4 (Continued)

11. $y = c_1 e^{m_1 x} + c_2 e^{m_2 x} + \dfrac{e^{mx}}{(m - m_1)(m - m_2)}$,

$$\text{if } m \neq m_1,\ m \neq m_2,\ m_1 \neq m_2;$$

$y = c_1 e^{m_1 x} + c_2 e^{m_2 x} + \dfrac{x e^{m_1 x}}{m_1 - m_2}$, if $m = m_1,\ m_1 \neq m_2$;

$y = e^{m_1 x}(c_1 + c_2 x) + \dfrac{e^{mx}}{(m - m_1)^2}$, if $m_1 = m_2,\ m \neq m_1$;

$y = e^{mx}(c_1 + c_2 x) + (x^2 e^{mx})/2$, if $m = m_1 = m_2$.

PAGE 107, SECTION 4–6

1. $[D - (-1 + \sqrt{5})I]\,[D - (-1 - \sqrt{5})I]$.

3. $(D - 3I)\left[D - \dfrac{1}{2}(3 + \sqrt{17})I\right]\left[D - \dfrac{1}{2}(3 - \sqrt{17})I\right]$.

5. $D^2 + 2D + 4I$.

7. $(D - I)(D + I)(D^2 + D + I)(D^2 - D + I)$.

PAGE 116, SECTION 4–7

1. $y = c_1 e^x + c_2 e^{-x} + c_3 \cos x + c_4 \sin x$.

3. $y = c_1 e^x + e^{-x/2}\left(c_2 \cos \dfrac{\sqrt{3}}{2} x + c_3 \sin \dfrac{\sqrt{3}}{2} x\right) - 1$.

5. $y = c_1 + c_2 x + c_3 e^x + c_4 e^{-x} - (x^5/20) - x^3$.

9. $A = (a - m)^{-3}$ if $a \neq m$, or $1/6$ if $a = m$.

PAGE 127, SECTION 5–2

1. $(D - I)^3 f = 0$ (equation of lowest order).

3. $(D - aI)^{n+1} f = 0$ (equation of lowest order).

5. $y_f = -x^4 - 8x^3 - 48x^2 - 190x - 357$.

7. $y_f = -(e^x/2) - (x/3)$.

9. $y_f = -(x^3 \sin x)/48$.

11. $y = c_1 e^{2x} + c_2 \cos x + c_3 \sin x - \dfrac{1}{8} e^x + e^{-x}\,[c_4 - (x/12)]$.

PAGE 133, SECTION 5–3

1. $y = C_1 e^x + e^{-x}(C_2 - 2x)$.

3. $y = C_1 \cos x + C_2 \sin x + \cos x \ln |\csc x + \cot x| - 1$.

5. $y_f = \displaystyle\int_{x_0}^x (t - 1)f(t)\, dt - x \int_{x_0}^x f(t)\, dt + e^x \int_{x_0}^x e^{-t} f(t)\, dt$.

7. $y = C_1 x + (C_2/x) + (x^2/3)$.

9. The $n + 1$ solutions are shown to satisfy a linear homogeneous equation of order $n + 1$; their wronskian is then proved to be zero.

PAGE 139, SECTION 5–4

1. $y = c_1 e^{-x} + c_2 x e^{-x} + e^{3x}\left(-\dfrac{24}{625} \cos 3x + \dfrac{7}{625} \sin 3x \right)$.

3. $y = c_1 + c_2 x + e^x\left(c_3 + c_4 x + \dfrac{x^2}{2} \right)$.

5. $y = c_1 \cos x + c_2 \sin x$
$$+ \dfrac{e^x}{25} [c_3 + (-5x - 8) \cos x + (-10x + 19) \sin x].$$

7. $y = e^{2x}(C_1 \cos x + C_2 \sin x - 1 + \sin x \ln | \sec x + \tan x |)$.

9. $y = C_1 \cos x + [C_2 + (x/2)] \sin x$.

PAGE 146, SECTION 5–5

1. $y_f = -\dfrac{1}{12} x^3 + \dfrac{1}{8} x^2 - \dfrac{1}{8} x$.

3. $y_f = -\dfrac{1}{2} x e^x (x + 2)$.

5. $y_f = -4x^5 + 6x^2 - 480x - 2$.

7. $y_f = -\dfrac{1}{2} (x^2 + 6x + 10)$.

9. $y = c_1 e^{-2x} + c_2 e^{-3x} + \dfrac{1}{6}\left(x^2 - \dfrac{5}{3} x + \dfrac{19}{18} \right)$.

11. $y = c_1 e^{2x} + c_2 e^{4x} + \dfrac{1}{3} e^x\left(x^2 + \dfrac{8}{3} x + \dfrac{26}{9} \right)$.

PAGE 149, SECTION 5–6

1. $y = c_1 x^{4/3} + c_2 x^{1/2}$.

3. $y = (c_1/x) + c_2 e^x$.

5. $y = x^2(c_1 \ln | x | + c_2)$.

7. $y = x^2(c_1 \ln | x | + c_2) + (3/2)$.

11. $y = c_1/(x - 1) + c_2 e^x$.

13. $W = - y_1^2 w_1$.

PAGE 154, SECTION 5–7

1. $y = x - e^x, \quad z = 2e^x - (x^2/2) + c.$

3. $y = 2c_1 + c_2 + 4c_3 + 2(c_2 + c_3)x + 2c_3x^2$
$\qquad + e^{-x/2} [c_4 \cos (\sqrt{3}x/2) + c_5 \sin (\sqrt{3}x/2)]$
$\qquad + (e^{2x}/14) + \sin x,$

$\qquad z = c_1 + c_2x + c_3x^2 + e^{-x/2} [c_4 \cos (\sqrt{3}x/2)$
$\qquad\qquad\qquad + c_5 \sin (\sqrt{3}x/2)] - (3/56) e^{2x} + \sin x.$

5. $y = 2c_1e^{x/4} - 3c_2e^{-x} + 2e^x/3),$
$\qquad z = c_1e^{x/4} + c_2e^{-x} + (e^x/3).$

7. $y = c_1e^{x/2},$
$\qquad z = c_2 - 5c_1e^{x/2} + x,$
$\qquad w = -10c_1e^{x/2} + 4 - x.$

9. $z = 1 + x - y' + y$, where y is an arbitrary differentiable function.

11. $y = -D^2z, \quad w = x + D^2z + C,$ where z is an arbitrary three-times differentiable function.

PAGE 160, SECTION 5–8

5. $y_f = x^2e^x.$

7. $y_f = -\dfrac{1}{5} e^x (2 \cos x + \sin x).$

9. $y = C_1 + C_2x + e^{2x}(C_3 + C_4x + 2x^2).$

11. $y = C_1e^x + C_2e^{2x} + e^{-x/2}\left(C_3 \cos \dfrac{\sqrt{3}}{2} x + C_4 \sin \dfrac{\sqrt{3}}{2} x\right)$
$\qquad\qquad\qquad - x^4 - 2x^3 - \dfrac{5}{2} x^2 - \dfrac{53}{2} x - \dfrac{53}{4}.$

13. $y = 2x^2 - 6x + 7 - 8e^{-x} + e^{-2x}.$

15. $y = \dfrac{1}{2} x^2 - \dfrac{1}{2} x.$

17. $y = e^{(6-x)/2} + (e^x/3).$

23. Do not commute.

PAGE 162, CHAPTER 5, MISCELLANEOUS

1. $y = c_1 + c_2e^x + c_3e^{-x} - \dfrac{1}{4} x^4 - 3x^2 - \dfrac{1}{6} e^{-2x}.$

3. $y = x(c_1 \cos \ln x + c_2 \sin \ln x) + \dfrac{1 + \ln x}{2}.$

5. $y = \sum\limits_{i=0}^{n} [c_{i+1}x^ie^x + (-1)^n(x + n)].$

7. $y = \sum_{k=0}^{4} e^{x \cos [(2k+1)\pi/10]} \left[c_{k+1} \cos \left(x \cos \dfrac{2k+1}{10} \pi \right) \right.$

$\left. + c'_{k+1} \sin \left(x \cos \dfrac{2k+1}{10} \pi \right) \right] + x^{10} - 10!.$

9. $x = c_1 \cos \sqrt{2}\, t + c_2 \sin \sqrt{2}\, t,$

$y = \left(c_1 + \dfrac{1}{\sqrt{2}} c_2 \right) \cos \sqrt{2}\, t + \left(c_2 - \dfrac{1}{\sqrt{2}} c_1 \right) \sin \sqrt{2}\, t.$

11. $y = (c_1 + c_2 x)e^x + e^x \ln (1 + e^{-x}).$

13. $y = c_1 e^x + c_2 e^{(1+\sqrt{5})x/2} + c_3 e^{(1-\sqrt{5})x/2}$
$+ x^5 + 40x^3 - 58x^2 + 480x - 472.$

15. $y = c_1 \cos 2x + c_2 \sin 2x + (1/4)x - 1;$

$y = \dfrac{3}{2} \cos 2x - \dfrac{1}{8} \sin 2x + \dfrac{1}{4} x - 1.$

17. $y = c_1 e^{(1+\sqrt{5})x/2} + c_2 e^{(1-\sqrt{5})x/2} - \cosh x.$

19. $y = c_1 \cos x + c_2 \sin x - \sin x \ln |\csc x + \cot x|.$

21. Reduces to $p_1 v'' + (2ap_1 + p_2)v' = f(x)e^{-ax}$, which is linear and of first order in v'.

PAGE 170, SECTION 6–2

1. At $y = -1/8$, $|\,\text{tension}\,| = |\,\text{weight}\,|$.
3. $y = -1/8$; no motion occurs.
5. $k = 10^6 \pi^2 m = 9.87 \cdot 10^6 m.$
7. $16g/\pi^2 = 51.88$ feet.
9. Major idealizations: Fluid is assumed incompressible; frictional effects are neglected; cube is assumed rigid and replaceable by a particle in the lower face; fluid is assumed to be at rest and undisturbed by motion of the cube; air currents causing forces on the cube are assumed absent.
11. $my'' + ky = 0$ $(k > 0)$, $y(0) = r$, $\dot{y}(0) = 0.$

PAGE 179, SECTION 6–3

1. $I_{\dot{E}} = \dfrac{E_0}{2514} \sin (120\pi t - \phi)$, $\phi = -78°32'.$
3. 2514 ohms at 60 cycles per second; 3024 ohms at 1000 cycles per second; natural: 211 cycles per second; resonant: 225 cycles per second.
5. $I_{\dot{E}} = \dfrac{E_0}{\sqrt{29}} (-5 \cos 10^6 t + 2 \sin 10^6 t).$

7. Graph is the portion of the rectangular hyperbola $z^2 - \omega^2 = 1$ in the first quadrant.

9. $z^2 = 1 + \dfrac{1}{\omega^2}$; as ω increases from 0 to $+\infty$, z decreases from $+\infty$ and approaches 1 asymptotically.

11. $x = \dfrac{1}{6} e^{-4t}(\cos 2\sqrt{2}\, t + \sqrt{2} \sin 2\sqrt{2}\, t)$.

13. $f_1, f_2 = \dfrac{1}{4\pi LC} (\pm\sqrt{3}\, RC + \sqrt{3R^2C^2 + 4LC})$;

$$f_1 < \frac{1}{2\pi\sqrt{LC}} < f_2.$$

15. $L = 4.42$ microhenrys; $R = 4.82$ ohms.

17. $R = 15,315$ ohms; p.f. $= 0.7559$.

PAGE 191, SECTION 6–4

1. $x_1 = -\dfrac{1}{10} (\cos t + 4 \cos \sqrt{6}\, t)$,

$\quad x_2 = -\dfrac{1}{5} (\cos t - \cos \sqrt{6}\, t)$.

3. $x_1 = -\dfrac{1}{26} (9 \cos \sqrt{15}\, t + 4 \cos \sqrt{2}\, t)$,

$\quad x_2 = \dfrac{3}{13} (\cos \sqrt{15}\, t - \cos \sqrt{2}\, t)$.

5. $\Delta(\omega)$

$$= \begin{vmatrix} -m_1\omega^2 + k_1 + k_2 & -k_2 & 0 \\ -k_2 & -m_2\omega^2 + (k_2 + k_3) & -k_3 \\ 0 & -k_3 & -m_3\omega^2 + k_3 \end{vmatrix}$$

$$= 0; \quad \omega_1^2 \omega_2^2 \omega_3^2 = \frac{\Delta(0)}{m_1 m_2 m_3} = \frac{k_1 k_2 k_3}{m_1 m_2 m_3} .$$

7. $I_R = c_1 e^{m_1 t} + c_2 e^{m_2 t}$, where

$$m_1 = \frac{1}{2RC}\left(-1 + \sqrt{1 - \frac{4R^2C}{L}}\right),$$

$$m_2 = \frac{1}{2RC}\left(-1 - \sqrt{1 - \frac{4R^2C}{L}}\right);$$

$$I_C = -RC \frac{dI_R}{dt} ; \quad I_L = I_R - I_C.$$

PAGE 191, SECTION 6-4 (Continued)

9. $I = E_0 \left[\dfrac{1}{R} \cos \omega t + \left(\dfrac{1}{\omega L} - \omega C \right) \sin \omega t \right].$

11. $L = \dfrac{L_1 L_2}{L_1 + L_2}.$

13. From (6-32), $h = a v_y.$

15. 5 miles per second.

17. $v_y = 26{,}650$ feet per second.

19. $\dfrac{2 k m_1}{(k^2 m_1^2 - c^2 h^4)^{3/2}} \tan^{-1} \dfrac{\sqrt{k^2 m_1^2 - c^2 h^4} \sin(\theta - \alpha)}{(k m_1 + c h^2)[1 + \cos(\theta - \alpha)]}$

$- \dfrac{c h^2}{k^2 m_1^2 - c^2 h^4} \cdot \dfrac{\sin(\theta - \alpha)}{k m_1 + c h^2 \cos(\theta - \alpha)} = h^{-3} t + c_1;$

$e = \dfrac{c h^2}{k m_1} < 1.$

21. Equations of motion: $\ddot{x} + \dfrac{f(r)}{r} x = \ddot{y} + \dfrac{f(r)}{r} y = 0;$ (6-23) holds here as in the text.

PAGE 193, CHAPTER 6, MISCELLANEOUS

1. For different unit rates, $x = x_0 e^{-kt}$, $y = y_0 e^{-lt}$

$+ \dfrac{k x_0}{l - k} (e^{-kt} - e^{-lt});$ for equal unit rates, $x = x_0 e^{-\kappa t},$

$y = (y_0 + k x_0 t) e^{-kt}.$

3. $5.2 \cdot$ radius of earth's orbit $= 4.83 \cdot 10^8$ miles.

5. $y = \dfrac{\sqrt{3}}{2} \left[(-2 - \sqrt{3}) e^{(-2 + \sqrt{3}) t} + (2 - \sqrt{3}) e^{(-2 - \sqrt{3}) t} \right].$

7. $I_R = \dfrac{E_0}{4007} [0.25 \cos 240 \pi t + 0.97 \sin 240 \pi t].$

9. Motion: $x = a \cos kt$, $y = \dfrac{v}{k} \sin kt$; path is an ellipse; Kepler's law holds for radius vectors from the origin: $\dfrac{d}{dt}(r^2 \theta) = av.$

11. Integrate (6-25), use $h = a v_y$ and the results of Example 6-7.

13. Steady state current through R satisfies

$$a\dot{I} + bI = \left(\dfrac{R_1}{R_1 + R_2} - \dfrac{C_2}{C_1 + C_2} \right) \dot{E},$$

where $a = R + R_1 R_2/(R_1 + R_2)$, $b = 1/(C_1 + C_2).$

PAGE 202, SECTION 7–2

1. $y = a_0 \left(1 + \sum\limits_{k=1}^{\infty} \dfrac{(-1)^{k+1} x^{3k}}{12^k k! (3k-1)} \right) + a_1 x;$

the series converges for all x.

3. $y = a_0 \left(1 + \sum\limits_{k=1}^{\infty} \dfrac{(-3)(-1) \cdot 1 \cdot \cdots \cdot (2k-5) x^{2k}}{2^k k!} \right);$

the series converges if $-1 < x < 1$.

5. $y = a_0 \left(1 + \sum\limits_{k=1}^{\infty} \dfrac{(-7) \cdot \cdots \cdot (2k-9) \cdot 4 \cdot \cdots \cdot (k+3) x^{2k}}{1 \cdot 3 \cdot \cdots \cdot (2k-1) k!} \right)$

$\qquad + a_1 \left(x - 9x^3 + \dfrac{99}{5} x^5 - \dfrac{429}{35} x^7 \right);$

the series converges if $-1 < x < 1$.

7. $y = a_0 \left(1 + \sum\limits_{k=1}^{\infty} \dfrac{(-1)^k (-1) \cdot \cdots \cdot (4k^2 - 4k - 1) x^{2k}}{2^k (2k)!} \right)$

$\qquad + a_1 \left(x + \sum\limits_{k=1}^{\infty} \dfrac{(-1)^k \cdot 1 \cdot \cdots \cdot (2k^2 - 1) x^{2k+1}}{(2k+1)!} \right);$

the series converge if $-\sqrt{2} < x < \sqrt{2}$.

9. $y = a_0 \left(1 + \sum\limits_{k=1}^{\infty} \dfrac{(-1)^k [1 \cdot \cdots \cdot (3k-2)]^2 x^{3k}}{2 \cdot \cdots \cdot (3k-1) 24^k k!} \right)$

$\qquad + a_1 \left(x + \sum\limits_{k=1}^{\infty} \dfrac{(-1)^k [2 \cdot \cdots \cdot (3k-1)]^2 x^{3k+1}}{4 \cdot \cdots \cdot (3k+1) 24^k k!} \right);$

the series converge if $-2 < x < 2$.

11. $y = a_0 \left(1 + \sum\limits_{k=1}^{\infty} \dfrac{2 \cdot \cdots \cdot (9k^2 - 21k + 14) x^{3k}}{(3k)!} \right)$

$\qquad + a_1 \left(x + \sum\limits_{k=1}^{\infty} \dfrac{2 \cdot \cdots \cdot (9k^2 - 15k + 8) x^{3k+1}}{(3k+1)!} \right)$

$\qquad + a_2 \left(x^2 + \sum\limits_{k=1}^{\infty} 2 \cdot \dfrac{4 \cdot \cdots \cdot (9k^2 - 9k + 4) x^{3k+2}}{(3k+2)!} \right);$

the series converge for all x.

PAGE 208, SECTION 7–3

See answers to exercises in Section 7–2, page 202.

7. $y = c_1 x^{-5} + c_2 x$.

9. $y = c_1 \mid x \mid^{1/5} \left(1 + \displaystyle\sum_{n=1}^{\infty} \dfrac{(-1)^n 2^n x^n}{5^n n! 2 \cdot \; \cdots \; \cdot (5n - 3)} \right)$

$\qquad + c_2 \mid x \mid^{4/5} \left(1 + \displaystyle\sum_{n=1}^{\infty} \dfrac{(-2x)^n}{5^n n! 8 \cdot \; \cdots \; \cdot (5n + 3)} \right)$;

the series converge for all x; the solutions are valid for $x > 0$ or $x < 0$.

11. $y = c_1 \mid x \mid^{-1/2} \left(1 + \displaystyle\sum_{k=1}^{\infty} \dfrac{(-1)^k (-5) \cdot \; \cdots \; \cdot (4k - 9) x^{2k}}{4^k k! 11 \cdot \; \cdots \; \cdot (12k - 1)} \right)$

$\qquad + c_2 \mid x \mid^{-1/3} \left(1 + \displaystyle\sum_{k=1}^{\infty} \dfrac{(-1)^k (-7) \cdot \; \cdots \; \cdot (6k - 13) x^{2k}}{6^k k! 13 \cdot \; \cdots \; \cdot (12k + 1)} \right)$;

the series converge for all x; the solutions are valid for $x > 0$ or $x < 0$.

1. $y = c_1 y_1 + c_2 y_2$, where

$$y_1 = 1 + \sum_{k=1}^{\infty} \frac{1 \cdot \; \cdots \; \cdot (8k - 7) x^{2k}}{4^k (k!)^2},$$

$$y_2 = y_1 \ln \mid x \mid + \sum_{k=1}^{\infty} \frac{1 \cdot \; \cdots \; \cdot (8k - 7)}{4^k (k!)^2} q(k) x^{2k},$$

and $q(k) = \dfrac{4}{1} + \cdots + \dfrac{4}{8k - 7} - \dfrac{1}{1} - \cdots - \dfrac{1}{k}$;

the series converge for all x; y_1 is a valid solution for all x, and y_2 is valid for $x > 0$ or $x < 0$.

3. $y = c_1 y_1 + c_2 y_2$, where

$$y_1 = x \sum_{n=0}^{\infty} \frac{(-x)^n}{n!} = x e^{-x},$$

$$y_2 = y_1 \ln \mid x \mid - x \sum_{n=1}^{\infty} \frac{(-x^n)}{n!} \left(1 + \cdots + \frac{1}{n} \right) ;$$

the series converge for all x; y_1 is a valid solution for all x, and y_2 is valid for $x > 0$ or $x < 0$.

5. $y = c_1 y_1 + c_2 y_2$, where

$$y_1 = 1 - 2x + \frac{1}{2} x^2,$$

$$y_2 = y_1 \ln \mid x \mid + 5x - \frac{9}{4} x^2 + \frac{1}{18} x^3 + \sum_{n=4}^{\infty} \frac{2(n - 3)! x^n}{(n!)^2} ;$$

the series converges for all x; y_1 is a valid solution for all x, and y_2 is valid for $x > 0$ or $x < 0$.

PAGE 220, SECTION 7–5 (Continued)

7. $y = c_1 y_1 + c_2 y_2$, where

$$y_1 = x^2 \left(1 + \sum_{k=1}^{\infty} \frac{(-2)^k 2 \cdot \cdots \cdot (3k-1)x^{3k}}{9^k k!(k+1)!} \right),$$

$$y_2 = \frac{2}{3} y_1 \ln|x| + x^{-1} \left(1 - \frac{8}{9} x^3 + \sum_{k=2}^{\infty} q(k)x^{3k} \right),$$

and $q(k) = \dfrac{(-2)^k(-1) \cdot \cdots \cdot (3k-4)}{3^{2k-1}k!(k-1)!} \left(-1 + \dfrac{1}{2} + \cdots + \dfrac{1}{3k-4} \right.$

$$\left. - \frac{2}{3} - \cdots - \frac{2}{3k-3} - \frac{1}{3k} \right);$$

the series converge for all x; y_1 is a valid solution for all x, and y_2 is valid for $x > 0$ or $x < 0$.

9. $y = c_1 y_1 + c_2 y_2$, where

$$y_1 = x^{7/3} \left(-\frac{2}{243} + \sum_{n=3}^{\infty} p(n)x^{n-2} \right),$$

$$y_2 = y_1 \ln|x| + x^{1/3} \left(3 + \frac{1}{9} x - \frac{13}{486} x^2 + \sum_{n=3}^{\infty} p(n)q(n)x^n \right), \text{ and}$$

$$p(n) = \frac{(-1)^{n-1}1 \cdot \cdots \cdot (3n-2)n(n-1)}{3^{3n-1}(n!)^2},$$

$$q(n) = \frac{3}{1} + \cdots + \frac{3}{3n-2} + 1 - \frac{1}{n} - \frac{1}{n-1} - \frac{2}{1} - \cdots - \frac{2}{n-2};$$

the series converge for all x; y_1 is a valid solution for all x, and y_2 is valid for $x > 0$ or $x < 0$.

11. $\alpha = -k$; $v = a_0$; $y = a_0 |x|^{-k}$; valid for all x if $k \leqq 0$ and valid for $x > 0$ or $x < 0$ if $k > 0$.

PAGE 226, SECTION 7–6

1. $y_n = \sum\limits_{k=0}^{n} \dfrac{(2x)^k}{k!}$, $\quad y = \sum\limits_{k=0}^{\infty} \dfrac{(2x)^k}{k!} = e^{2x}$.

3. $y_n = 1 + 2x + x^2 + 4 \sum\limits_{k=3}^{n} \dfrac{x^k}{k!} + \dfrac{2}{(n+1)!} x^{n+1}$

$$+ \frac{2}{(n+2)!} x^{n+2},$$

$$y = 1 + 2x + x^2 + 4 \sum_{k=3}^{\infty} \frac{x^k}{k!} = 4e^x - x^2 - 2x - 3.$$

PAGE 226, SECTION 7–6 (Continued)

5. $y_n = a + \sum\limits_{k=1}^{n} \dfrac{7^{k-1}(2 + 7a)x^k}{k!} - 4! \sum\limits_{k=5}^{n+4} \dfrac{7^{k-5}x^k}{k!}$,

$\quad y = a + \sum\limits_{k=1}^{\infty} \dfrac{7^{k-1}(2 + 7a)x^k}{k!} - 4! \sum\limits_{k=5}^{\infty} \dfrac{7^{k-5}x^k}{k!}$;

conventional method of solution yields

$y = \left(a + \dfrac{4778}{7^5}\right) e^{7x}$

$\qquad + 7^{-5}\left[(7x)^4 + 4(7x)^3 + 12(7x)^2 + 24(7x) - 4778\right].$

7. $y_1 = x$, $y_2 = x + \dfrac{1}{3}x^3$, $y_3 = x + \dfrac{1}{3}x^3 + \dfrac{2}{15}x^5 + \dfrac{1}{63}x^7$.

9. $y_1 = 1 + x + \dfrac{1}{2}x^2$,

$\quad y_2 = 1 + x + \dfrac{1}{2}x^2 + \dfrac{2}{3}x^3 + \dfrac{1}{2}x^4 + \dfrac{1}{5}x^5 + \dfrac{1}{24}x^6$,

$\quad y_3 = 1 + x + \dfrac{1}{2}x^2 + \dfrac{2}{3}x^3 + \dfrac{1}{2}x^4 + \dfrac{7}{15}x^5 + \dfrac{31}{72}x^6 + \dfrac{31}{105}x^7$

$\qquad + \dfrac{257}{1440}x^8 + \dfrac{19}{180}x^9 + \dfrac{67}{1200}x^{10} + \dfrac{23}{990}x^{11} + \dfrac{49}{7200}x^{12}$

$\qquad + \dfrac{1}{780}x^{13} + \dfrac{1}{8064}x^{14}.$

11. $y_1 = x - 1$, $y_2 = (x - 1) + \dfrac{1}{2}(x - 1)^2 + \dfrac{1}{3}(x - 1)^3$,

$\quad y_3 = (x - 1) + \dfrac{1}{2}(x - 1)^2 + \dfrac{1}{2}(x - 1)^3 + \dfrac{5}{24}(x - 1)^4$

$\qquad + \dfrac{1}{15}(x - 1)^5.$

PAGE 238, SECTION 7–7

For exercises 1, 3, 5 the sine series is given first, then the cosine series, and finally the mixed series.

1. $\sum\limits_{k=1}^{\infty} \dfrac{4}{(2k - 1)\pi} \sin \dfrac{(2k - 1)\pi x}{2}$; 1; **1.**

3. $\sum\limits_{n=1}^{\infty} \dfrac{2}{n\pi}\left[1 - (-1)^n - 2\cos\dfrac{n\pi}{3} - \dfrac{3}{n\pi}\sin\dfrac{n\pi}{3}\right]\sin\dfrac{n\pi x}{3}$;

PAGE 238, SECTION 7–7 (Continued)

$$\frac{1}{3} + \sum_{n=1}^{\infty} \frac{2}{n^2\pi^2} \left[2n\pi \sin\frac{n\pi}{3} + 3(-1)^n - 3\cos\frac{n\pi}{3} \right] \cos\frac{n\pi x}{3} ;$$

$$\frac{1}{3} + \sum_{n=1}^{\infty} \left(\frac{3}{2n^2\pi^2} \sin\frac{n\pi}{3} - \frac{2}{n\pi} \cos\frac{n\pi}{3} \right) \sin\frac{2n\pi x}{3}$$

$$+ \sum_{n=1}^{\infty} \left(-\frac{2}{n\pi} \sin\frac{n\pi}{3} + (-1)^n \frac{3}{2n^2\pi^2} - \frac{3}{2n^2\pi^2} \cos\frac{n\pi}{3} \right) \cos\frac{2n\pi x}{3} \cdot$$

5. $\displaystyle \sum_{n=1}^{\infty} \frac{4}{n^3\pi^3} \left[16(-1)^n - 16 - 3n^2\pi^2(-1)^n + n^2\pi^2 \right] \sin\frac{n\pi x}{4} ;$

$$\frac{4}{3} + \sum_{n=1}^{\infty} \frac{8}{n^2\pi^2} \left[5(-1)^n + 3 \right] \cos\frac{n\pi x}{4} ;$$

$$\frac{4}{3} + \sum_{n=1}^{\infty} (-1)^{n+1} \frac{4}{n\pi} \sin\frac{n\pi x}{2} + \sum_{n=1}^{\infty} (-1)^n \frac{16}{n^2\pi^2} \cos\frac{n\pi x}{2} \cdot$$

7. $c_1 \cos x + c_2 \sin x$

$$+ \sum_{n=1}^{\infty} \frac{2}{n\pi} \left[1 - (-1)^n - 2\cos\frac{n\pi}{3} - \frac{3}{n\pi} \sin\frac{n\pi}{3} \right] \frac{9}{9 - n^2\pi^2} \sin\frac{n\pi x}{3} \cdot$$

9. $\displaystyle E(t) = \sum_{n=1}^{\infty} (-1)^{n+1} \frac{2}{n\pi} \sin n\pi t;$

$$q = \sum_{n=1}^{\infty} (-1)^{n+1} \frac{2}{n\pi} \left[\frac{(1 - n^2\pi^2) \sin n\pi t - n\pi \cos n\pi t}{(1 - n^2\pi^2)^2 + n^2\pi^2} \right].$$

Index

Acceleration, 57, 65
Analogy, between applied systems, 168
Antiderivative, 2, 101
Applications
  to geometry, 57, 71
  to natural science, 57, 163
Areal law, 188, 193*, 194*

Bandwidth, 180*
Bessel functions, 220
Bessel's equation, 219, 220*
Binary relations, 98
Boundary conditions, 15, 17
Bridge network, 194*

Cauchy-Riemann equations, 80*
Cauchy's equation, 213*
Characteristic equation, 87, 106
Characteristic polynomial, 87
Characteristic roots, 87, 106
Charge, electrostatic, 78
Chemical reactions, 62
Clairaut's equation, 26*
Coefficients, undetermined,
    85, 97, 124, 202
Combination, chemical, 62
Complementary function, 94
Complete solution, 9
  of linear equations, 46, 83–84, 90,
    95–96, 109, 112
Complex conjugates, method
    employing, 138–139
Complex functions, 89, 91
Components
  of force, 66
  of vector fields, 74
Conics, confocal, 26*, 74*
Conjugate fields, 80
Conservative vector fields, 75
Constant of integration, 2, 5

Continuity, 244
  equation of, 61
Convergence, 224
  interval of, 197, 198
  of series, 244
Convolution, 86, 98*, 161*
Cooling, 60
Coulomb's law, 78
Current, 172
Curvature, locus of centers of, 29*
Curves
  equipotential, 77
  families of, 14
  level, 24
Cusp locus, 28

Damping, 173, 177
  constant of, 177
Decay, 60
Degree(s) of freedom, 64–65
Dependence, linear, 117
Derivative(s)
  of complex functions, 92, 93*
  of products, 207
Derivative operator (D), 100, 104
  factorization of polynomials in, 106
  polynomials in, 105
Determinant(s)
  differentiation of, 245–246
  operator, 152
  van der Monde, 117
  wronskian, 117
Direction field, 14
Discontinuity, 230–231, 244
Domains
  of functions, 3, 18, 32, 98, 244
  natural, 3–4
  of operators, 99

e, value of, 247
Economic competition, 64*

NOTE: The asterisk(*) indicates references to exercises.